THE STRAIN GAGE PRIMER

THE STRAIN GAGE PRIMER

C. C. PERRY

*Associate Professor of Engineering Mechanics,
Wayne State University
and Research Consultant*

H. R. LISSNER

*Professor and Chairman
Department of Engineering Mechanics,
Wayne State University*

SECOND EDITION

McGRAW-HILL BOOK COMPANY, INC.

New York Toronto London

THE STRAIN GAGE PRIMER

 Library of Congress Catalog Card Number: 62-14220

49461

PREFACE

Experimental stress analysis has been a major factor in most of the significant mechanical achievements since 1940. The widespread growth and application of experimental stress analysis is due, in turn, almost entirely to the advent of the bonded resistance strain gage. The electrical resistance strain gage is unique among scientific tools because of its versatility. Besides its fundamental use for measuring strains as such, the strain gage can be adapted to measure loads, torques, pressures, vibrations, and numerous other physical variables, limited principally by the imagination of the user. "The Strain Gage Primer" has been written to describe this phenomenal instrument and its capabilities, as well as to set forth the information and data necessary for the proper use of the strain gage and its associated instrumentation.

The resistance strain gage is in itself so basically simple that some users have acquired erroneous impressions as to the amount of knowledge and experience required for its proper utilization. It is not at all unusual, for instance, to find investigators taking data from a single strain gage placed on a two-dimensionally strained surface in the direction of the maximum tensile stress as inferred from, say, a brittle fracture. This procedure does not produce strain data from which the true magnitude of the maximum principal stress can be calculated. There are many other, and often more subtle, aspects of strain gage usage which have not previously been gathered in one publication or presented in a manner that can be understood by anyone familiar with algebra and trigonometry.

Aside from the theoretical aspects of strain gage technology, there are the practical laboratory methods of bonding strain gages and protecting them from the effects of extraneous variables. Resistance strain gages are now being employed at temperatures ranging from the boiling point of liquid hydrogen to near the melting point of steel (with varying success, we might add); in locations of zero relative humidity, and completely

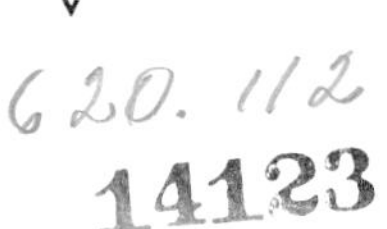

submerged in water and other liquids; and subjected to any number of other adverse environmental conditions. The more generally applicable techniques for a wide range of strain gage installations are described in this book and supplemented liberally by selected bibliographical references.

There are three basic steps in the ritual of experimental stress analysis with strain gages. The first involves selecting an appropriate strain gage and cementing it in the proper location. The second step is that of employing suitable instruments to obtain electrical signals proportional to the strains being measured. The final step includes translation of the strains to stresses. Lack of care and precision in performing any one of these rites can result in data which are at best worthless and which may actually be dangerous or costly.

The material in the first half of the book treats the above three steps in the order listed. The remainder of the book is devoted to extensions of the basic principles to various classes of "special" applications. It might be noted here parenthetically that in the use of bonded resistance strain gages, nearly every application is somewhat special.

Chapter 1 presents an abridged history of the growth and development of strain measurement. The second chapter describes the bonded resistance strain gage itself—its appearance, composition, manufacture, and fundamental characteristics. Chapter 3 gives detailed instructions for proper application (bonding) of strain gages under commonly encountered conditions. In Chapter 4 the basic instrument for strain measurement, the Wheatstone bridge, is described and its operating characteristics analyzed, while Chapter 5 discusses the extension of this principle to the practical measurement of static and dynamic strains.

Chapters 6 and 7 constitute a simplified presentation of the laws of elasticity and their significance in the proper use of strain gages and the translation of strains into stresses. The next five chapters describe the use of strain gages under various special conditions and for special purposes and include representative techniques as well as bibliographical references for extended reading. Chapter 13 is an introduction to brittle-lacquer strain analysis as a tool for use in conjunction with strain gages, and Chapter 14 describes the recently developed photoelastic strain gage.

A few simple exercises—some analytical and some experimental—have been appended to each chapter. These may be of interest to the individual reading the book for self-study, and they may also serve the instructor of a formal laboratory course in experimental stress analysis, at least as a source of ideas from which better exercises, more applicable to his particular circumstances, may be devised.

Experimental stress analysis in particular, and the entire field of engineering mechanics in general, is indebted to E. E. Simmons and A. C. Ruge for the original conception and development of the bonded wire strain gage. The present widespread use and popularity of the resistance strain gage must, however, be credited in large measure to F. G. Tatnall. Mr. Tatnall has been the foster father of the strain gage—presiding at its christening, watching over its development and maturation, and energetically evangelizing it for over two decades. One of Mr. Tatnall's strongest allies in this effort has been the Society for Experimental Stress Analysis, for many years under the able guidance of Dr. W. M. Murray. The names of all those individuals who have made substantial contributions to strain gage technology are too numerous to mention here, but they will be found repeatedly throughout the bibliographies in this book and in the *Proceedings of the Society for Experimental Stress Analysis.*

Since the "Primer" first appeared in 1955, a veritable river of strain gage cement has flowed under the (Wheatstone) bridge. Although the resistance strain gage has probably achieved its majority as an instrument for experimental stress analysis, the last decade has seen a number of significant changes. The basic patents on wire gages have expired. New companies have entered the field . . . and some have departed again. The foil strain gage has achieved increasing prominence, and the wire gage is apparently on the wane. Adhesive technology has steadily improved—largely in the direction of fast-curing cements. Strain-measuring instruments have changed also. Transistors are gradually displacing vacuum tubes; and there is a distinct trend toward digital strain display. Reliable and accurate high-temperature static strain measurement, however, remains a largely unconquered province. Another problem area is that of nuclear radiation-resistant strain gages.

The "Primer" has had a little history of its own during this period, too. In its peregrinations it has suffered burial in a "time vault" of engineering memorabilia at George Washington University (to be unearthed a century later, on June 20, 2056); it was translated into Russian in 1957 under the title OSNOVY TENZOMETRIROVANIA and it has, we are told, served countless purposes in various stress laboratories, ranging from its use as a weight (approximately 1½ lb) for holding strain gages in place during curing, to shimming up the short leg of a work bench.

The authors have been pleased by the reception given the first edition of the "Primer" and sincerely hope that the second edition may prove useful to those who find themselves engaged in experimental stress analysis or other measurement problems involving strain gages. They are grateful to the many individuals and organizations who have contributed data and illustrative material, and to Miss Diane Marvicsin for her efforts in the preparation of the revised manuscript.

The authors cheerfully disavow any claim to originality in the material presented in this book. Actually, it represents an accumulation of the experiences of hundreds of investigators, each of whom had the will to solve his particular measurement problem with the best materials, techniques, and processes available to him. The book is dedicated to these people and to the spirit of honest inquiry which motivates them.

C. C. Perry
H. R. Lissner

CONTENTS

1 AN INTRODUCTION TO STRAIN MEASUREMENT

STRAIN

Strain is a fundamental engineering phenomenon. It exists in all matter at all times, due either to external loads or to the weight of the matter itself. Strains vary in magnitude from atomic dimensions to distances easily discernible by the naked eye, depending upon the materials and loads involved. Scientists and engineers have worked for centuries in the attempt to measure strain accurately, but only the last few decades have seen outstanding advancement in the art of strain measurement. The terms *strain* and *linear deformation* are synonymous and, as used in engineering, refer to the change in any linear dimension of a body, usually due to the application of external forces. The strain of a piece of rubber, when loaded, is ordinarily apparent to the eye—the strain of a bridge strut as a locomotive passes may not be. Strain as defined above is often spoken of as "total strain" in order to distinguish it from *unit strain.* Average unit strain is the total deformation of the body in a given direction divided by the original length in that direction and, as such, because of its dimensionless character, has much greater significance than total strain. *Strain gages are used to determine unit strain.*

Because unit strain is in most cases more significant than total strain, the word "strain" when used alone commonly refers to unit strain. As thus defined, strain has units of inches per inch. This could be looked upon as merely a ratio because, as noted above, it is mathematically dimensionless; however, the physical concepts of strain will be emphasized if it is thought of in terms of a change in length per unit length.

THE NEED FOR STRAIN INSTRUMENTATION

The measurement of strain has been of importance ever since the seventeenth century, when Hooke pointed out that for many common materials there is a constant ratio between stress and strain.[1] The constant of proportionality between stress and strain implied in Hooke's law is known as the *modulus of elasticity*[2] of the material, or, after the man who is credited with defining it, *Young's modulus*. Mathematically, this can be expressed as

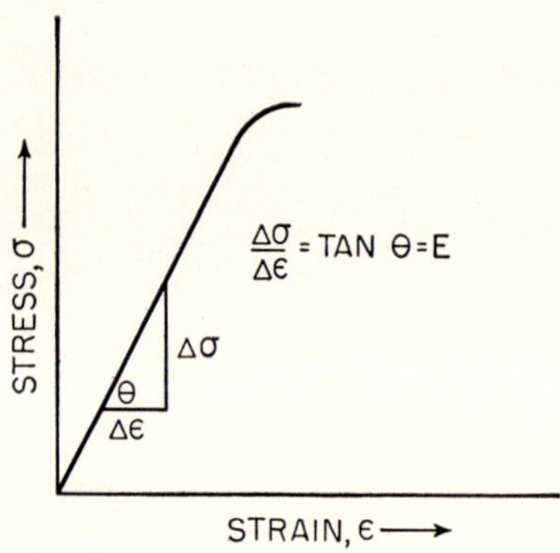

Fig. 1-1. Typical stress-strain diagram for a metal.

$$E = \frac{\sigma}{\epsilon} \tag{1-1}$$

where the modulus of elasticity and stress, E and σ, are commonly expressed in pounds per square inch. In a graphical representation (Fig. 1-1) E is the slope of the stress-strain curve.

The ability of a material to support applied loads or forces is usually expressed in terms of stress rather than in terms of strain. For economic reasons—material cost, transportation and handling cost—and for general convenience it is desirable to keep the functional components of any machine as small and light as possible. This means that the parts should be stressed in service to the highest permissible

[1] Notice from the following quotation that Robert Hooke apparently failed to recognize the existence of a proportional limit:

"Take then a quantity of even-drawn Wire, either Steel, Iron, or Brass, and coyl it on an even Cylinder into a Helix of what length or number of turns you please, then turn the ends of the Wire into Loops by one of which suspend this coyl upon a nail, and by the other sustain the weight that you would have to extend it, and hanging on several Weights observe exactly to what length each of the weights do extend it beyond the length that its own weight doth stretch it to, and you shall find that if one ounce, or one pound, or one certain weight doth lengthen it one line, or one inch, or one certain length, then two ounces, two pounds, or two weights will extend it two lines, two inches, or two lengths; and three ounces, pounds, or weights, three lines, inches, or lengths; and so forwards. And this is the Rule or Law of Nature . . . in every springing body . . . that the force or power thereof to restore itself to its natural position is always proportional to the Distance or space it is removed, therefrom." "De Potentia Restitutiva," The Cutler Lectures of Robert Hooke, Early Science in Oxford, Vol. VIII, R. W. T. Gunther, Oxford, 1931.

[2] Note: It must be pointed out that Hooke's law is true only when a stress exists in one direction and when the strain is measured in the direction of that principal stress. Under these conditions transverse strain exists without a transverse stress.

value. Prior to the advent of accurate strain (hence, stress) determination it was necessary to design complex mechanical parts principally on a cut-and-try basis. This involved making some calculations based on a theory only approximately true, multiplying by a "safety factor" of 3 to 5, building and testing the piece, and, in the event of failure, adding material in the critical section until a suitable component was evolved. Designing by this method was often extremely wasteful of both time and material. For instance, if the piston of an internal-combustion engine is made unnecessarily heavy, a thicker and heavier connecting rod is required, thereby necessitating a larger crankshaft and larger bearings, and finally a heavier engine block. The cut-and-try process became increasingly unsatisfactory as the demand for higher-performance machinery embodying very complex parts grew toward its present state. A further stimulus was provided by the need in aircraft construction for minimum weight and maximum performance from every part. It was desirable to accurately determine local stresses so that the least amount of material could be distributed to the greatest advantage in new designs or in modifications of old designs.

Keeping in mind the relationship between stress and strain, it becomes apparent that we can determine the average intensity of stress in a body under some given external load by measuring the strain and multiplying by the modulus of elasticity. This is basically the only manner in which stress can be determined, since stress is not a fundamental physical quantity like strain, but only a derived quantity. For example, in the derivation of the torsion and flexure formulas, the stress is determined by multiplying the geometrically obtained strains by the elastic moduli.

It is no wonder then that a great deal of effort has been expended toward perfecting a universal strain gage. In attempting to develop such a strain gage an "ideal" might be set up as a goal. This ideal strain gage would be:

1. Extremely small in size.
2. Of insignificant mass.
3. Easy to attach to the member being analyzed.
4. Highly sensitive to strain.
5. Unaffected by temperature, vibration, humidity, or other ambient conditions likely to be encountered in testing machine parts under service loads.
6. Capable of indicating both static and dynamic strains.
7. Capable of remote indication and recording.
8. Inexpensive.
9. Characterized by an infinitesimal gage length.

The ideal gage as described here is one whose primary purpose is for the determination of stress in the material and not for laboratory studies of the characteristics of the material itself.

To date there is no one instrument that fully meets all the above specifications, which are, after all, rather extensive. As one authority in the strain gage field puts it: "While it is theoretically possible to develop a strain gage which is infinitesimal in size and weight, has an infinite sensitivity to strain, and an infinitesimal sensitivity to all other variables, the cost of such a strain gage would be . . . infinite." Although the bonded resistance strain gage with which this book largely concerns itself fails to reach the ideal on specifications 4, 5, and 9, it is so much superior on all counts to any of its predecessors that the latter have almost passed out of existence except for laboratory use.

MECHANICAL STRAIN MEASUREMENT

Early attempts at measuring strain involved the use of a screw micrometer to measure the over-all change in length of a body under load (total strain). The unit strain was obtained by dividing this quantity by the original length. This, of course, actually gives the *average* strain over the entire gage length required for this type of instrument and gives no indication of what the local strain may be in the neighborhood of a discontinuity. To illustrate the importance of this last handicap, consider the difficulties involved in determining the strain distribution in a complicated piece such as an automotive connecting rod. With an average stress of 50,000 psi, peak stresses of 90,000 psi might exist. If the part were designed on the basis of average stresses, it would fail under load at one of the highly stressed sections. In the past the practice was to compute the average stresses, then multiply by a safety factor to cover the highly stressed points about which little was known. The result of this was that often most of the connecting rod was overdesigned—that is, certain portions of the rod were unnecessarily strong for the applied loads. In stress analysis it is common to find that a piece which fails under load does not need more material added, but merely requires redistribution of the material already present so that all sections are stressed to approximately the same level. Often, in fact, stress analysis will show that the piece can be made stronger (more resistant to fracture) simply by removing material!

The next step in the development of strain-measuring apparatus yielded a series of instruments called *extensometers*. To start with, extensometers magnified the minute strains by a system of purely mechanical levers. Later, light-beam and mirror arrangements were added, resulting in increased sensitivity and smaller, less cumbersome instruments.

The highest level of purely mechanical magnification of strain was probably reached by the extensometers of the Huggenberger and Porter-Lipp type. These gages can measure strains as low as 0.00001 in. per in. with a magnification ratio of 2,000 to 3,000. They are characterized, however, by bulkiness, weight, and a minimum gage length of ½ in. The term *gage length* as related to extensometers refers to the unstrained distance between the two points at which the extensometer is attached to the piece being tested. Because fatigue failures (by far the most common type in metal parts) originate from *local* overstraining—often in a minute area such as a small fillet—it is highly desirable to measure strains over a very short span or gage length in the critical area. The best mechanical extensometers fulfill hardly any of the specifications laid down for the ideal strain gage for stress determination.

It should probably be emphasized at this point that the field of strain measurement can be divided roughly into two areas of activity. One includes the measurement of strain for purposes of securing information about the physical properties of a material. The second, the principal subject matter of this book, embraces strain measurement as an indication of stress or load. The instruments which are best suited for laboratory determination of material properties may not be satisfactory for stress indication, and, of course, the inverse is equally true.

OPTICAL STRAIN MEASUREMENT

Since a beam of light is easier to manipulate than a mechanical device and is weightless and free of friction, it is not surprising that efforts were directed toward applying light-beam amplification to the problem of strain measurement. One of the extensometers using this principle is the Tuckerman gage. This instrument employs an optical lever system (where the lever transmits only motion, not force), not unlike the mechanical extensometers. The Tuckerman extensometer has a relatively high sensitivity, indicating strains as low as 0.000002 in. per in. The minimum gage length is approximately ¼ in. This extensometer has been used for dynamic strains up to 150 cycles per second (cps). Figure 1-2 illustrates a commercial form of the Tuckerman optical strain gage.

Optical interference phenomena have also been employed in strain measurement. The interference method uses two optical flats fastened either directly or through levers to the structure being tested. Relative motion of the optical flats causes interference fringes to move past a reference point. These fringes are counted as a measure of the strain.

The interference method is extremely sensitive and accurate as well as delicate. The instrument is most suited to precise laboratory work under ideal conditions. A number of similar instruments employing optical or optical-mechanical amplification have been developed, but they are generally characterized by gage lengths of ½ in. or more and by inconvenient and slow determination of strains.

A comparatively recent high-magnification extensometer is the photoelectric instrument developed by General Motors Research Laboratories Division. This gage employs a combination of mechanical, optical, and electrical magnification. The gage operates through a single mechanical lever which shifts a fine grating with respect to a second grating. These gratings intercept a parallel light beam which is directed to a photocell. The current generated by the photocell is read on a very sensitive ammeter. Thus, as strain occurs in the part to which the gage is attached, the grating shifts slightly, altering the amount of light received by the photocell, which in turn alters the meter reading as a measure of the strain. The photoelectric gage has an over-all amplification of some 30,000 and comes in gage lengths of ¼, ⅛, and 1/16 in. It is a small, lightweight instrument and is very successful in general static strain analysis; but it is still a long way from the ideal strain gage pictured earlier, principally because of its cost, delicacy, and lack of convenience and versatility.

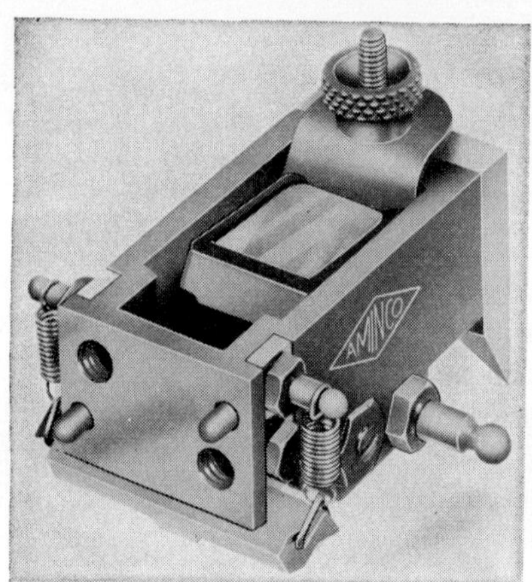

FIG. 1-2. Tuckerman-type optical strain gage consists of an extensometer (photograph) and an autocollimator or precision telescope with light source and reticule for measuring strain from motion of the light beam. (*Courtesy of American Instrument Company.*)

ELECTRIC STRAIN MEASUREMENT

While the mechanical and optical extensometers were being perfected, other investigators turned to basic electrical phenomena as tools for strain measurement. Electrical strain gages are instruments so constructed that any strain in the body to which they are attached is accompanied by a proportional change in some electrical characteristic of the gage. The electrical variables commonly used are resistance, inductance, and capacitance. The capacitance strain gage is composed of a condenser, the capacity of which can be made to vary with strain. A capacitor, or condenser, is fundamentally two plates separated by an insulator (which may be, and often is, air). The impedance to an alternating current depends upon the capacity of the condenser, which in turn depends upon the distance between the plates and the area of the plates. Either variable can be used as a strain transducer. The instrument, then, is so constructed and so mounted on the structure being tested that the surface strains in the immediate vicinity of the gage act to alter either the plate spacing or the plate area of the condenser. Capacitance strain gages have a number of disadvantages, including an undesirable sensitivity to vibration, mounting and clamping difficulties, and electrical circuit complexities.

The inductance strain gage is essentially an iron-core coil, the inductance of which can be varied with strain. Inductance variations can be achieved by changing the length of the air gap in the magnetic flux circuits or by changing the position of an armature relative to the coil. In general, the inductance strain gage has all the handicaps of the capacitance gage, with several more of its own, including weight, bulkiness, and susceptibility to magneto-mechanical resonance.

Another electrical property which can be employed for strain measurement is the *piezoelectric* effect of certain types of crystals. These crystals (quartz or Rochelle salt) have the curious property that a voltage difference appears across the face of the crystal when it is distorted or strained. This voltage difference is proportional to the strain and of a relatively high magnitude. The crystal gages, however, are bulky (compared with the resistance wire type), very fragile, and not suitable for measuring static strains because the charge gradually leaks off. Capacitance and inductance, as well as piezoelectric, strain gages have been developed and used, but never with the success obtained by the resistance wire and foil gages.

The immediate forerunner of the resistance wire strain gage was the carbon-resistor gage. This operated on the principle that any lengthening or shortening of a carbon resistor is accompanied by a change in the electrical resistance of the carbon. This effect is presumably due to changes in mutual contact of the carbon particles as the resistor is stretched or compressed. Thus, if a strip of flexible insulating material which has been coated with a conductive layer of carbon on its upper side were cemented to the surface of a machine member, the strain in the member would strain the carbon and alter its electrical resistance. This makes a very sensitive strain gage—many times as sensitive as the bonded wire and foil resistance strain gages. While this gage satisfies several of our requirements for the ideal gage very well, it turns out to be very poor with respect to some others. For one thing, along with its high sensitivity to strain it has an equally high sensitivity to temperature changes, and it is markedly affected by changes in humidity. Thus, a few degrees increase in temperature of the gage would cause the gage resistance to decrease noticeably, and since gage resistance is being used to measure strain, this resistance change would indicate an apparent strain where none existed. The temperature effect can be partially compensated or canceled by appropriate electrical circuits, but it always stands as a limitation to the accuracy of the carbon strain gage. A further and equally serious disadvantage of carbon gages is their tendency to "age," or change their calibration with time. Because these gages

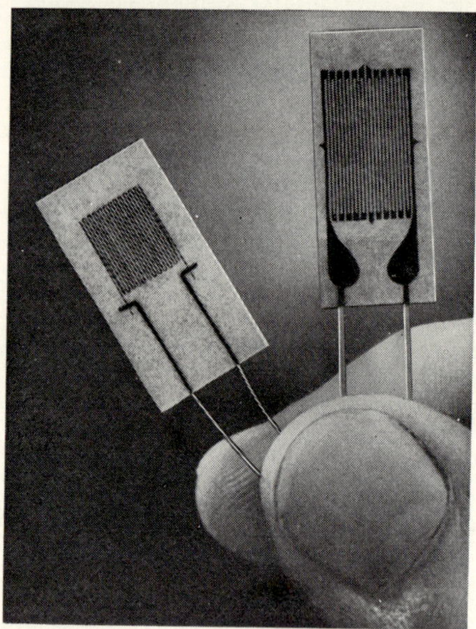

Fig. 1-3. Wire and foil bonded resistance strain gages. (*Courtesy of Baldwin-Lima-Hamilton Corporation.*)

are inexpensive to manufacture and have a high sensitivity to strain, they have obtained some popularity for measuring dynamic strains in which the cycle of straining is too rapid for temperature or aging effects to be of much importance.

The ultimate in strain-measuring devices to date is the bonded resistance gage, two examples of which are illustrated in Fig. 1-3. The most widely used gage consists of a short length of very fine wire or thin conductive foil, which is attached to the piece being tested so that the filament of the gage is strained equally with the surface of the test piece. The electrical resistance of the filament material used for these gages changes with strain. This change in resistance (small fraction of an ohm), when detected by the proper instruments, is an accurate measure of the strain in the filament and, hence, the strain in the underlying material being tested.

THE BONDED STRAIN GAGE

The bonded resistance strain gage is by far the most important single tool available to the stress analyst. This gage is about the size of a postage stamp and generally much lighter. It consists of a grid or filament of very small diameter wire or thin metallic foil mounted on paper or plastic. The filament material used has the property of linear variation of electrical resistance with strain. In order to measure the strain in a machine or structural member, one or more of these strain gages are cemented to the surface of the part. The next step is to connect the strain gage to some electrical instrument which will indicate small changes

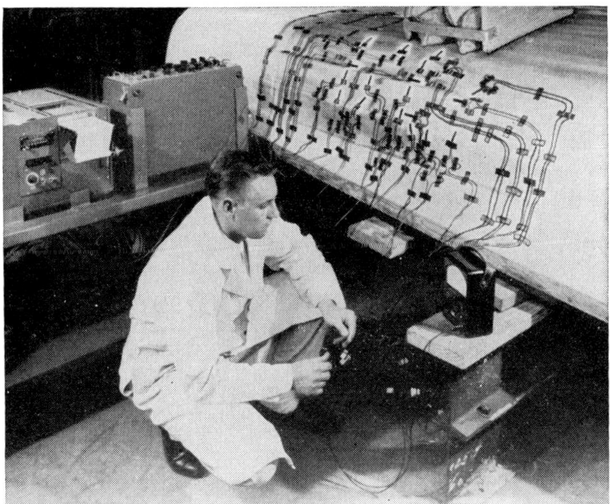

Fig. 1-4. Strain gages used in stress analysis of boat hull under dead-weight loading. (*Courtesy of Traveler Manufacturing Company, Division of Stanray Corporation.*)

in resistance, such as a Wheatstone bridge. Once this is done, the strain gage will faithfully follow and report any strains occurring in the test surface in the direction of the gage axis.

The bonded wire strain gage was perfected independently and almost simultaneously in 1938 by two men working in widely separated laboratories. Simmons at the California Institute of Technology and Ruge at the Massachusetts Institute of Technology both developed techniques for bonding a length of fine wire to the surface to be investigated so that any and all surface strains were transmitted directly to the wire. This resulted in the bonded wire strain gage and, for the first time, made large-scale experimental stress analysis really practical. Although Simmons received official credit for priority in inventing the wire resistance strain gage, all gages operating on this principle sold by the Baldwin-Lima-

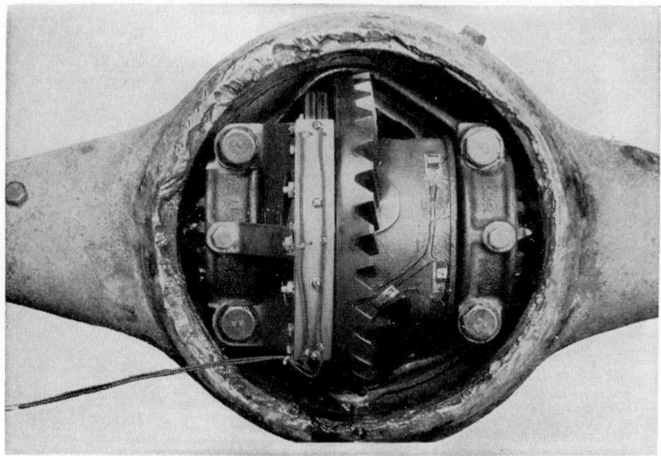

Fig. 1-5. Stress analysis of a rear-axle assembly with strain gages. Notice the slip rings used to maintain continuous electrical connection with the rotating differential carrier. (*Courtesy of Chrysler Corporation, Engineering Department.*)

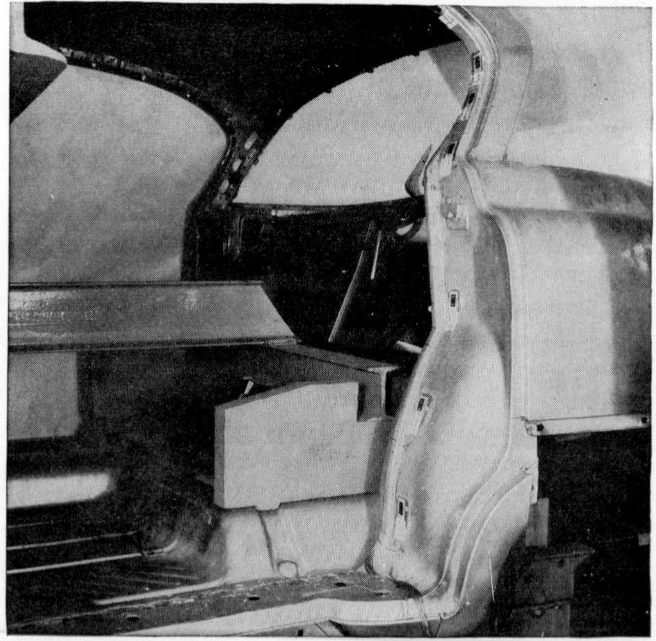

Fig. 1-6. Strain gage study of stresses in an automobile body. (*Courtesy of Chrysler Corporation.*)

Hamilton Corporation (the original strain gage manufacturer in the United States) are referred to as SR-4 strain gages, which name embodies the initials of both men.

The resistance strain gage is versatility itself. Because of the relatively low cost of the gages, it is now economically possible to plaster hundreds of them all over a structure such as an airplane and then obtain recordings of actual service strains at all critical points on the airplane during flight and landing maneuvers. Figure 1-4 illustrates the application of strain gages to a boat hull for stress studies. The gages have been widely used in the automotive industry (Figs. 1-5 and 1-6); on locomotives, rails, and other railroad components; on structures such as bridges, buildings, and highways; and on all types of machinery like presses, machine tools, and cranes. These applications barely scratch the surface of possible uses for the wire strain gage and fail to mention its use as a sensing unit in fluid pressure pickups, torque meters, comparators, accelerometers, load cells, and other instruments.

Reviewing the specifications for the ideal strain gage as applied to the bonded resistance strain gage, the final score might look something like this:

Specification	*Resistance Strain Gage*
1. Size	Very small
2. Weight	Insignificant
3. Ease of attachment to test piece	Relatively simple
4. Sensitivity to strain	Fair—higher output would be very advantageous
5. Sensitivity to ambient variables	Slightly affected, but the gages can usually be protected or the variables compensated for
6. Static and dynamic strain indication	Will indicate both with equal ease
7. Remote indication and recording	Easily accomplished
8. Expense	Most gages are comparatively inexpensive
9. Gage length	Shortest gage length presently available is $\frac{1}{64}$ in.

PIEZORESISTIVE STRAIN GAGES

In 1957 strain gages based upon the piezoresistive effect in certain crystals such as silicon and germanium were first used experimentally. Commercial piezoresistive gages followed shortly. The piezoresistive or semiconductor strain gage is remarkable for its high output signal with strain (some fifty to sixty times that of a conventional wire or foil gage). The principal disadvantages of the piezoresistive gage consist in resistance and output variations with temperature and, in some instances, nonlinearity in compression.

The piezoresistive effect is to be distinguished from the piezoelectric effect. The latter designation refers to the phenomenon by which a voltage appears across the faces of a quartz or similar crystal when it is deformed, while the former is associated with the change in resistance of a semiconducting crystal accompanying deformation. The piezoelectric crystal, which requires no external source of current, produces a voltage only with dynamic or varying deformation. Its output for static or steady-state strain is zero. The piezoresistive crystal must be supplied with current from an external source. It exhibits a resistance change proportional to strain and independent of the deformation rate down to and including static deformation.

PHOTOELASTIC STRAIN GAGES

Photoelasticity is a precision experimental stress-analysis technique of classical origin and long standing. A recent offspring of photoelasticity has been the reduction to practicability of the photoelastic-coating method. A coating of birefringent plastic is applied and bonded directly to the surface of a metal part and used in conjunction with a reflection polariscope to measure surface strains in areas of interest. Among its other advantages, the photoelastic coating constitutes a strain gage with an effective gage length approaching the infinitesimal. Photoelastic coatings are available in the United States under the trade name of PhotoStress, along with many convenient accessory instruments for determining strain magnitudes.[1]

A further development of photoelastic coatings has resulted in the evolution of comparatively small uniaxial and biaxial strain gages based upon the same principle. These ordinarily consist of coupons of birefringent plastic (rectangular or circular) in which an initial stress pattern has been frozen. The initial stress pattern is discernible to the eye under ordinary lighting because the photoelastic plastic is aluminized on its reverse side and covered with a polarizing film on its face.

After bonding the photoelastic strain gage to the test member and applying a load, the initial fringe pattern shifts or distorts noticeably. The movement of the fringe pattern is proportional to the strain in the underlying material. Measurement of the fringe shift is then interpreted in terms of strain with reasonable precision. The circular gages also indicate principal stress directions since the latter coincide with the axes of symmetry of the photoelastic pattern as distorted by the strain field. Figure 1-7 illustrates two types of photoelastic strain gages.

Photoelastic strain gages, and the techniques for utilizing them effectively, are described in Chap. 14.

[1] PhotoStress is a product of the Budd Instruments Division, P.O. Box 245, Phoenixville, Pa.

BRITTLE LACQUERS

A convenient tool for use in conjunction with any strain gage is the brittle-lacquer technique. This had its origin years ago when it was noted that fine cracks developed in the mill-scale surface of hot-rolled steel parts in the regions of high stresses. This effect could be made more pronounced by applying a coat of whitewash on top of the scale. Whitewash or a brittle cement paint could be applied to machined parts. The mill scale or brittle paint, however, was not uniform in thickness or in sensitivity to strain, and had the further limitation that strains of 0.001 in. per in. or higher (at the yield point of mild hot-rolled steel) were necessary to produce cracks. Thus, the cracks indicated yielding, but not elastic strain.

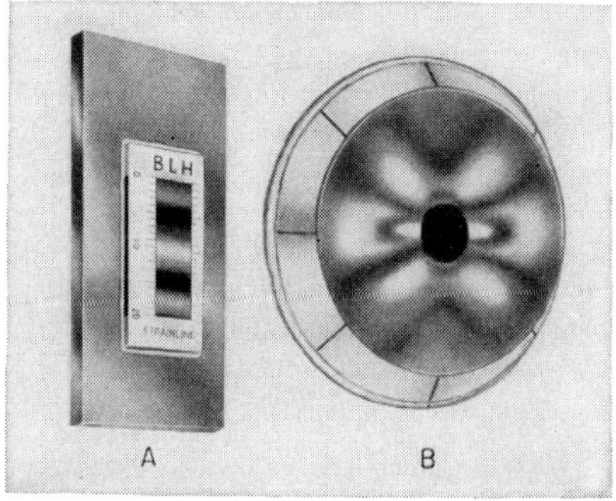

FIG. 1-7. Photoelastic strain gages: (*A*) for measuring linear strain; (*B*) for indicating the directions of the principal axes (along the axes of symmetry of the fringe pattern). (*Courtesy of Baldwin-Lima-Hamilton Corporation.*)

From this knowledge was evolved the brittle-lacquer technique of strain indication. The process consists in first painting the part to be studied with a coat of brittle lacquer, then loading the part as it would be loaded in service. The brittle lacquer will crack wherever surface strains exceed a certain value (approximately 0.0006 in. per in.). These cracks serve to point out the regions of high strain (or stress) at which to place resistance strain gages for accurate measurement. They also indicate the direction of the strain and, under favorable circumstances, the magnitude of the strain to a fair degree of accuracy. This art has reached a remarkably high degree of mastery in the United States. There is commercially available a product known as Stresscoat, which is really a series of brittle lacquers for use under different conditions of temperature and humidity.[1] For more severe ambient conditions, including

[1] Stresscoat is available from the Magnaflux Corporation, 7300 West Lawrence Avenue, Chicago 31, Ill.

temperatures as high as 600°F, Stresscoat AllTemp, a ceramic brittle coating, can be used. Stresscoat lacquers, and the basic techniques for using them in conjunction with strain gages, are described further in Chap. 13.

BIBLIOGRAPHY

Strain Measurement—General and Historical

Benson, R. W., and V. J. Raelson: From Ultrasonics a New Stress-analysis Technique; Acoustoelasticity, *Product Eng.*, vol. 30, pp. 56–59, July 20, 1959.

Black, W. A.: Uses of Resistance Wire Type Strain Gages in Steel Plants, *Iron & Steel Engr.*, vol. 31, no. 11, pp. 57–63, November, 1954.

Carlson, R. W.: Five Years' Improvement of the Elastic-wire Strain Meter, *Eng. News-Record*, vol. 114, pp. 696–697, May 16, 1935.

Clark, D. S., and G. Datwyler: Stress-Strain Relations under Tension Impact Loadings, *ASTM, Proc.*, vol. 38, pp. 98–111, 1938.

deForest, A. V., and H. Leaderman: The Development of Electrical Strain Gages, *NACA, Tech. Note* 744, January, 1940.

Durelli, A. J., and E. A. Phillips: Criteria for Selecting Experimental Stress Analysis Methods, *Product Eng.*, vol. 26, no. 1, pp. 182–191, January, 1955.

Eaton, E. C.: Electric Resistance Strain Gage Measures Stresses in Concrete, *Eng. News-Record*, vol. 107, pp. 615–616, Oct. 15, 1931.

Greenspan, M., and L. R. Sweetman: Transfer Strain Gage for Large Strains, *J. Research Natl. Bur. Standards*, vol. 34, pp. 595–597, June, 1945.

Hathaway, C. M., and E. S. Lee: The Electric Gage, *Mech. Eng.*, vol. 59, pp. 653–658, September, 1937.

Lamble, J. H., and S. S. Gill: Measurement of Strain, *Trans. Liverpool Eng. Soc.*, vol. 68, pp. 3–24, 1947.

McCollum, B., and O. S. Peters: A New Electrical Telemeter, *Natl. Bur. Standards (U.S.) Tech. Papers* 221–247, vol. 17, pp. 737–777, 1922–1924.

Meier, J. H.: The Development of an Electrical Strain Gage and Its Application to the Stress Problem in Elevated Water Tanks, Sc. D. thesis, Massachusetts Institute of Technology, Department of Civil Engineering, 1939.

Oppel, G. U.: Photoelastic Strain Gages, *Experimental Mechanics*, vol. 1, no. 3, pp. 65–73, March, 1961.

Rohrbach, C.: Die Wichtigsten Verfahren der Spannungs- und Dehnungsmessung, *Materialpruefung*, vol. 2, no. 12, pp. 468–472, Dec. 20, 1960.

Rusher, M. A., and A. V. Mershon: Electric Strain Gauge, *Elec. Eng.*, vol. 57, no. 11, pp. 645–648, November, 1938.

Simmons, E. E., Jr.: Material Testing Apparatus, U.S. patent No. 2,292,549, Feb. 23, 1940.

Extensometers

Cuykendall, T. R., and G. Winter: Characteristics of the Huggenberger Strain Gage, *Civil Eng.*, vol. 10, no. 7, pp. 448–450, July, 1940.

deForest, A. V.: Measurement of Impact Strains, *Proc. Fifth Intern. Congr. Appl. Mech.*, p. 673, John Wiley & Sons, Inc., New York, 1938.

Donnell, L. H., and W. T. Savage: Mechanical Gages and Extensometers, "Handbook of Experimental Stress Analysis," pp. 72–116, John Wiley & Sons, Inc., New York, 1950.

Gadd, C. W., and T. C. Van DeGrift: A Short-gage-length Extensometer and Its Application to the Study of Crankshaft Stresses, *Trans. ASME*, vol. 64, pp. A-15 to A-20, March, 1942.

Greenspan, M., and L. R. Sweetman: Transfer Strain Gage for Large Strains, *J. Research Natl. Bur. Standards*, vol. 34, pp. 595–597, June, 1945.

Lamble, J. H., and S. S. Gill: Measurement of Strain, *Trans. Liverpool Eng. Soc.*, vol. 68, pp. 3–24, 1947.

Lee, G. H.: "An Introduction to Experimental Stress Analysis," pp. 86–111, John Wiley & Sons, Inc., New York, 1950.

Linge, J. R.: Mechanical Interference in Measurement of Strain, *Aircraft Eng.*, vol. 29, no. 337, pp. 70–74, March, 1957.

Lyon, W. C., *et al.*: Strain Measurement in the Reinforcement for the Dome of the Natural History Building, *J. Research Natl. Bur. Standards*, vol. 6, pp. 183–194, February, 1931.

Maulbetsch, J. L.: Optical Methods of Strain Measurement, "Handbook of Experimental Stress Analysis," p. 118, John Wiley & Sons, Inc., New York, 1950.

Palmer, P. J.: Bending Stresses in Cantilever Plates by Moiré Fringes, *Aircraft Eng.*, vol. 29, no. 346, pp. 377–380, December, 1957.

Smith, K. F.: Types of Strain Measuring Devices and Their Range of Utility, *Product Eng.*, vol. 18, pp. 107–110, January, 1947.

Weaver, P. R.: An Optical Strain Gage for Use at Elevated Temperatures, *Proc. SESA*, vol. 9, no. 1, pp. 159–162, 1952.

Wilson, B. L.: Characteristics of the Tuckerman Strain Gage, *ASTM, Proc.*, vol. 44, pp. 1017–1026, 1944.

Linkage Measures Bending Stress, *Product Eng.*, vol. 29, p. 65, June 9, 1958.

Recording Strain Meter for Ships' Structures, *Engineering*, vol. 132, p. 87, July 17, 1931.

Strain Gages, *Mech. Eng.*, vol. 69, p. 774, September, 1947.

Electrical Strain Gages

Bloch, A.: New Methods for Measuring Mechanical Stresses at Higher Frequencies, *Nature*, vol. 136, no. 3432, pp. 223–224, Aug. 10, 1935.

Carter, B. C.: Electric Capacitance Gages, "Handbook of Experimental Stress Analysis," p. 273, John Wiley & Sons, Inc., New York, 1950.

Carter, B. C., *et al.*: Measurement of Displacement and Strain by Capacity Methods, *Inst. Mech. Engrs. (London), J. & Proc.*, vol. 152, no. 2, pp. 215–221, September, 1945.

Chapman, J. C.: Stud-welded Vibrating Wire Strain Gauge, *Engineer*, vol. 206, no. 5361, pp. 640–641, Oct. 24, 1958.

Dohrenwend, C. O.: New Developments in Strain Measurement, *J. Western Soc. Engrs.*, vol. 49, pp. 3–14, March, 1944.

Dorey, S. F.: Use of Wire Wound Electrical Resistance Strain Gages (as Applied to Engineering Problems) for Measurement of Static Strains, *Trans. Inst. Naval Arch.*, vol. 86, pp. 61–71, 1944.

Fanning, R., and W. V. Bassett: Measurement of Impact Strains by a Carbon-strip Extensometer, *Trans. ASME*, vol. 62, pp. A-24 to A-28, March, 1940.

Grave, M. M.: Electric Strain Gage in Service of Shipbuilding, *Pacific Marine Rev.*, vol. 41, no. 7, pp. 94–97, 116, July, 1944.

Hull, E. H.: Alternating Stress Measurement by Resistance Strip Method, *Gen. Elec. Rev.*, vol. 40, no. 8, pp. 379–380, August, 1937.

Jerrett, R. S.: The Acoustic Strain Gauge, *J. Sci. Instr.*, vol. 22, no. 2, p. 29, February, 1945.

Lamble, J. H., and S. S. Gill: Measurement of Strain, *Trans. Liverpool Eng. Soc.*, vol. 68, pp. 3–24, 1947.

Langer, B. F.: Electric-inductance Gages, "Handbook of Experimental Stress Analysis," p. 238, John Wiley & Sons, Inc., New York, 1950.

Mainstone, R. J.: Vibrating-wire Strain Gauge for Use in Long-term Tests on Structures, *Engineering*, vol. 176, no. 4566, pp. 153–156, July 31, 1953.

Mason, W. P., and R. N. Thurston: Use of Piezoresistive Materials in the Measurement of Displacement, Force, and Torque, *J. Acous. Soc. Am.*, vol. 29, pp. 1096–1101, October, 1957.

Meyer, R. D.: Application of Unbonded-type Resistance Gages, *Instruments*, vol. 19, no. 3, pp. 136–139, March, 1946.

Mittelberger, F.: Electric Strain Gages for Measuring Loads on Machine Parts, *Product Eng.*, vol. 13, pp. 337–339, June, 1942.

Murray, W. M.: Stress Analysis Methods, *Materials & Methods*, vol. 23, pp. 1002–1006, April, 1946.

Potocki, F. P.: Vibrating-wire Strain Gauge for Long-term Internal Measurements in Concrete, *Engineer*, vol. 206, pp. 964–967, Dec. 19, 1958.

Redshaw, S. C.: The Electrical Measurement of Strain, *J. Roy. Aeronaut. Soc.*, vol. 50, pt. 2, no. 428, pp. 568–602, August, 1946.

Shamberger, J. P.: A Magnetic Strain Gage, *ASTM, Proc.*, vol. 30, pt. 2, pp. 1041–1047, 1930.

Smith, K. F.: Types of Strain Measuring Devices and Their Range of Utility, *Product Eng.*, vol. 18, pp. 107–110, January, 1947.

Vibration; Stress Determination by Electrical Means, *Automobile Eng.*, vol. 33, p. 184, May, 1943.

Brittle Coatings

deForest, A. V., and G. Ellis: Brittle Lacquers as Aid to Stress Analysis, *J. Aeronaut. Sci.*, vol. 7, no. 5, pp. 205–208, March, 1940.

Ellis, G.: Practical Strain Analysis by Use of Brittle Coatings, *Proc. SESA*, vol. 1, no. 1, pp. 46–60, 1943.

EXERCISES

1-1. From the description of the General Motors Research Division photoelectric extensometer, sketch your concept of this instrument.

1-2. List and describe six methods of electrical strain measurement.

1-3. How would you determine the stress from strain measurements on steel, aluminum, cast iron, and magnesium? What relationship between stress and strain will you use for each of these materials?

1-4. List and describe three methods of optical strain measurement.

1-5. What, if any, are the effects of the end loops in the strain gages (Fig. 1-2) on the strain indicated by the gages?

1-6. How is it possible to obtain Hooke's law ($\sigma = E\epsilon$) from the footnote describing the experiments of Robert Hooke?

1-7. Determine the stress at which the mill scale begins to flake off from a hot-rolled steel specimen when tested in tension in the laboratory. Compare this with the yield stress for the material.

1-8. Coat a brass, aluminum, or mild-steel tensile specimen containing a transverse hole with whitewash, neat cement, or other brittle substance, and attempt to determine the stress concentration factor for the hole. List and assess the probable sources of error in this method.

2 BONDED RESISTANCE STRAIN GAGE

RESISTANCE VERSUS STRAIN

In 1856 Prof. William Thomson (Lord Kelvin) delivered before the Royal Society of London a very interesting paper describing numerous experiments which he had performed in investigating the electrodynamic properties of metals. Among other findings, he reported that the electrical resistance of certain wires varied with the tension to which the wires were subjected. More recently (1923), in America, P. W. Bridgman confirmed Thomson's results in a series of tests involving wires under hydrostatic pressure. Little use was made of this knowledge until after 1930, when attempts were made to apply the phenomenon of strain sensitivity in wires to the actual measurement of strain in other bodies. These attempts were naturally accompanied by the usual growing pains—difficulty in developing satisfactory techniques for securing the strain-sensitive wire to the test structure, a search for the best wire with which to build the gages, calibration troubles, and the apparent impossibility of ever manufacturing such a delicate instrument on a mass-production basis.

While the original strain gages built by Simmons and Ruge had been assembled in place by cementing the wire itself directly to the test structure, it was felt that commercial wire strain gages required individual calibration to be dependably accurate. Early strain gages were therefore made by embedding the fine wire in cast thermoplastic-resin coupons which were individually calibrated. These gages were rather bulky compared with the currently available strain gages and did not allow the strain-sensitive wire to be in intimate contact with the surface of the body being tested. It was found, however, that, by exercising a sufficiently rigid control of manufacturing processes, gages could be made with a uniformity of resistance and gage factor such that individual calibration was no longer necessary. These developments soon led to the

SR-4 strain gage in the easy-to-use and versatile form which served as a prototype for the many resistance strain gages commercially available today.

In using electric strain gages, two physical quantities are of particular interest—change in gage resistance and change in length, or strain. The dimensionless relationship between these two variables is called the "gage factor" of the strain gage and is expressed mathematically as

$$F = \frac{\Delta R/R}{\Delta L/L} \tag{2-1}$$

In this relationship R and L represent, respectively, the initial resistance and initial length of the strain gage filament, while ΔR and ΔL represent the small changes in resistance and length which occur as the gage is strained along with the surface to which it is bonded. The *gage factor* of a strain gage, then, is a measure of the amount of resistance change for a given strain and is thus an index of the strain sensitivity of the gage.[1] The higher the gage factor, the more sensitive the gage and the greater the electrical output for indication or recording purposes, other variables remaining the same. Naturally, efforts have been made to develop strain gages with the highest possible gage factors. The limiting element in determining gage factor is the conductor material, and, to date, all those materials which have demonstrated high gage factors have had other unpleasant characteristics which made them unsuitable for strain gages.

The ideal strain gage conductor would have high resistance, a large change in resistance with strain, and a high elastic limit and would be insensitive to temperature in both its physical and its electrical properties. Furthermore, the very form of the gage-factor expression implies a *constant* ratio between resistance change and unit strain. In other words, the resistance change must be proportional to, or a linear function of, the unit strain in the filament. All filament materials do not exhibit this latter characteristic. The strain gage filament should be very small in cross section so that the cement in which it is incased will be consider-

[1] A naive approach might lead to the conclusion that this change in resistance is due solely to the dimensional changes accompanying longitudinal strain of the wire. Taking into account the lengthening of the wire and the reduction in cross-sectional area results in the following relationship for the gage factor,

$$F = 1 + 2\mu$$

where μ is Poisson's ratio. For example, if the Poisson's ratio of a metal were 0.3, the indicated gage factor would be 1.6. It is an interesting commentary on this derivation that nickel with a Poisson's ratio of 0.31 has a gage factor of approximately -10.

ably stronger than the conductor. This allows the cement to transmit the strains from the part being tested to the conductor. With 0.001-in.-diameter (1-mil) wire or 0.0001-in.-thick foil, the cement is sufficiently stronger than the conductor so that under compressive strains the conductor is actually made shorter without buckling. This is not strange considering, for example, the fact that a 1-in. length of 1-mil wire has a surface area 4,000 times its cross-sectional area. The bonding and supporting effect of the cement on the wire or foil is so great that the cement can control the filament up to strains of 0.03 in. per in. or more in either compression or tension. Of course, if the strain gage conductor is to be a fine wire or thin foil, this imposes another limitation on the physical properties of the material; that is, it must be capable of withstanding severe drawing or rolling operations during processing.

In Table 2-1 are listed a number of possible strain gage materials (including carbon, for comparison purposes). From this list it is apparent that we must select some compromise wire with the best over-all characteristics. Nichrome, for instance, has a comparatively high ther-

TABLE 2-1. PROPERTIES OF STRAIN GAGE CONDUCTORS*

Common name	Composition	Gage factor	Temp coef of resist-ance†	Resist-ance, ohms per ft, in 1-mil diam	Stress equivalent to 10°C on steel, psi
Nichrome	Ni—0.80, Cr—0.20	+2.0	+300	638	+2,000
Manganin	Ni—0.04, Mn—0.12, Cu—0.84	+0.47	Nil	260	−400
Advance	Ni—0.45, Cu—0.55	+2.1	....	......	−66
Copel	Ni—0.45, Cu—0.55	+2.4	±2	290	−200
Constantan‡	Ni—0.45, Cu—0.55	+2.1	....	......	−60
Chromel—C	Ni—0.64, Fe—0.25, Cr—0.11	+2.5	....	640	+980
Iso-elastic	Ni—0.36, Cr—0.08, Fe—0.52, Mo—0.005	+3.5	+175	680	+5,000
Nickel	....	−12.1	+6,000	70	−13,500§
Platinum	....	+4.8	+3,000	80	
Soft iron	....	+4.2	+5,000	68	
Carbon	....	+20.0	−500	45,000	

* These data are not to be taken too literally, since most of the characteristics vary markedly with small changes in composition, with degree of cold-working, etc.

† Ohms per ohm per degree centigrade $\times 10^6$.

‡ Constantan is the name also applied to a 60-40 alloy with somewhat different properties.

§ Unstable.

mal coefficient of resistance, while Manganin, though it has many desirable properties, has too low a strain sensitivity or gage factor. Similarly, nickel has a very high gage factor but unstable thermal properties. Furthermore, when nickel and some of the other materials are bonded to steel, because of the differences in thermal coefficients of expansion, an additional error is introduced due to the apparent strain which occurs with temperature changes. These temperature effects and the methods for compensating for them are discussed in detail in Chap. 4. It will be noted also that nickel has a negative gage factor, indicating that the resistance of the wire decreases as it is stretched and increases as it is compressed. Negative gage factors are just as useful as positive ones, since all that is significant in the strain gage is obtaining the greatest change in resistance for a given strain. Whether the change in resistance is positive or negative is incidental.

The materials used in most gages are principally of two types, Advance and Iso-elastic. Advance alloy, because of its very low sensitivity to temperature, is employed in gages to be used for measuring static strains where it is necessary to maintain stability of gage resistance over extended periods of time and possible changing ambient temperatures. Although the gage factor of Advance is comparatively low, resistance changes due to strain are large enough to be indicated on a Wheatstone-bridge circuit or other sensitive instrument. Iso-elastic alloy (a severely cold-worked Elinvar) is used only for dynamic strain measurement because of its relatively high temperature sensitivity. In the case of dynamic or rapidly varying strains it is usually possible to take advantage of Iso-elastic's higher gage factor since the strain is changing fast enough so that resistance variations due to temperature are insignificant.

COMMERCIAL RESISTANCE STRAIN GAGES

Basically, the metallic resistance strain gage consists of a length of strain-sensitive conductor mounted on a small piece of paper or plastic backing. The backing serves as a carrier for ease in handling the filament and also acts to insulate the conductor from the metal surface on which it is to be bonded.

In the case of wire strain gages, the filament consists of several inches of 1-mil wire in the form of a grid as shown in Fig. 2-1. In the manufacturing process the grid is mounted on a piece of thin paper and fixed in place with a suitable cement. Large-diameter leads are then welded or soldered to the two ends of the grid wire, and a second piece of paper is cemented over the wire as a cover. The preceding method of assembly is satisfactory when gage lengths of ½ in. or more are being constructed. The shorter gages, however, may involve a different form of grid construction. For strain gages of $\frac{3}{8}$ in. or less in length, the strain-sensitive wire is sometimes wound around a cylindrical core in the form of a close-wound helix. This core is flattened and cemented between layers of paper for purposes of protection and insulation.

The metallic-foil strain gage has a grid made from thin (approximately 0.0001 in.) strain-sensitive foil. The grid configuration is obtained by printing the desired pattern on a sheet of foil with acid-resistant ink and subsequently etching away the unprotected metal. Another method of manufacture involves precision punching of the gages from a foil sheet. As shown in Fig. 2-1, the filament of the foil gage grid commonly ends

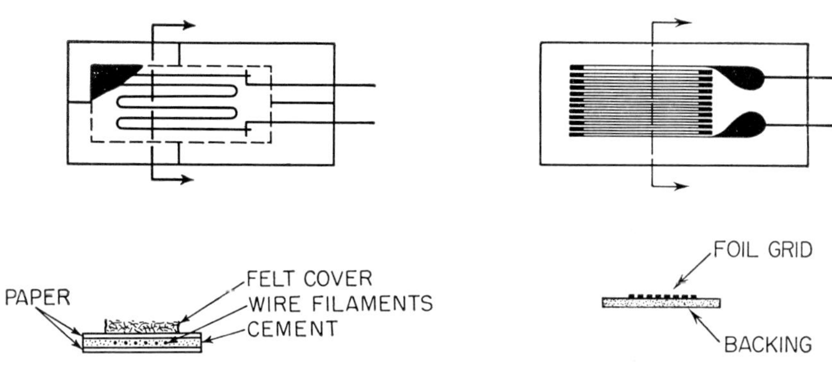

FIG. 2-1. Wire and foil strain gage construction.

in enlarged tabs to which lead wires can be soldered or welded. Foil gages are also produced with integral leads. These gages, like their wire counterparts, come mounted on paper or plastic backing.

The principle of the foil strain gage offers a number of advantages. The width of the foil at the end of each loop can be greatly increased to reduce the sensitivity of the gage to transverse strains. The cross section of the conductor is rectangular, resulting in a higher ratio of surface area to cross-sectional area. This in turn yields augmented heat-dissipation characteristics and improved adhesion between the grid and the backing material. The gage factors of foil gages are characteristically 5 to 10 per cent greater than those of equivalent wire gages. A major benefit derived from the foil strain gage construction is the ease with which a variety of grid sizes and configurations can be manufactured. Essentially, any pattern which can be drawn can be produced.

As is readily apparent, the total cost of materials in the metallic resistance strain gages is very slight. Gage costs arise largely from the practice of maintaining accurate control of gage resistance and gage factor.

Continual improvement of manufacturing techniques, with the aid of statistical quality-control methods, has resulted in making these strain gages available at a price which allows their use in relatively large quantities. Incidentally, the same is not especially true for the instruments which are necessary to translate the strain gage language into numbers usable by the engineer. These instruments are apt to be both complex and expensive, particularly for those cases in which it is desired to record simultaneously the output of a large number of strain gages. If only a few gages are to be used and the strains being measured are static or incremental, the equipment can be quite inexpensive and simple. With

Fig. 2-2. Silicon semiconductor strain gage (Strainistor). *(Courtesy of Century Electronics and Instruments, Inc.)*

piezoresistive strain gages the output signal is great enough so that amplification equipment can be drastically reduced or eliminated altogether.

The piezoresistive strain gage (Fig. 2-2) is composed of a piece of semiconducting material such as silicon cut from a large single crystal of the same material (or vapor-grown in the form of a whisker) and cemented to a paper, plastic, or mica carrier for handling and bonding. The crystals are grown under closely regulated conditions, with controlled amounts of impurities added to obtain the desired performance characteristics. Both the gage resistance and gage factor can be adjusted over wide ranges by comparatively small changes in the impurity content. In the same physical size, for instance, the resistance can be varied by a factor of 1,000, and the gage factor can be varied from -100 to $+200$.

TYPES OF RESISTANCE STRAIN GAGES

In order to adapt the resistance strain gage to use under specialized and extreme conditions, a great variety of gage types has been developed. The elements of the gage which are varied in these modifications include the filament material, the backing material, the grid configuration and resistance, and the cements employed in bonding the filament to the carrier and the gage to the test surface.

For gages which are to be used at temperatures below 180°F, a thermoplastic cement is very satisfactory. For higher gage-operating temperatures, up to 300 or 400°F, a thermosetting cement is employed. Temperatures above 400°F will generally necessitate special ceramic cements. Carrier materials may be paper, plastic, mica, ceramic, etc., and must, of course, be selected for compatibility with the cement and the expected operating conditions. When static, slowly varying, or incremental strains are to be measured, a gage made with an Advance filament is commonly selected because of its low temperature coefficient of resistance. For situations involving dynamic strains, gages with Iso-elastic filaments may be used in order to take advantage of the accompanying higher gage factor. Advance gages, incidentally, are perfectly usable for measuring dynamic strains, but their output will be only a little over half as great as can be obtained from the Iso-elastic gages.

While the basic strain gage consists of a single foil or wire grid, it may be necessary in measuring strains in complex parts to employ a multigrid gage known as a *rosette*. This type of gage has two, three, or four separate grids with various angular orientations, and such a gage can be used to determine principal strain magnitudes and directions in general biaxial stress fields.

Among other refinements in special attributes of strain gages, there are gages available with special thin-base paper for rapid evaporation of the cement solvent for those instances in which fast-drying time is a factor. There are also gages with special dual leads for use in cyclic strain applications which might otherwise result in fatigue of the strain gage; and gages with their grid elements so disposed that when used on a particular material their output is proportional to stress rather than strain. These latter gages are known as "stress gages." Other strain gages are made with self-temperature-compensating filaments, and still others with the capacity to follow strains beyond the yield point, to elongations as high as 10 per cent.

Installation techniques and methods of protecting the gages have developed to the point that strain gages can now be used in almost any place and under a wide range of environmental conditions. Whether one wishes to know the strain in the hot, oily crankcase of an internal-combustion engine, or in a reinforcing rod buried deep in the concrete columns of a building, or in the whirling inferno of a gas turbine, the answers to these questions are now within our grasp.

While all the statements made here refer to strain gage practices in the United States, in general strain gages are similar in materials and construction, bonded with similar cements, and subject to about the same instrumentation problems the world over.

BASIC INSTRUMENTATION

Since the bonded resistance strain gage operates on the principle that the electrical resistance of the gage varies with strain, in order to make use of the gage it must be connected in some circuit for measuring small changes in resistance. The amount of resistance change in the gage corresponding to a particular load on the piece being tested is the value of ΔR in Eq. (2-1). The values of R, the nominal gage resistance, and F, the gage factor, are also known because this latter information is supplied by the strain gage manufacturer. The only unknown quantity then remaining in the equation is $\Delta L/L$, the unit strain. Equation (2-1) can be rewritten in the form

$$\epsilon = \frac{\Delta L}{L} = \frac{\Delta R/R}{F} \tag{2-2}$$

In other words, unit strain equals the unit change in resistance ($\Delta R/R$) divided by the gage factor. The unit strain caused by a particular load is determined by merely substituting the known and measured quantities in the above equation. If a greater load is placed on the same test piece, greater surface strains will result, which in turn will strain the filament of the gage and increase ΔR. When the new value of ΔR is substituted into the above equation, it can be solved for the magnitude of the surface strains corresponding to the increased load.

This procedure is all very simple except for one item. Some device is needed for measuring ΔR. ΔR is a very small quantity and could be determined by accurately measuring the initial (unstrained) resistance R_0 and the resistance of the gage under loaded conditions R_1 and then subtracting the smaller from the larger. Notice that the value of R (the nominal gage resistance, and the denominator in the term $\Delta R/R$) need be known only to an accuracy of approximately plus or minus 1 per cent since errors in calculated strain due to errors in R will be of the same order. R_0 and R_1, however, whose difference is ΔR, must be known to an accuracy of one-thousandth of 1 per cent or better, since in the subtracting process the first four or more significant figures will drop out.

To illustrate the size of ΔR, consider a 120-ohm strain gage with a gage factor or strain sensitivity of 2.0. If this is cemented to a steel piece and then the piece is subjected to a stress of, say, 1,000 psi, it is possible to calculate the magnitude of ΔR from Eqs. (1-1) and (2-1).

By Eq. (1-1)

$$E = \frac{\sigma}{\epsilon} \qquad \text{or} \qquad \epsilon = \frac{\sigma}{E}$$

Since E for steel is approximately 30×10^6 psi, then the unit strain is 1,000/30,000,000, or 0.000033 in. per in.

Now substituting this quantity of strain for $\Delta L/L$ in Eq. (2-1), along with the known gage factor and nominal gage resistance,

$$\frac{\Delta R}{R} = F\frac{\Delta L}{L} \qquad \text{and} \qquad \Delta R = RF\frac{\Delta L}{L}$$

Therefore,

$$\Delta R = 120 \times 2.0 \times 0.000033 = 0.008 \text{ ohm}$$

It is apparent from these calculations that, in order to determine ΔR accurately, an instrument is required which can measure R_0 and R_1 to within about 1/1,000 ohm. Conventional ohmmeters are not capable of measuring resistance with sufficient precision to detect such minute differences. There is a form of electrical circuit, however, known as the *bridge* type, which can perform this task adequately.

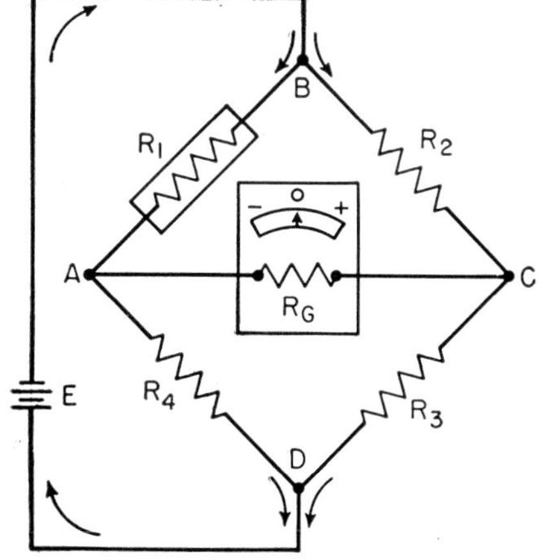

FIG. 2-3. Basic Wheatstone-bridge circuit for precision measurement of resistance.

Figure 2-3 is a schematic diagram of a form of bridge circuit widely used for precision measurement of resistance. The bridge is composed of four resistors connected in a definite pattern, a battery or current source, and a sensitive galvanometer. This system, devised by S. H. Christie in 1833, and named the *Wheatstone bridge* after Sir Charles Wheatstone, who first made significant use of the principle, is one of the most convenient and accurate methods of resistance measurement ever conceived. In Fig. 2-3 assume that R_1 is an unknown resistance, R_2 and R_3 are "ratio arms," and R_4 is a resistance whose value is known precisely. It can be shown (and will be, in Chap. 4) that, when resistance values in this circuit are such that no current flows through the galvanometer, then R_1 is to R_4 as R_2 is to R_3. That is,

$$\frac{R_1}{R_4} = \frac{R_2}{R_3}$$

From this,

$$R_1 = \frac{R_2}{R_3} R_4$$

A mechanical analog of the Wheatstone bridge is a simple lever balance system as illustrated in Fig. 2-4. The unknown weight in the figure represents the unknown resistance R_1 and the small known weight the resistor R_4. Similarly the respective moment arms of these

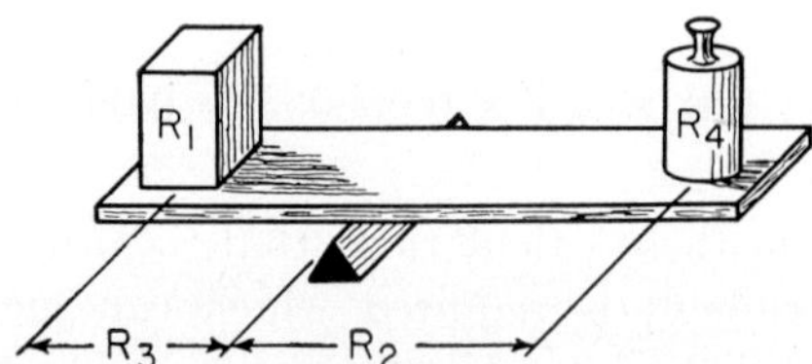

FIG. 2-4. Mechanical analog of the Wheatstone bridge.

weights from the fulcrum are equivalent to R_2 and R_3. From elementary statics it is obvious that when the lever is in a state of balance, then $R_1R_3 = R_2R_4$, or $R_1/R_4 = R_2/R_3$, from which $R_1 = (R_2/R_3)R_4$. Thus the weight of R_1 can be obtained by multiplying the known weight R_4 by the ratio R_2/R_3. Just as the lever system is termed "balanced" when there is no motion of the ends of the lever, so is the Wheatstone bridge *balanced* when there is no current through the galvanometer. With a resistor R_4 whose value is known to a high degree of precision and with means for measuring the ratio R_2/R_3 precisely, the resistance of R_1 can be determined very accurately with the Wheatstone-bridge circuit. In practice the resistor R_1 will be the resistance of a strain gage.

After the strain gage is cemented to a test piece and connected into the Wheatstone bridge as R_1, the bridge can be balanced by adjusting the ratio R_2/R_3, thus determining the exact resistance of the gage which corresponds to zero load. The process of adjusting the ratio R_2/R_3 is equivalent to moving the fulcrum of the lever system until the weights just balance each other. As the part to which the strain gage is bonded is loaded, the surface strains will be transmitted to the filament, changing its resistance. This is like adding weight to the left-hand side of the lever system and results in unbalancing the Wheatstone bridge, causing current to flow through the galvanometer. The bridge can be rebalanced by again adjusting the ratio R_2/R_3 until there is no current through the galvanometer. In this manner the new strain gage resistance corresponding to a particular load is determined. The difference between the two resistances (obtained before loading and while loaded) is the ΔR which can be substituted into Eq. (2-2) to obtain the unit strain. In actual practice the process is much simpler than outlined above. There are special Wheatstone bridges designed specifically for use with strain gages. These are constructed so that the bridge balancing control is calibrated in micro-inches per inch, and thus it is possible to read the unit strain directly from the instrument without any of the above arithmetic.

WHAT THE STRAIN GAGE WILL DO

The strain gage has been extolled as an extremely useful tool, but in a large part its utility will depend upon what the user asks of it. The experimental stress analyst should have a broad knowledge of what can be and has been done with strain gages. Coupled with this, incidentally, he should have enough imagination to be able to adapt strain gages to his own particular uses, since seldom are two applications identical. Basically, of course, the strain gage is used to procure accurate information about the magnitude, distribution, and directions of strains in loaded bodies. This means that the stress analyst should also have a complete understanding of the relationships between stress and strain.

The subject of experimental strain analysis can be broken down arbitrarily into four major divisions as follows:

1. Analysis of new designs.
2. Trouble shooting and correcting old designs.
3. Service-load analysis.
4. Theoretical investigations.

In designing machine parts it is now but rarely necessary, because of technological advances, to multiply design calculations by safety factors as high as 4 or 5 as was at one time general practice. On the other hand, it is not yet possible to design parts with no provision for unknowns. There are still a number of variables for which the designer must make either intelligent estimates or out-and-out allowances in order not to have too many unpredicted failures on his hands. As an example, one factor for which allowance must always be made is that of material variations. These arise through variations in composition, heat-treatment, work hardening, and other factors which are difficult to control accurately. There is little which the designer can do about this unknown except to overdesign by 10 or 20 per cent to cover most of the material variations. Another unknown facing the designer is that he usually lacks information as to the exact nature and magnitude of the loads to which the part will be subjected in service. Here, thanks to the strain gage, he is not completely helpless. By taking strain gage records of typical service loads, sufficient data can often be accumulated so that much of the variability of actual service conditions can be reduced by statistical and other methods to usable design information. While it is obviously impossible in most cases to make a precise prediction of service loads or stresses purely on the basis of past data, it is possible to make a logical and reasonably accurate estimate. Figure 2-5 illustrates the use of strain gages by the

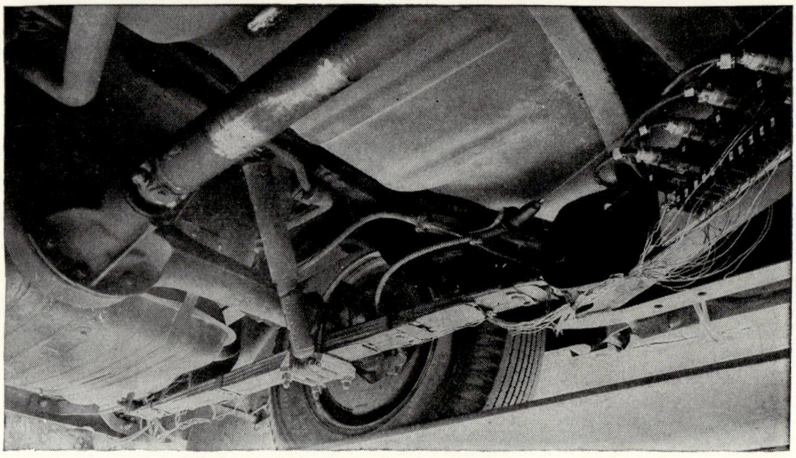

FIG. 2-5. Underneath view of passenger car with strain gages installed on the leaf-spring assembly. (*Courtesy of General Motors Proving Ground.*)

General Motors Proving Ground for studying the service stresses in an automobile leaf-spring assembly. The purpose of this series of tests was to determine the effectiveness of a deflection-limiting bumper in controlling spring stresses under extreme operating conditions.

The designer must also be able to evaluate the severity of any stress concentrations which he may be forced to include in his design. There are quite extensive data available on isolated stress concentrations of conventional form. Many design cases, however, such as complex forgings and castings, involve multiple interfering stress concentrations for which there are no data and in which the stresses are impossible to calculate. Once again the strain gage can come to the designer's aid. He can actually measure strains in the critical regions of the part and with this knowledge adjust the design for better stress distribution. In Fig. 2-6 a group of foil strain gages is being used to determine the stress in the fillet of a stud.

In developing new designs of machines or their parts, there is often a great deal to be gained from constructing a "pilot model" and subjecting this model to an intensive experimental stress analysis. For one thing, the study may point out design weaknesses which could have led to undesirable field failures if not corrected. Secondly, such an investigation can give sufficient information to bring about a more uniform

FIG. 2-6. Foil strain gage installation for determination of radial and tangential stresses in the fillet of a stud. (*Courtesy of The Budd Company.*)

stress distribution and in some cases reduce the amount of material in the part.

It is not uncommon for a manufacturer of mechanical equipment to experience an "epidemic" of a certain type of service failure. Without knowing anything about the real cause of the failure he may, if physical conditions permit, rectify the situation by merely increasing the size of the apparently weak part, that is, by "beefing it up." However, an investigation with strain gages might have shown him that the part which failed was not inherently weak but was being greatly overloaded by unappreciated service conditions such as vibration, misalignment, or deflection. In this case strengthening the part which had been failing may result only in transferring the failure to some other member of the same assembly. Thus, with judicious application of strain gages, it is possible to learn a great deal about the loads and stresses which are encountered by a machine part under service conditions.

For example, a shaft designed for pure torque may be subjected to combined bending and torsion. A turbine blade may be vibrating because of aerodynamic loading. Part of the traction gear of a locomotive may be receiving unpredicted shock loading, or the inertia loads on a heavy-duty crane may occasionally be much in excess of the calculated values. These and countless other examples could be given to indicate the value of experimental strain analysis with the bonded wire strain gage.

Besides directly applicable uses such as are indicated above, the strain gage is capable of significant utility in what might be termed "theoretical investigations." For instance, residual stresses can be measured with strain gages by cementing the gages in place, taking a zero reading, and then releasing the stresses by the most expedient cutting or drilling method and taking a second reading. Strain gages are also used in checking elasticity theories by actually measuring strains under various forms of loading and comparing the data with calculated theoretical results. Strain gages are widely used to give general information which can lead indirectly to superior designs. Strain gage records have been taken of vessels subjected to explosive pressures. Studies have been made of rail stresses at railroad-track curves. There have also been investigations of the stresses induced in ship plates during the launching process. In brief, any indeterminate loading can be brought into the realm of actual numbers; and it is numbers which are important to the designer. To repeat an often-quoted but no less applicable idea, "We know really very little about a phenomenon until we can express its manifestations numerically."

The foregoing illustrations give but a glimpse of the possible applications and versatility of the bonded wire strain gage. Ultimately, the principal limitation to strain gage applications is nothing more than the imagination of the user. Besides all those cases in which the strain gage is utilized directly for strain (or stress) indications, it has limitless potentialities as a device for measuring forces, torques, loads, pressures, and other physical phenomena. One of the peculiar characteristics of the strain gage and Wheatstone-bridge combination is its ability to separate forces from moments electrically. Methods and techniques of using strain gages as physical sensing units, or transducers, will be dealt with in detail in a later chapter.

BIBLIOGRAPHY

Strain Gage Construction

Aughtie, F.: Electrical Resistance Wire Strain Gauges, *Inst. Mech. Engrs. (London), J. & Proc.*, vol. 152, pp. 213–214, September, 1945.

Dorey, S. F.: Wire-wound Electrical Resistance Strain Gauges, *Engineer,* vol. 177, pp. 375–376, May 12, 1944, pp. 386–387, May 19, 1944.

Edwards, J.: Electrical Resistance Wire Strain Gauges, *Metal Treatment,* vol. 14, nos. 52, 53, pp. 213–221, Winter, 1947–1948, pp. 17–26, Spring, 1948.

Hooton, F. W., and P. H. Sulzberger: Strain Gauges of Electrical Resistance Type, *Elec. Eng. and Merchandiser,* vol. 23, no. 9, pp. 302–306, December, 1946.

Savic, P.: Wire Resistance Strain Gage, *Research (London),* vol. 1, no. 3, pp. 98–106, December, 1947.

Van Leeuwen, E. G., and W. F. Gunning: Resistance Wire Strain Gage Applications and Circuits, *Product Eng.,* vol. 16, pp. 443–449, July, 1945.

Woodford, C. G. A.: Electrical Resistance Strain Gauge, *Aircraft Production,* vol. 6, no. 67, pp. 245–249, May, 1944.

Strain Gauging, *Iron and Steel,* vol. 20, no. 11, pp. 492–493, October, 1947.

Strain Gage Conductor Properties

deForest, A. V.: Characteristics and Aircraft Applications of Wire Resistance Strain Gages, *Instruments,* vol. 15, no. 4, pp. 112–114 and 136–137, April, 1942.

Kammer, E. W., and T. E. Pardue: Electrical Resistance Changes of Fine Wires during Elastic and Plastic Strains, *Proc. SESA,* vol. 7, no. 1, pp. 7–20, 1949.

Thomson, W. (Lord Kelvin): On the Electrodynamic Qualities of Metals, *Phil. Trans. Roy. Soc. (London),* vol. 146, pp. 649–751, 1856.

Tomlinson, H.: The Influence of Stress and Strain on the Action of Physical Forces, *Phil. Trans. Roy. Soc. (London),* vol. 174, pp. 1–172, 1883.

Elementary Applications

Fehr, R. O.: Practical Strain-gage Applications, *Electronics,* vol. 18, no. 1, pp. 112–115, January, 1945.

Heth, S. C.: Use of Strain Gages for Farm Equipment Design, *Agri. Eng.,* vol. 28, no. 11, pp. 509–511, 516, November, 1947.

Nolan, R. W.: Strain Gages, *Chem. Eng.,* vol. 60, no. 9, pp. 217–228, September, 1953.

Thomson, W. T.: Airframe Stress Analysis by Electrical Strain Gage, *Aero Dig.,* vol. 42, no. 5, pp. 259, 261, 263, May, 1943.

Applications of the Electric Strain Gage in the Solution of Aircraft Structure Design Problems, *Automotive Inds.,* vol. 87, no. 12, pp. 40–42, 64, Dec. 15, 1942.

Strain Gauge Issue, *Instruments & Automation,* vol. 31, no. 3, pp. 446–473, March, 1958.

Stress Analysis, Electric Systems for Gauging Static and Dynamic Strains, *Automobile Engr.,* vol. 36, no. 479, pp. 401–406, September, 1946.

EXERCISES

2-1. Take a suitable length of 0.001-in. Advance wire (obtainable in spools from Driver-Harris Corp.) and suspend it from the ceiling of the laboratory. Hang a small lightweight pan of about 2-in. diameter (say, cardboard, or thin sheet plastic) on the lower end of the wire. Add small weights to the pan and measure the changes in length and resistance of the wire. Plot the results, and determine the gage factor of the wire. (Advance and other strain gage wires may also be obtained from strain gage manufacturers.)

2-2. Examine a flat-wound, a coil-wound, and a foil strain gage with a magnifying glass and backlighting. Sketch the grid configurations in detail.

2-3. Calculate the expected resistance change in a 55-ohm strain gage mounted at the root of a 1-in.-square cross-section aluminum cantilever beam 30 in. long carrying a 10-lb load at its extremity. The gage factor of the strain gage is 1.75, and its gage length is 0.85 in.

2-4. Account for the difference between the gage factor of a strain gage and that of the conductor from which it is made.

2-5. Compare the expected performance obtained from a flat-wound and coil-wound strain gage mounted on a very thin metal sheet in bending.

2-6. From the data presented in Table 2-1, design a strain gage having a gage factor of zero.

2-7. In Fig. 2-3 resistances R_1 and R_2 are 120 ohms each and R_3 and R_4 480 ohms each. The bridge is initially in balance. R_1 is a strain gage having a gage factor of 1.9 and is subjected to a strain of 875 micro-inches per in. Determine the change in resistance R_4 necessary to rebalance the bridge.

2-8. What effect, if any, would you expect from replacing the direct-current voltage source in Fig. 2-3 by an alternating current?

2-9. Derive the formula $F = 1 + 2\mu$, which gives a purely geometrical relationship between gage factor and change in dimension of a cylinder. Why do the actual gage factors of many materials fail to fit this relationship?

2-10. The gage factors for most materials in the plastic region are 2.0. Why?

2-11. Devise a system for loading an unmounted strain gage as a tensile member and proceed to test the gage in this fashion, recording resistance versus load for a series of loads.

2-12. Devise an instrument to measure pressures up to 100 psi using a strain gage as the sensing element.

2-13. Describe the apparatus used by Thomson when he first observed the strain-sensitivity effect in conductors.

3 BASIC STRAIN GAGE TECHNIQUES

BONDING TECHNIQUES

The resistance strain gage has been shown to be an extremely versatile, accurate, and sensitive device. Fundamentally, though, its performance is absolutely dependent on the bond by which it is attached to the test piece. It is readily apparent that if a precise measure of the surface strain is desired, then the sensitive filament in the gage must have this strain transmitted to it undiminished by the bonding cement. This can be accomplished only by a perfect bonding job. The methods of strain gage installation described in this chapter in general parallel those of the gage manufacturers, and in some cases may be direct quotations from such sources without further acknowledgment. While parts of the forthcoming instructions may appear unduly elaborate, these techniques represent standard recommended procedures for obtaining maximum accuracy and stability from the gages.

The choice of a cement for bonding the strain gage to the test piece is dictated by three principal considerations: the materials used in the gage construction, the environmental conditions within which the gage must perform satisfactorily, and the time available for making the gage installation. For example, some strain gages employ paper backing and a nitrocellulose cement in their construction. It is obvious that the adhesive for bonding the gage to a test surface must be selected for compatibility with these materials, and the bonding procedure required for the adhesive should not subject the gage to a high temperature or to other deleterious conditions.

Commercial strain gages for operation at 350°F and below (gages and techniques for temperatures from 350 to 2000°F are described in Chap. 12) fall into three major categories, according to the backing material:

1. Paper, with nitrocellulose adhesive ($T < 160°F$).
2. Bakelite, with cellulose fiber ($T < 350°F$) or glass fiber ($T < 450°F$).

3. Epoxy ($T < 200°F$).

The most commonly used cements for application at temperatures below 350°F include Duco (nitrocellulose), epoxy, bakelite, and acrylic.

Table 3-1 provides a summary of strain gage cements, their principal characteristics, and the general types of strain gages with which they are compatible. Strain gages from different manufacturers will differ in materials and construction, and each manufacturer will generally supply instructions and recommendations for the proper cements and bonding procedures with the gages. Deviations from these recommended practices should be made only with knowledge of the consequences, or after testing, to be certain that the modification in procedure does not detract from the expected performance of the gage.

Generally speaking, gages embodying paper, cellulose cements, or epoxy plastic, or bonded with cellulose, epoxy, or acrylic cement, must be employed at temperatures below about 160°F in static strain measurements to avoid slip or "creep" in the cement. At higher temperatures the cement becomes too soft to transmit all the strain from the test piece to the strain gage filament. This malfunction can lead to serious errors when measuring static strains. Applications for service at temperatures above 200°F and up to 350°F will commonly require bakelite or epoxy strain gages and bakelite or high-temperature epoxy cements. The bakelite strain gage and cement combination is also to be recommended for extended-service installations in which long-time stability is desired.

The epoxy and acrylic cements have come into use as the result of efforts to obtain room-temperature-curing adhesives with short curing times and superior mechanical properties. These epoxy cements generally cure in less time than nitrocellulose cements and produce a bond which is satisfactory for static strain measurement at temperatures 30 to 50°F greater than for the nitrocellulose cements. The salient feature of cyanoacrylate cement is the near-instantaneous bond obtained. This adhesive can be considered a contact cement, and through its use gage-installation time can be radically reduced.

SURFACE PREPARATION FOR BONDING STRAIN GAGES

Before cementing any strain gage to a test part, certain surface requirements should be met in order to ensure a strong bond between the gage and surface. Preparation of the test surface prior to cementing the gage is nominally the same for all gages and cements. The surface on which the gage is to be mounted should be smooth in a gross sense, but not too highly polished, since the latter condition does not promote adhesion. Naturally, all scale, rust, and paint should be removed from metal surfaces. This can usually be accomplished by successive application of

Table 3-1. Strain Gage Cement Summary*

Item	Organic							Ceramic			
	Solvent release, room-temperature curing		Thermo-plastic, melting	Chemical setting				Drying, heat curing	Chemical setting, heat curing	Fusing	
				Room-temperature curing		Heat curing				Molten spray	Heat curing
Base	Nitro-cellulose		Shellac	Acrylic	Epoxy	Epoxy	Phenolic	Silicate	Phosphate	Refractory oxide	Glass
Cements and properties	SR-4 and post yield	Duco	DeKhotinsky hard	Eastman 910, F-88	EPY-150	EPY-400	Bakelite	RX-1	AL-P1, PBX, Brimor	Rokide A, Rokide C	L6AC
Cure temperature, °F	Room to 150	Room to 150	Melts at 275	Room	Room to 150	250–500	250–350	220	600	None	1,800
Cure time	2–10 hr	12–48 hr	When cool	1–5 min	10–70 hr	2–10 hr	5–6 hr	1 hr at temperature	1 hr	None	½ hr
Cure pressure psi	1–5	1–5	1–15	1–15	5–15	5–50	50–100	None	None	None	None
Maximum operating temperature, °F	150	150	100	150	150	400 normal, 500 after proper cure	300 continuous to 500 for short time	500	>1,000	>1,000	Approx. 1,500
Strain gage compatibility	Use with quick-drying thin paper-backed gages	All paper-backed gages	All	All except paper wrap-around construction	All	All that will stand cure temperature. Exception: all paper-backed	Phenolic-backed only	Strippable, transferable, and ceramic-insulated	Strippable, transferable, and ceramic-insulated	Strippable, transferable, and ceramic-insulated	Strippable, transferable, and ceramic-insulated
Specimen material compatibility	All except plastics soluble in MEK and acetone and unbondable plastics	All except plastics soluble in MEK and acetone and unbondable plastics	All except some plastics	All except some plastics	All except some plastics	All except some plastics and reactive metals	All except some plastics and reactive metals	All except some plastics and reactive metals	All except some plastics and reactive metals	All except some plastics	All metals that will stand cure temperature
Strain limit	>10% at room, ½% at −320 °F	>10% ½% at −320	2–3%	>2% >½% at −320	>2% ½% at −320	2% 1% at −320	2–3% ½% at −320	½%	½%	2%	½%
Electrical properties	Excellent over operating temperature range	Excellent over operating temperature range	Excellent	Excellent	Excellent	Excellent	Excellent to 300°F. Poor in 400–500°F range	Deteriorates with increase in temperature. Limits useful temperature	Deteriorates with increase in temperature. Limits useful temperature	Excellent but deteriorates at high temperature	Excellent
Humidity resistance	Fair, absorbs up to 2% water	Fair, absorbs up to 2% water	Good	Fair, absorbs up to 0.3% water	Good, absorbs up to 0.1% water	Good, absorbs up to 0.1% water	Fair, absorbs up to 0.2% water	Poor, is hygroscopic, soluble in water	Fair, is hygroscopic	Good, is porous and somewhat hygroscopic	Excellent

* Courtesy of Baldwin-Lima-Hamilton Corporation.

two or three grades of abrasive paper, finishing with the fine paper (say, 180 grit) in a figure-eight or random-motion pattern. If the metal is pitted or rough, as is apt to be the case for forgings and castings, it may be necessary to lightly grind off a spot a little larger than the gage. Initially highly polished surfaces should be roughened slightly with a medium-fine-grit abrasive paper or light sandblast to improve adhesion.

With a surface of approximately the correct degree of roughness, it is next necessary to do a thorough cleaning job. Gages will not adhere well except to immaculately clean surfaces. Some volatile solvent such as acetone, trichloroethylene, toluene, or methyl ethyl ketone will ordinarily perform this function adequately. Adhesion can sometimes be augmented by the application of a metal conditioner to the surface, followed by a neutralizing agent.

To secure maximum bond strength, it is imperative that cleanliness be maintained until the gage is firmly in place. A clean bottle of solvent and clean cloths should be used, and neither the gage nor test surface should be touched by the fingers after cleaning. The cement and strain gage should be applied immediately after cleaning the test surface. If gages have been handled prior to use, the backs of the gages can be cleaned by wiping with a clean cotton gauze or swab dampened slightly with solvent. This should be done with extreme care in the case of paper gages to avoid damaging the gages with the solvent. Since a certain amount of contact between the fingers and the strain gage or test surface seems unavoidable, it is considered good practice to wipe the fingers as frequently as necessary with solvent-dampened clean cotton gauze.

In order to orient the strain gage in the desired direction it is advisable to scribe guide lines on the prepared surfaces. The guide lines can either outline the gage boundary or coincide with the longitudinal and transverse center lines of the strain gage if the latter are provided. The scribed lines should not pass under the strain gage, since a burr raised by the scriber may pierce the gage and result in a short or open circuit.

NITROCELLULOSE CEMENT

Nitrocellulose cement is ordinarily used only with paper-backed strain gages. Since the cement cures by the evaporation of a solvent, it is not suitable for use with the impermeable epoxy or bakelite strain gages. For paper gages the manufacturer commonly supplies a cellulose cement, but ordinary Duco household cement, which is available in the "dime store," will work very successfully for this purpose. After preparing the test surface as described in the preceding section, the actual cementing process is about the same as would be used in repairing a broken piece of china. A fairly liberal layer of cement is spread on both the gage and the prepared surface, and the gage is set in place at once. In the first few seconds after the gage has been applied to the surface it will be possible to slide the gage around slightly in order to align it with the guide lines and orient it in the desired direction. Then the gage is pressed or rolled lightly with a finger to squeeze out most of the excess cement. It is not necessary to try to squeeze out all the excess cement since this will be taken care of by the clamping pressure which is applied while the gage is drying. A properly cemented gage should look something like Fig. 3-1, with a small bead of excess cement entirely around the edge of the gage, indicating that there was cement under the whole gage when it was applied. Scraping off this excess will shorten the required drying time.

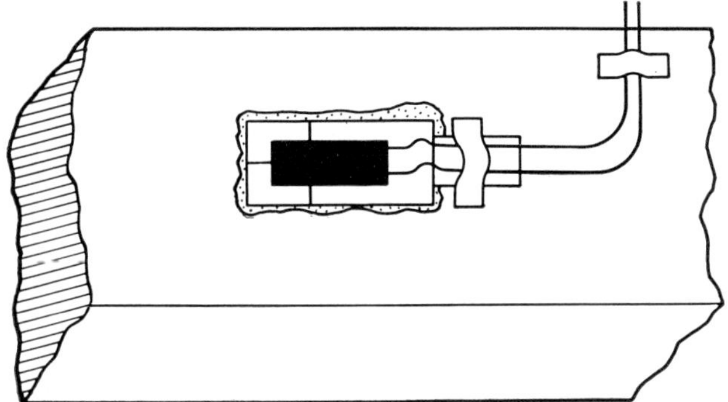

Fig. 3-1. Appearance of a properly applied strain gage.

While the gage is drying, it should be held in place with about a 1-lb clamping force. Greater pressures may result in grounding of the gage wire or lead to the underlying material. If conditions permit, a 1-lb weight placed on the gage makes a very suitable clamp. For gages which are mounted so that it is impossible to use a weight, some form of spring clamp should be used. If a C clamp is used, there should be a spring between it and the strain gage in order to keep the force relatively constant as the cement flows or shrinks. An ideal clamp for this purpose is the Neg'ator constant-force clamp.[1] Figure 3-2 illustrates the use of this spring in clamping a strain gage for drying.

The drying time allowed for paper-backed strain gages of the Duco type will depend partly upon experience and judgment and partly upon the degree of stability required of the gage. The drying time will also

[1] The Neg'ator Spring, manufactured by the Hunter Spring Company of Lansdale Pa., exhibits the unique property of constant force regardless of its extension. Because of certain prestressing techniques employed in the manufacturing process, the spring has a zero rate.

vary somewhat with the type of gage construction and the temperature and humidity of the surrounding atmosphere. Strain gages are available made with a special paper which allows extra-fast evaporation of the cement solvent and thus shorter drying time. With standard flat grid gages and household cement the clamp can be left on the gage for an hour or so and then removed and the gage left to air-dry for 18 to 24 hr at room temperature. The reason for removing the clamp is to permit

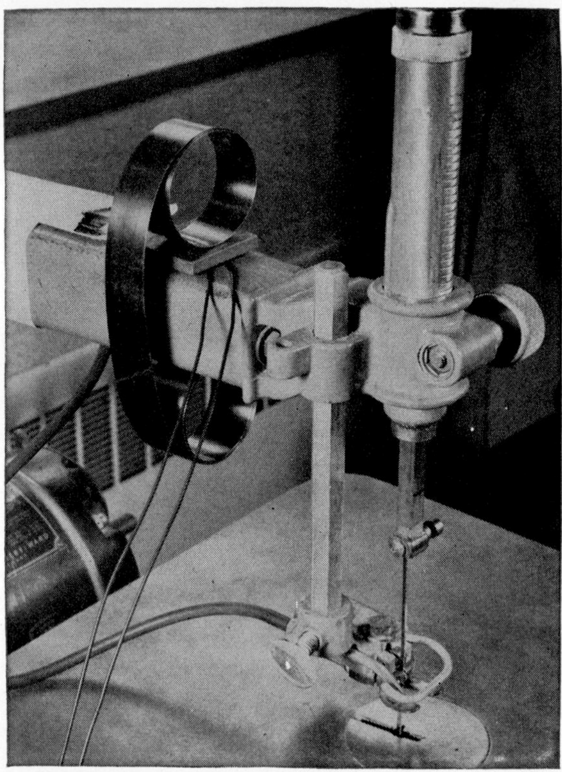

FIG. 3-2. Duco strain gage clamped with Neg'ator constant-force spring while drying.

the free circulation of air over the surface of the gage. Naturally the drying process can be accelerated by heating the strain gage. A small electric hair dryer with a built-in heater can be used for this purpose by blowing warm air directly on the gages. Temperatures for the thermoplastic gages should not be increased too rapidly because the cement may bubble. If radiant heat is employed, it is advisable to heat the metal adjacent to the gage and not the gage itself. After the gage has been left to air-dry for about an hour, the temperature can be gradually increased to as high as 170°F. At this temperature the strain gage will be dry in a few hours. If, during drying, the electrical resistance is measured between either strain gage lead and the metal surface to which the gage is being bonded, it will be found that, as the gage dries, the resistance increases. When the resistance levels off, the gage is dry. It is also possile t o somewhat accelerate the drying process by thinning the Duco cement slightly with acetone before applying it or by using the Baldwin SR-4 cement, which is comparatively fast-drying. Specific recommendations for drying procedures for the various paper-backed gages will be found in the manufacturers' bulletins. In general, however, it is not inconvenient merely to let the gages dry for a day, and this will result in essentially complete evaporation of the solvent. The two major exceptions to this would be cases in which the gages were located where the humidity was extraordinarily high or the temperature very low. In the latter case, particularly, heat drying is an absolute necessity in order to drive the solvent out of the cement.

BAKELITE CEMENT

Bakelite (phenol resin) cement is employed only with bakelite strain gages. This combination of cement and gage type is called for when operating temperatures exceed 200°F but not 350 or 450°F. For highly precise static strain measurements, the upper temperature is usually limited to 350°F, while in dynamic strain applications the allowable temperature may go over 450°F. In special cases, bakelite bonded strain gages have been used at temperatures as high as 600°F.

Bakelite strain gages are notably less flexible than paper- or epoxy-backed gages and correspondingly more difficult to bond to fillets and curved surfaces. Because of this characteristic and the special curing process required for the cement, bakelite gages bonded with bakelite cement are, as a rule, employed only when conditions demand the attributes obtainable with this combination. In general, bakelite gages and cement are used for any one or any combination of the following circumstances:

1. Where temperatures are between 150 and 450°F.
2. Where gage stability is required despite high humidity.
3. Where long-time gage stability or stability under generally adverse conditions is necessary.

Specific methods for dealing with extremes of time, temperature, and humidity are dealt with in detail in Chaps. 8, 9, and 12.

Bonding of bakelite strain gages with bakelite cement is preceded, as usual, by the surface-preparation procedures already described. The bakelite strain gage can be cleaned on its underside with a piece of clean cotton gauze saturated with acetone or a similar solvent. Once cleaned, it should be handled by the lead wires or with a pair of tweezers to preserve the freedom from contamination.

The next step is to apply a coat of bakelite cement to both the metal surface and the underside of the gage, eliminating any air bubbles that may have formed. The gage is placed in the proper position and correctly oriented while the cement is wet. The gage should next be covered by a strip of cellophane or scotch tape and a felt or neoprene pad for distributing the clamping pressure uniformly. A metal plate about ¼ in. thick can then be placed over this sandwich and the clamping pressure

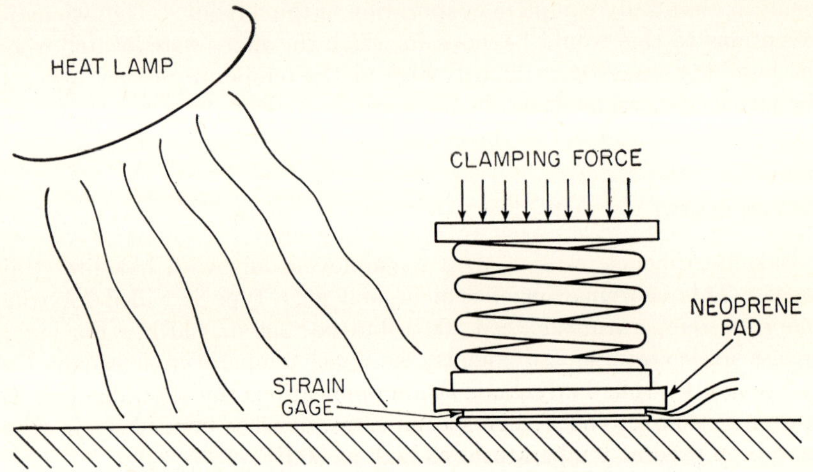

Fig. 3-3. Clamping and curing a bakelite-type strain gage.

applied. It is important, as in the case of the paper-backed gages, to exert the clamping force through some resilient member such as a compression spring or a thick piece of neoprene in order that the pressure will remain essentially constant while the cement is being cured. For best results, a clamping pressure of 100 to 200 psi should be employed, although satisfactory bonding can be accomplished at considerably lower pressures. Thirty pounds per square inch is considered a bare minimum. The clamping pressure should be left applied during the following recommended baking cycle:

1. One hour at 140°F.
2. Two hours at 175°F.
3. Two hours at 250°F.

The sketch in Fig. 3-3 illustrates the clamping and curing technique for bakelite strain gages. Gage stability will be improved noticeably if the gage is given an additional hour of baking at 275°F after removing the clamp. Best practice, as in the case of paper gages, is to apply the heat to the metal surface immediately adjacent to the gage rather than to the gage itself. If the strain gage is to be exposed in use to comparatively high temperatures (over the highest curing temperature in the above recommendations), the gage should be cycled to the maximum expected temperature once or twice before being put in use in order to obtain optimum stability. After the gage has been applied and baked according to the above recommendations, it should be tested in the manner described later in this chapter. Checks of gage resistance and of the resistance between the gage and ground are absolutely necessary if accurate work is to be done and gage results are to be trusted.

EPOXY CEMENTS

The epoxy cements can be used with paper, epoxy, or bakelite strain gages. These cements are available in a number of different formulations, requiring different curing procedures and exhibiting somewhat different characteristics. The room-temperature-curing epoxy cement will withstand temperatures to 200°F, is significantly less hygroscopic than nitrocellulose cement, is unaffected by oils and most common solvents, and can be cured by heating to allow using a strain gage in less than an hour after cementing.

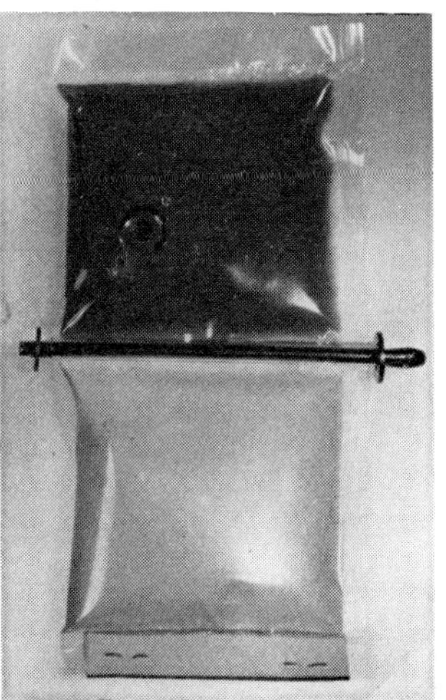

FIG. 3-4. Epoxy cement packaged for convenient mixing of two components. (*Courtesy of Baldwin-Lima-Hamilton Corporation.*)

This adhesive is sold commercially as two components—a resin and activator—packaged separately or in a two-compartment plastic mixing bag. In the more convenient latter form (Fig. 3-4), the user breaks the seal between the compartments, kneads the bag until complete mixing has occurred, and cuts off a corner of the bag to produce an opening from which the cement is squeezed. When the two components are packaged separately, it will be necessary to exercise considerable care in obtaining precisely the recommended proportions and in achieving complete mixing, if the cement is to develop its full potential strength when cured.

Some of the epoxy cements are self-polymerizing at room temperature and begin to cure immediately upon mixing. These cements will develop half their strength in 16 hr at room temperature, and full strength after about a week. Heating to 160°F will drastically shorten the curing time to approximately an hour. A method occasionally used in curing epoxy adhesives is to conduct from 30 to 50 milliamperes of current through the strain gage filament. The resulting heat will accelerate the curing process at least as effectively as an external heat source. The actual amount of current used will depend upon the type of metal and size and shape of the piece to which the gage is being bonded.

Different epoxy formulations, combined with different activators, produce a variety of operating characteristics and necessitate modifications in application and curing techniques. There are, for example, high-temperature epoxy cements which can be used, after a corresponding high-temperature cure, to 500°F. Epoxy cements are also formulated with or without filler materials. The nonfilled cements must be cured with very low clamping pressures (3 to 5 psi) to avoid squeezing too much cement from beneath the gage. Filled epoxy cements can be cured at somewhat higher clamping pressures (5 to 15 psi).

The gage application procedure when using epoxy cements is similar to that for nitrocellulose adhesives. After the mounting surface has been prepared, an adequate amount of cement is spread evenly over the gage area. The gage can be set in place immediately and oriented to match previously scribed guidelines. Gentle pressure with a finger can be used to squeeze out the excess adhesive. After this, the gage can be covered with a thin piece of teflon tape, and the clamping force applied. The clamping force should be applied through a sponge-rubber pad to distribute the pressure uniformly. The force can be obtained by a small weight on the pad or by taping the pad in place. Because many of the epoxy cements exhibit very little tackiness or strength when first applied, it is necessary that the strain gage be held in alignment by some positive means such as the above until cured. The gage installation is now ready for curing, and the manufacturer's instructions for time and temperature should be followed religiously. When the curing cycle has been completed, the clamping force, pad, and teflon tape can be removed, and the solder connections made to the strain gage.

An alternative procedure, first used with contact cements because of the precipitous bonding action, involves handling the gage during application with a piece of pressure-sensitive tape. Once the mounting surface is prepared and scribed, the strain gage is picked up by pressing over it a 2- or 3-in. length of masking tape (or similarly compliant transparent adhesive tape such as polyvinyl chloride). One end of the tape is pressed against the mounting surface adjacent to the gage area, and after spreading a uniform layer of cement over the gage area, the free portion of the tape (carrying the gage) is wiped down into place. The clamping force is then applied as before through a soft rubber pad over a piece of teflon. When curing is complete, the pad, teflon, and tape are removed. When using this technique, the adhesive on the pressure-sensitive tape should not, of course, be strong enough to damage the strain gage when the tape is removed. Should this condition exist, it can be remedied by dusting the adhesive side of the tape slightly with fine talcum powder. Removal of the tape is accomplished by peeling it slowly and gently back over the strain gage in a fashion such that the pull on the tape is exerted parallel to the mounting surface.

All other application procedures, such as surface preparation and cleaning, and the wiring and testing of the finished gage installation are nominally the same for the epoxy cements as for other adhesives.

CONTACT CEMENT

In order to avoid the curing time associated with most strain gage adhesives, a contact cement can be used. As implied by the name, this cement forms an immediate bond when the strain gage is placed in contact with the mounting surface. The gage can be used as soon as connections have been made to the leads.

A cyanoacrylate monomer (trade name, Eastman 910) is widely used as a strain gage contact cement. Hardening of the cement can be induced simply by applying pressure to a thin film of the liquid. For use with strain gages, however, it is common to accelerate the polymerization by employing a catalyst. This cement can be used with paper, epoxy, or bakelite strain gages. The upper temperature limit for the acrylic cement is approximately 200°F when used in static strain measurement.

The procedure for applying a strain gage with contact cement is simple and direct (Fig. 3-5). Since the gage cannot be moved or adjusted once it has touched the mounting area, it is common practice to handle the gage with a piece of transparent pressure-sensitive tape during application. Following preparation of the mounting surface, the strain gage is picked up on a convenient length of adhesive tape. The thick plastic carrier for the gage (if one is used) is stripped off. A uniform film of accelerator is applied over the back of the strain gage. One end of the tape is then pressed onto the mounting surface adjacent to the gage area in such a fashion that when the tape is rolled or wiped out straight, the gage will contact the surface properly oriented. Before wiping the tape and gage down against the surface, a generous bead of contact cement is applied in the fillet between the tape and mounting surface. With a firm, progressive pressure the tape is then wiped into place. Gentle thumb pressure over the gage area will ensure that all sections of the gage are in intimate contact with the surface. After at least a minute the tape can be gently pulled from the gage. This should be done by slowly peeling back the tape over the gage, with the pull exerted parallel to the mounting surface. The strain gage is ready for use after the lead wires are connected. Several precautions should be noted when using the cyanoacrylate adhesive. The bond strength of this cement is severely weakened by water or alkali agents. As an example, evaporation of the volatile constituent in the catalyst after it has been applied to the back of the strain gage may cool the gage sufficiently to cause condensation

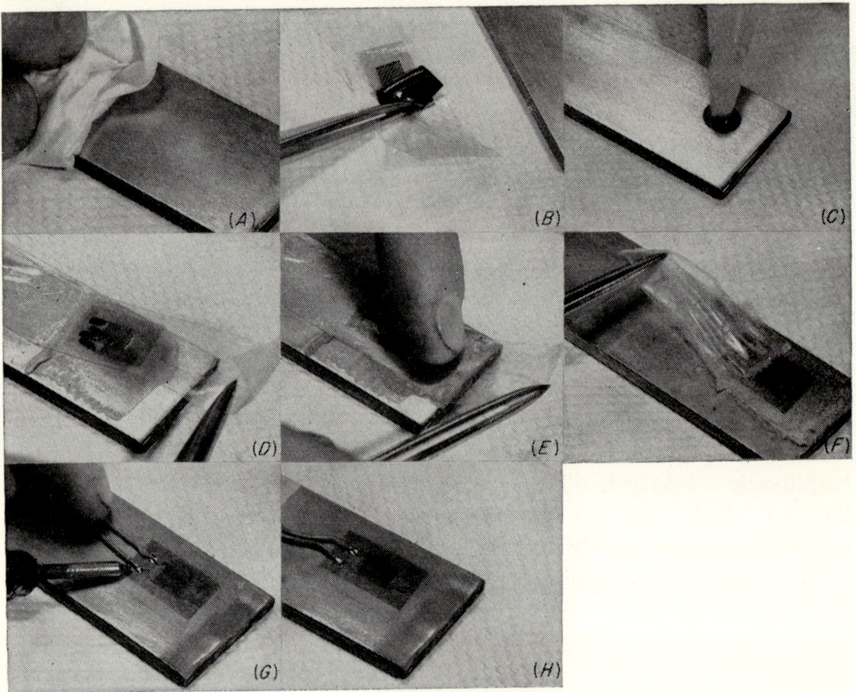

FIG. 3-5. Installation procedure for use with contact cement: (*A*) surface preparation and cleaning; (*B*) removal of plastic carrier after picking up with transparent cellulose tape; (*C*) application of contact cement; (*D*) tape and gage in position, ready to be wiped into place; (*E*) gage pressed firmly onto surface and bonded; (*F*) removal of transparent tape; (*G*) soldering leads; (*H*) completed installation. (*Courtesy of The Budd Company.*)

of a small amount of water vapor. To avoid this condition, it is well to warm the gage slightly. Similarly, once the gage has been cemented in place, the adhesive should be protected from water or vapor by adequate moistureproofing. Because of its sensitivity to moisture and alkali agents, the cyanoacrylate cement is not recommended for use on concrete. The bottle of cement should be stored under refrigeration at 40 to 50°F to prolong its shelf life. For the corresponding reason, bonding at temperatures below 70°F will require more than a 1-min wait between placement of the gage and removal of the tape. In extreme cases, polymerization can be accelerated by the application of mild heat from a hair dryer or an infrared lamp.

The cyanoacrylate adhesive forms an immediate tenacious bond to most materials, and once solidified, the cement is resistant to many solvents. The liquid cement can be removed with acetone, methyl ethyl ketone, or toluene. The removal of a strain gage bonded with cyanoacrylate cement can be accomplished by soaking the gage installation in dimethyl formamide for 5 to 15 min. Soaking in boiling water is also effective for this purpose.

OTHER STRAIN GAGE CEMENTS

Although the majority of strain gage installations have in the past been made with the adhesives described in the preceding paragraphs, numerous other cements have also been used successfully, and still others will undoubtedly be used in the future. The expanding adhesive technology can be expected to produce new bonding agents with short curing times and superior electrical and mechanical properties.

Among the rapidly setting adhesives that have been used for strain gage bonding, mention should be made of the dental cements. F-88[1] dental cement consists of a resin in powder form and a liquid activator. When all preparations for installing the strain gage have been completed, appropriate amounts of the powder and liquid are combined and mixed to a thin, pastelike consistency. A uniform layer of cement is then spread over the back of the gage and on the mounting surface, and the strain gage is set in place without delay. Firm thumb pressure over the strain gage is necessary to squeeze out the excess cement. Curing commences immediately at room temperature and is complete within a few minutes.

The F-88 cement not only cures quickly, but also demonstrates the capacity for bonding in the presence of moisture—even when the surface to which it is applied is wet or submerged in water. For gage installations where it is impossible to provide a dry surface, this cement is invaluable.

Another strain gage adhesive with rather unique properties is deKhotinsky cement. This is a thermoplastic material which acts as a fusible adhesive. The cement comes in stick form and is applied by heating the test surface until it will melt cement from the end of the stick. The actual procedure used in bonding a strain gage with deKhotinsky cement is first to clean and prepare the surface in the usual manner and then to heat the surface to approximately 285°F. The end of the cement stick is next applied to the hot area, and a thin layer of cement deposited over

[1] F-88 dental cement is available from American Consolidated Manufacturing Company, Incorporated, Industrial Division, Philadelphia, Pa.

a space large enough for the strain gage. The gage is immediately set in position and held there under light pressure for several minutes until the cement has cooled and hardened. This process is recommended only for use with bakelite gages because of the temperature to which the gage is subjected when first installed. These gages can later be removed by heating the cement to its melting temperature, and are suitable for reuse if handled with reasonable care.

LEAD WIRE INSTALLATIONS

As in other phases of strain gage technique, lead-wire installations to the gages must be made very carefully to assure precision and stability in the electrical output. The lead wires should be selected for low electrical resistance, quality of insulation, and flexibility and ease of handling. For room-temperature applications, 20-gage Belden No. 8014 has been widely used. This is a stranded wire covered with thermoplastic insulation. Higher-temperature applications require other insulating materials such as teflon, fiberglass, or ceramics.

The probability of damaging a strain gage during wiring will be greatly reduced if the instrument leads are firmly tied or cemented to the structure at a point near the gage *before* making the soldered connections to the gage. In order to prevent the application of any strain on the gage leads once the installation is completed, it is recommended that a small loop be placed in each of the leads as shown in Fig. 3-1. The usual procedure is to place a small piece of tape on the metal surface immediately adjacent to the gage and to tape down the soldered lead joints at this point. This gives a sort of shock absorber for the strain gage leads, and may often prevent an accidentally shorted gage circuit, as well as eliminating external strains on the gage. All lead wires from the instrument to the strain gage should be securely taped or cemented to the structure bearing the gage so that no relative motion occurs. If a large number of wires is employed, it may be desirable to cable the wires. This can be done by gathering the wires into a compact bundle, tying them at one point with one end of a long piece of cord, and continuing along the group of wires, placing a half hitch as often as necessary to retain the wires neatly.

The solder and flux used in joining lead wires to strain gages also deserve consideration. A noncorrosive flux such as rosin should always be used when making strain gage connections. Choice of a solder will depend upon the operating temperatures of the strain gage, but for routine work at temperatures below 300°F, the tin-lead solders (63-37 or 50-50) are commonly used. At temperatures below 0°F, however, these solders should be used with care since they may exhibit brittleness and a loss in strength. Tin-antimony and lead-tin-silver solders are satisfactory to 400 and 500°F, respectively.

The actual procedure for making soldered connections to strain gages coincides with standard practice for all electronic soldering. The lead wires and the strain gage leads (or tabs on some foil gages) should first be tinned with solder. The lead wires are then held in place and connected with a pencil-type soldering iron or small soldering gun until the solder is shiny and liquid. Additional solder may be introduced as necessary. In general, no more solder than is required to form the connection should be used. The joint should be heated sufficiently to burn out the rosin, but care must be taken that the strain gage is not damaged by excessive heating.

TESTING STRAIN GAGE INSTALLATIONS

After the gage has been installed and the cement cured, there are several quick tests which can be made to ascertain that the gage will function properly. First, the gage resistance is checked. If it shows an open circuit but all soldered connections are conductive, then the gage may have been damaged during bonding, and, of course, it is useless. If, on measuring the gage resistance, a value noticeably different from the manufacturer's specifications is obtained, the gage should be regarded with extreme suspicion, for this, too, indicates probable damage in handling or bonding of the gage—assuming that the ohmmeter used is accurate.

Next, the resistance between the strain gage filament and the metal surface to which the gage is attached should be measured. A thoroughly dried or cured gage will show a resistance of 1,000 megohms or higher, although much lower resistances can be tolerated without too serious consequences. A minimum of 50 megohms is considered necessary for accurate, stable functioning of the gage. Attempts should not be made to use gages with resistance to ground of less than 10 megohms except for dynamic strain indication. In testing the high resistance which exists between the gage filament and ground, a vacuum tube or conventional high-range ohmmeter should be used. A "megger" or other high-voltage insulation tester should *not* be used since there is danger of damaging the gage by breakdown of the insulation, particularly if the gage is not thoroughly cured when the voltage is applied.

A final check on the gage—particularly on the gage bond—can be made by the following process: connect the gage to a static strain indicator, balance the bridge, bringing the meter needle to the zero point, and then press lightly on the strain gage with the eraser end of a lead pencil. When this pressure is applied, the needle should show a slight deviation (corresponding to a few micro-inches per inch of strain), but when the pressure is released, the meter needle should return to zero or nearly so. If the pointer fails to return at all or becomes unsteady, then the gage is probably either imperfectly bonded (which might be caused by an air bubble under the gage) or accidentally damaged and will have to be replaced.

SUMMARY OF FACTORS INVOLVED IN SELECTING THE PROPER STRAIN GAGE

A prerequisite to strain gage bonding is the selection of the appropriate gage. In the present state of development of the bonded resistance strain gage, there is no single gage type which is truly universal. Because of this, a great many special-purpose strain gages have been made available. The strain gage user should be well aware of the limitations of each type of gage, and he should also know what gages to select in order to secure the most dependably accurate and useful information from his tests. If the gage is to be used at room temperature and comparatively low humidity, and for a short-time static strain within the proportional limit, then the least expensive available gage (of appropriate size) will commonly suffice. Under these circumstances, the strain gage can be bonded to the member with any compatible cement. However, as gage-operating conditions become more extreme, or as special characteristics are demanded of the gage, it is necessary to select gages specifically designed for these conditions.

There are seven principal variables in the construction of strain gages which can be modified to obtain specialized characteristics. These are (1) the filament material, (2) the base carrier material upon which the filament is mounted for handling and bonding, (3) the cement (if any) used to mount the filament to the carrier, (4) the type of lead construction, (5) the grid pattern, (6) the number and orientation of grids, and (7) the grid and gage dimensions. Of these seven factors, the filament material and the cement and backing material used in the construction of the gage probably represent the most basic and important variables which can be altered to modify gage characteristics.

Strain gages exhibiting a great variety of attributes are available commercially for use under special circumstances, as indicated by the partial list below:

Applications requiring insensitivity to temperature change (temperature-compensated gages).
Strain measurement on two or more axes (multigrid rosettes).
Measurement of plastic strains to 10 per cent or more (post yield).
Repeated dynamic strains (fatigue-resistant).
Direct indication of stress.
Embedment in concrete.

Measurement of tangential strain in diaphragms (spiral grid).
Separate measurement of bending and direct strains from one side of a plate.

The actual procedure of selecting a strain gage for a particular application can be summarized in the following steps:

1. Selection of broad gage type (base material) as determined largely by the maximum expected temperature.
2. Selection of filament material on the basis of operating temperature and temperature range, strain range, and whether strain is static or dynamic.
3. Selection of grid and lead configurations to meet application requirements.
4. Consideration of special characteristics necessitated by the application (Chap. 12).
5. Selection of gage length (Chap. 12).

After selecting the optimum strain gage type for the application, the cement used in bonding the gage to the mounting surface is determined by consideration of compatibility with the strain gage, the stability requirements, the expected operating temperature, and the time available for curing the cement.

SIMPLE STRAIN GAGE APPLICATIONS

In the following paragraphs three typical strain gage installations are described. Discussion of temperature compensation and many of the instrumentation details is reserved for Chap. 4. The most basic measurement which can be made with strain gages is probably that of direct strain in the form of unidimensional tension or compression. The investigation of the tensile strain in the shank of a crane hook such as that shown in Fig. 3-6 will serve as an example. First a relatively smooth surface is prepared at the point where the gage is to be attached. Next the appropriate strain gage for the task is selected. In this case it is assumed that the tests are to be conducted in the laboratory, where normal room conditions of temperature and humidity exist. With this in

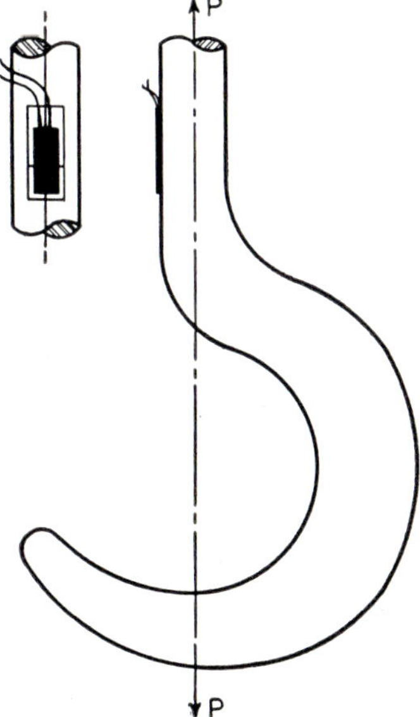

Fig. 3-6. Strain gage installation on the shank of a crane hook.

mind and the fact that the hook would ordinarily be loaded with a series of incremental loads (static strain), the logical choice for a strain gage is one of the paper- or epoxy-backed types constructed with a thermally insensitive Advance filament. A single grid gage suffices for this application because it is relatively certain that the strains are parallel to the axis of the shank. With the surface smoothed and cleaned, the selected gage is cemented in place with its axis (marked by centerlines on the strain gage itself) properly oriented so that it coincides with the shank axis. After the strain gage has been cured and tested for resistance to ground and for stability as outlined in the foregoing paragraphs, strain measurements can be taken.

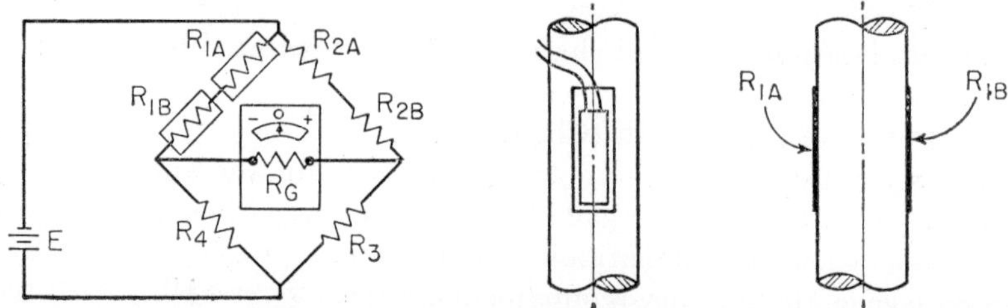

FIG. 3-7. Electrical and physical arrangement of strain gages for canceling the effects of bending strains and indicating only axial strains.

This setup will be improved considerably by cementing a second strain gage of the same type (and preferably from the same lot so that it has very nearly the same resistance and gage factor) on the shank at a point diametrically opposite the first one. This latter gage must be connected in the same leg of the Wheatstone-bridge circuit in series with the first gage, as shown in Fig. 3-7, and performs the function of eliminating any stray bending strain which may be present due to eccentric loading. This is fairly important since it is almost impossible to obtain *purely* axial loading in any body. How the foregoing gage arrangements operate can be readily seen if the strain at a section of the shank is diagramed as shown in Fig. 3-8: first for pure bending, then for pure tension, then for the combination of the two. It is apparent from this illustration that if the shank is being bent slightly by nonaxial loading, gage A will "feel" a strain somewhat greater than the uniform strain representative of pure tension. On the other hand, the net strain felt by gage B will be lower than it should be by exactly the same amount. If these gages are placed in series electrically, the circuit effectively adds their results and divides by 2, which gives the true tensile strain and eliminates all the strain indication due to bending.

It should be noted that if the strain in the curved portion of the hook is desired, it is necessary to obtain separate readings of strain on the inner and outer surfaces since the bending strain is not linear across the section.

To measure the bending stress or strain in a cantilever beam such as that in Fig. 3-9, a very similar procedure will be followed. From elementary mechanics it is known that the strain and stress are maximum for any given load at the root of the beam adjacent to the point of support.

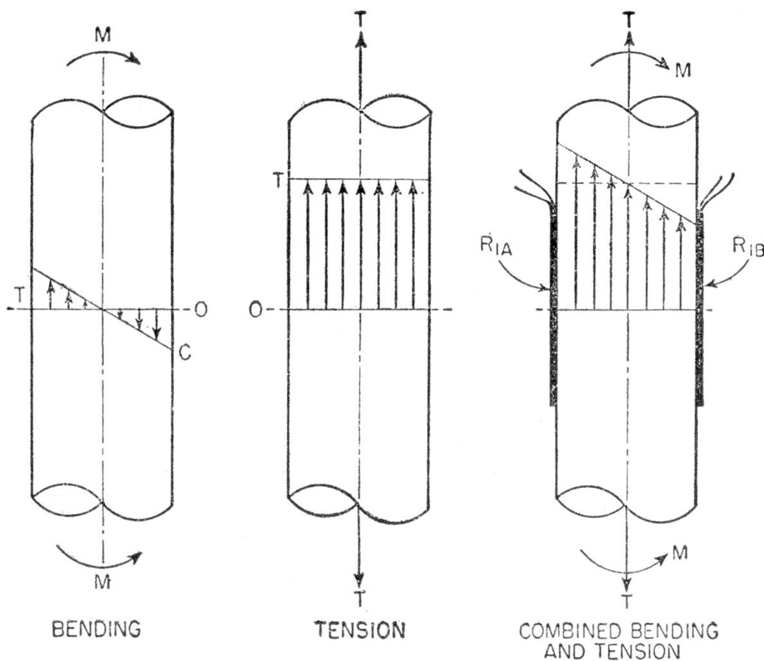

Fig. 3-8. Strain distribution in the shank of a crane hook under combined bending and tension.

This is the point at which the strain gages should be placed in order to secure the maximum electrical output for a particular load on the beam. The gage will be selected on the basis of the temperature and humidity conditions to be encountered, and cemented in place as recommended by the manufacturer. The strain gage can be cemented to the top of the beam, in which case it will indicate tensile strain as the load is applied; or it can be cemented to the underside of the beam, where it will indicate a theoretically equal compressive strain. Either installation, if properly made, will function equally well.

Again, however, the situation can be improved by applying two gages, one to the top and one exactly opposite on the bottom of the beam. It should be noted that if these gages were connected in the Wheatstone-bridge circuit in the same manner as the gages in the previous tension example (Fig. 3-7), there would be absolutely no electrical output from the bridge, since the two strains and resistance changes would be of opposite mathematical sign and, when placed electrically in series, would cancel each other. In this case, the gages will be connected in the Wheat-

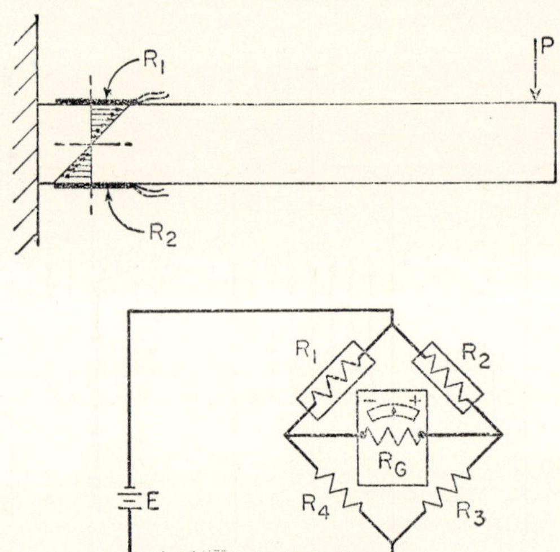

Fig. 3-9. Electrical and physical arrangement of strain gages for indicating the strain in a cantilever beam. This system results in temperature compensation and doubled electrical output.

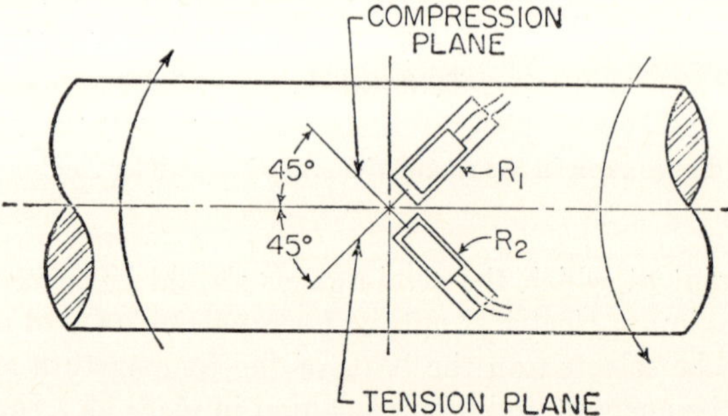

Fig. 3-10. Disposition of strain gages on a shaft for sensing torsional strains.

stone bridge as shown in Fig. 3-9. Two very significant gains arise from this arrangement: (1) the electrical output of the Wheatstone bridge is twice what it would be for one gage alone at a given beam load; (2) both gages are automatically temperature-compensated; that is, thermal variations in resistance of the two gages will be mutually canceled. These advantages will be derived and proved in detail in Chap. 4.

To measure torsional strain with conventional strain gages, it must be kept in mind that these gages indicate only tensile or compressive strains. Upon examining the strain in a cylinder under torsion, it is apparent that while on those planes parallel to and normal to the axis of the cylinder only shear strains exist, on the planes at 45° to the axis the principal strains (tension and compression) are to be found. Therefore, in measuring torsional strains, it is necessary to mount the axes of the strain gages along 45° lines as shown in Fig. 3-10. Again it is possible to measure the strain with only one strain gage, but better results and twice the electrical output will be obtained if two gages are used—one on the tension plane and one on the compression plane as illustrated in the figure. The electrical arrangement of these gages is the same as for the cantilever beam and is illustrated in Fig. 3-9.

BIBLIOGRAPHY

Brewer, G.: Electrical Strain Gage, *Metal Prog.*, vol. 48, no. 1, pp. 91–96, July, 1945.

Hizer, R. C.: Testing Vehicle Components with Strain Gages, *Product Eng.*, vol. 20, pp. 134–137, April, 1949.

MacNair, C. S.: Use of Electronic Gages to Determine the Fatigue Point in Corrugated Containers, *Tappi*, vol. 36, suppl. 138A–142A, January, 1953.

Miller, B. L., and L. D. Anderson: The Performance of Wire-resistance Strain Gages as Influenced by the Drying Time of Three Mounting Cements, *David Taylor Model Basin, Rept.* R-213, January, 1946.

Nielsen, D. M.: Strain Gages, *Electronics*, vol. 16, no. 12, pp. 106–111, 192, 194, December, 1943.

Reinhart, Frank W.: Selecting Engineering Adhesives, *Product Eng.*, vol. 22, no. 9, pp. 123–129, September, 1951.

Tatnall, F. G.: Field Testing Techniques Using Bonded-wire Strain Gage, *ASTM Bull.*, no. 199, pp. 62–66, July, 1954.

EXERCISES

3-1. Prepare a flat metal surface for strain gage mounting. Mount a reject gage in a specified location and direction with Duco cement (available in quantities from gage manufacturers at a nominal cost, reject gages are ordinarily perfectly usable except that the resistance may be outside of the tolerance range). Make proper lead wire attachments to the gage. Test the gage for internal conductivity and resistance to ground. This exercise should be repeated using epoxy and cyanoacrylate cements.

3-2. Apply a paper gage to a properly prepared surface with Duco or nitrocellulose cement. After attaching the lead wires and connecting an ohmmeter from one side to the base metal, apply heat to the installation with a hair dryer. Record impedance to ground at regular intervals to observe the curing of the cement.

3-3. Use a static strain indicator or other sensitive Wheatstone bridges to test the gages mounted in the above exercises for bond integrity.

3-4. Apply paper-backed or epoxy gages to a properly prepared surface on a circular shaft at a 45° angle using epoxy cement. Wire and test the installation for integrity of bond.

3-5. Design a strain gage transducer (device for converting mechanical effects to electrical signals) for the purpose of weighing automobiles while in motion. This might consist of a platform set flush with the highway. The strain gage instrumented supports for the platform should respond to vertical force components only.

3-6. Apply a bakelite strain gage to a wrench with deKhotinsky cement and plot the gage reading versus load applied to the end of the handle.

3-7. Cement a $\frac{1}{16}$-in. strain gage to one of your incisor teeth using F-88 cement. Attach lead wires before installation. Determine the strain resulting from a moderate bite. CAUTION: Be sure to determine how to remove the cement from your tooth before undertaking this experiment.

3-8. Determine the current necessary to destroy one of the gages applied in Exercise 1.

3-9. Cure the installation of a gage applied with epoxy cement by passing a current through the gage. Experiment with different currents applied to the gage, checking speed of cure and stability of installation.

4 THE WHEATSTONE BRIDGE

THEORY OF THE BALANCED BRIDGE

Although the Wheatstone-bridge circuit has been described briefly in the preceding chapters, its universal application in measuring static strains makes a further, more detailed investigation of this circuit well worthwhile. With the assistance of several electrical laws and some comparatively simple mathematics, the circuit can be subjected to a rather thorough analysis. The basic Wheatstone-bridge circuit is repeated in Fig. 4-1. It will be recalled that by suitably proportioning

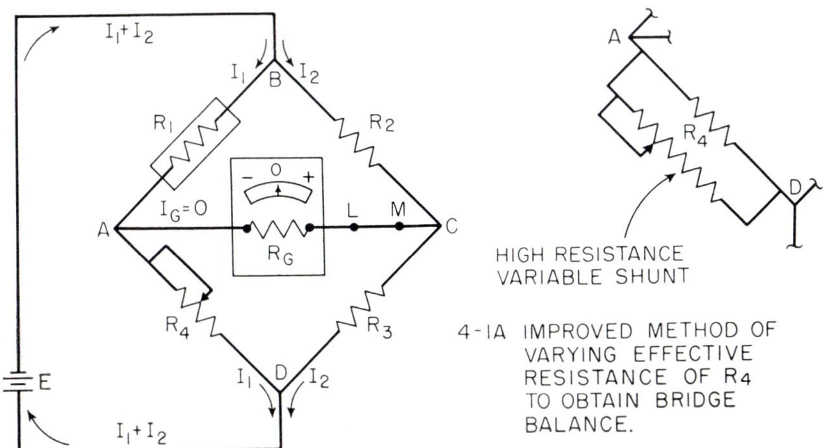

FIG. 4-1. Wheatstone-bridge circuit—balanced.

the resistances R_1, R_2, R_3, and R_4, it is possible so to balance the bridge that no current flows in the galvanometer branch. When such a condition exists, there must of necessity be a certain definite relationship among the values of the various resistances, and this can be calculated with very little effort.

First, consider Ohm's law, $E = IR$, in reference to the galvanometer branch alone. It becomes evident that if the bridge is balanced and I_G, the current through the galvanometer, is by definition zero, then E_G, the voltage across the galvanometer, must also be zero. This is apparently the same as saying that the voltage at A equals the voltage at C. If the voltages at these two points are equal, then it follows that the voltage drop from B to A, $(I_1 \times R_1)$, must be equal to the voltage drop from B to C, $(I_2 \times R_2)$. Similarly, the voltage drop from A to D must equal the voltage drop from C to D. Furthermore, since no current is passing across the center, or galvanometer branch, the current through R_1 must be the same as the current through R_4, and the current through R_2 must equal that through R_3.

From these observations several useful relationships can be derived.

$$E_{B-A} = E_{B-C}$$

or

$$I_1R_1 = I_2R_2 \tag{4-1}$$

and

$$E_{A-D} = E_{C-D}$$

or

$$I_1R_4 = I_2R_3 \tag{4-2}$$

In the above equations the currents I_1 and I_2 can be eliminated by dividing Eq. (4-1) by Eq. (4-2). This gives

$$\frac{I_1R_1}{I_1R_4} = \frac{I_2R_2}{I_2R_3}$$

or

$$\frac{R_1}{R_4} = \frac{R_2}{R_3} \tag{4-3}$$

This important relationship for the balanced bridge can be easily recalled with the aid of a simple memory crutch. Note that the positions of R_1, R_2, R_3, and R_4 in the equation correspond exactly to their relative positions in the circuit of Fig. 4-1. Solving Eq. (4-3) for R_1,

$$R_1 = \frac{R_2}{R_3} R_4 \tag{4-4}$$

This latter equation states that when the bridge has been adjusted to balance, R_1 can be accurately determined by knowing R_4 and the ratio R_2/R_3 with a high degree of precision. The accuracy with which R_1 can be determined will also depend upon the sensitivity of the galvanometer by which zero current in the horizontal branch of the bridge is detected.

In actually measuring static strains with the Wheatstone bridge, one of the resistances, say R_1, will be a strain gage. With the strain gage in the circuit, the bridge can be balanced by adjusting any one of the other resistances so that Eq. (4-3) is satisfied. For the moment, R_2 and R_3 can be left fixed and R_4 considered a variable resistance. Now if the structural member to which the strain gage is bonded were to be loaded and strained, there would be a resultant change in the resistance of R_1 according to the relationship $\Delta R = R_1 F \, \Delta L/L$. This change, even though it is only a few hundredths of an ohm, will upset the relationship expressed in Eq. (4-3) and unbalance the bridge. The unbalance will be indicated by departure of the galvanometer needle from the zero point. By readjusting R_4, the bridge can be brought back to a balanced state and the relationship of Eq. (4-3) reestablished. R_4 could be a resistor so accurately calibrated that its precise resistance is known no matter what the point of adjustment. Then the values of R_4 before and after straining could successively be substituted into Eq. (4-4), and the respective values of R_1 obtained. The difference between the values of R_1 before and after straining will be ΔR_1. This can then be substituted into Eq. (2-2), from which the strain can be obtained.

There is an easier method, however, for, instead of calibrating R_4 in terms of ohmic resistance, it can be calibrated directly in micro-inches per inch of strain. This is true since the amount of adjustment required in R_4 will obviously be related to the resistance change in R_1 and hence to the strain itself. In this case, all that is needed is to note the micro-inch reading of R_4 when the bridge is initially balanced and the strain gage R_1 unstrained; then, after straining, to readjust R_4 to balance the bridge and to note the second micro-inch reading. The difference in these two readings will then be the amount of strain suffered by the strain gage. It would be more practical, since the actual resistance changes being dealt with are so small, to place a variable high-resistance shunt (as shown in Fig. 4-1*A*) across R_4 and adjust this in order to get a much finer control and calibration.

This line of thought suggests a still easier method of using the Wheatstone bridge to indicate static strains. Instead of rebalancing the bridge after loading the piece to which the strain gage is attached, the galvanometer deflection itself might be taken as a measure of the strain. For small changes in the resistance of R_1 (corresponding to moderate strains) the galvanometer indication is proportional to the resistance change or strain. This method would be still more convenient if the galvanometer were calibrated in units of micro-inches per inch of strain.

THEORY OF THE UNBALANCED BRIDGE

As already noted, the Wheatstone bridge can be employed in either of two distinct modes of operation: as a null-balance system or as a direct-reading "deflection" instrument. In either case, it is desirable to have an expression for the output signal from the unbalanced bridge. Whether the output signal is used directly as a measure of strain or whether it is used to indicate lack of null balance, its magnitude is very important. A large signal for a particular strain increases the accuracy with which the strain can be indicated or the null-balance condition detected. In the former case, with direct indication, the linearity of the output signal with strain is also significant.

Under unbalanced conditions, Eq. (4-3) is no longer valid; so it will be necessary to develop some new equations. Fortunately, this is not so difficult as it might at first appear since, as in many other phases of modern technology, someone else has been here ahead of us. In this case it was Kirchhoff who formulated several important rules about the currents and voltages in the complicated electrical systems known as networks. His two most significant laws are (1) that the sum of the individual currents entering a junction of several branches of the network must always equal the sum of the currents leaving the same junction, and (2) that the sum of the voltages around any one closed circuit in the network equals zero.

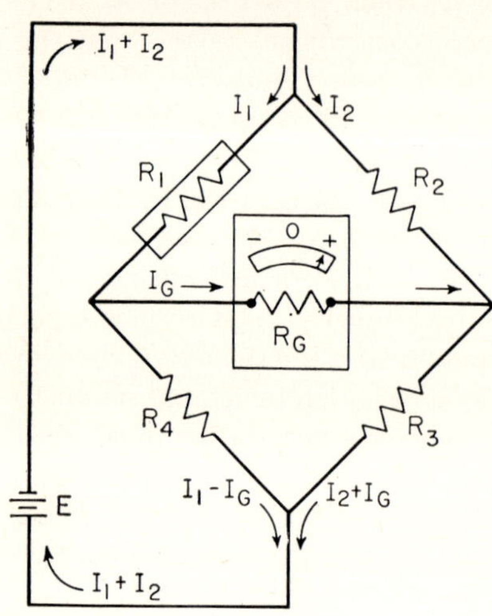

FIG. 4-2. Wheatstone-bridge circuit—unbalanced.

For the unbalanced bridge illustrated in Fig. 4-2 the voltage equations for three different paths can be written using Kirchhoff's second law. Taking the path through the battery E and through R_1 and R_4,

$$R_1I_1 + R_4(I_1 - I_G) = E$$

or, by rearranging,

$$I_1(R_1 + R_4) - I_GR_4 = E \qquad (4\text{-}5)$$

For the path through R_1, R_2, and R_G,

$$R_1I_1 + R_GI_G - R_2I_2 = 0 \qquad (4\text{-}6)$$

For the path through R_G, R_3, and R_4,

$$R_GI_G + R_3(I_2 + I_G) - R_4(I_1 - I_G) = 0$$

or

$$-R_4I_1 + R_3I_2 + I_G(R_G + R_3 + R_4) = 0 \qquad (4\text{-}7)$$

These three equations can be solved for the galvanometer current I_G in terms of the strain-gage resistance R_1. The method of determinants makes a very easy solution for these equations but is not shown because only the result is significant. The solution for the galvanometer current gives the following equation:

$$I_G = \frac{E(R_2R_4 - R_1R_3)}{R_2(R_1 + R_4)(R_G + R_3 + R_4) + R_1R_3R_4 - R_2R_4^2 + R_GR_3(R_1 + R_4)} \tag{4-8}$$

Notice that if the bridge is balanced, and by Eq. (4-3) $R_1/R_4 = R_2/R_3$, or $R_1R_3 = R_2R_4$, the numerator of Eq. (4-8) becomes zero and therefore the galvanometer current, as might be expected, is zero. With this equation one can now inquire into the variation of I_G as the bridge is unbalanced by straining and changing the resistance of the strain gage, R_1. For the special, but convenient, case in which all four legs of the Wheatstone bridge have the same nominal resistance R, and for a small change ΔR in the resistance of one leg, Eq. (4-8) can be reduced to the following expression if higher-order nonlinearities are ignored:

$$I_G = \frac{E\,\Delta R}{4R(R + R_G)} \tag{4-9}$$

Or, noting that $\Delta R/R = F\epsilon$,

$$I_G = \frac{EF\epsilon}{4(R + R_G)} \tag{4-10}$$

Equations (4-9) and (4-10) give the output current of a Wheatstone bridge in terms of the bridge parameters E, R, the galvanometer resistance R_G, and either the strain ϵ or resistance change $\Delta R/R$ in one leg of the bridge. The galvanometer resistance can be looked upon as the load impedance sensed by the bridge circuit. Whether the resistance corresponds to the coil of a galvanometer, or microammeter, or to the input impedance of an amplifier or other instrument is incidental.

The output voltage across the load resistance is

$$E_0 = I_GR_G = \frac{EF\epsilon R_G}{4(R + R_G)} \tag{4-11}$$

The open-circuit output voltage (for $R_G = \infty$) can be obtained by taking the limit of E_0 as R_G approaches ∞.

$$E_0' = \lim_{R_G \to \infty} E_0 = \frac{\dfrac{d}{dR_G}(EF\epsilon R_G)}{\dfrac{d}{dR_G}[4(R + R_G)]} = \frac{EF\epsilon}{4} \tag{4-12}$$

This is the maximum attainable output voltage from a bridge circuit with a resistance change in only one leg. Equation (4-11) demonstrates that the output voltage is attenuated by current flow through the load resistance, and the smaller the resistance, the greater the attenuation. Figure 4-3 shows the ratio E_0/E_0' as a function of R_G/R. It is apparent that the load resistance must be considerably larger than the strain gage resistance in order to develop an appreciable fraction of the available signal.

In order to appreciate the problems associated with the indication and recording of strain gage signals, some numerical values can be substituted

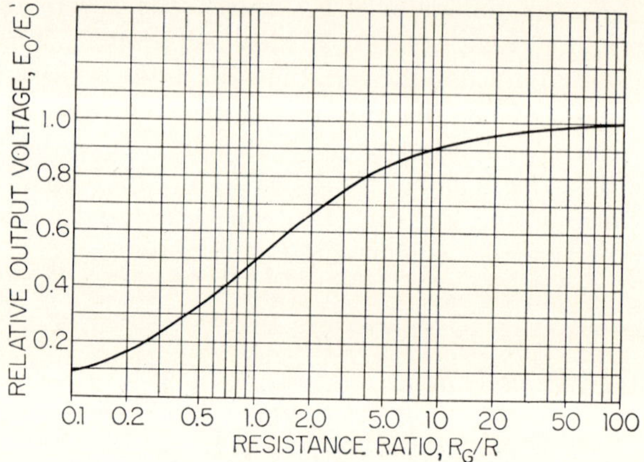

FIG. 4-3. Variation of relative output voltage with galvanometer impedance for Wheatstone bridge with nominally equal resistances in all legs.

into Eqs. (4-10) and (4-11). Consider a wire strain gage with a resistance of 350 ohms and a gage factor of 2 subjected to a strain of 1,000 microinches per in. Assume a meter with an internal resistance of 150 ohms. Battery voltage will ordinarily be determined by the maximum current the strain gage can carry without heating noticeably. The battery voltage could be calculated on the following basis: since most wire strain gages will carry approximately 0.030 amp (30 milliamperes) without overheating, E will equal $I_1(R_1 + R_4)$, or [1]

$$E = 0.030 \times 700 = 21 \text{ volts}$$

The nearest even battery voltage is 22.5 volts, which is not sufficiently different to worry about.

[1] Foil strain gages, because of their heat-dissipation characteristics, will have two to three times the current-carrying capacity of wire gages.

Performing the substitutions,

$$I_G = \frac{22.5 \times 2 \times 1 \times 10^{-3}}{4(350 + 150)} = 22.5 \text{ micro-amperes}$$
$$E_0 = 22.5 \times 10^{-6} \times 150 = 3.38 \text{ millivolts}$$

The sensitivity of the Wheatstone-bridge circuit with its associated galvanometer or load resistance can be expressed in several different ways. Output current per unit strain and output current per unit change in resistance in one leg of the bridge are given here.

$$\frac{dI_G}{d\epsilon} = \frac{EF}{4(R + R_G)} \tag{4-13}$$
$$\frac{dI_G}{dR} = \frac{E}{4R(R + R_G)} \tag{4-14}$$

Substituting from the preceding numerical example,

$$\frac{dI_G}{d\epsilon} = \frac{22.5 \times 2}{4(350 + 150)} = 22.5 \text{ milliamperes per in. per in.}$$
$$\frac{dI_G}{dR} = \frac{22.5}{4 \times 350(350 + 150)} = 32.1 \text{ micro-amperes per ohm}$$

By the same process as shown above, but allowing resistance changes in all four legs of the Wheatstone bridge, it can be shown that the output signal is

$$E_0 = \frac{ER_G}{4(R + R_G)}\left(\frac{\Delta R_1}{R_1} - \frac{\Delta R_2}{R_2} + \frac{\Delta R_3}{R_3} - \frac{\Delta R_4}{R_4}\right) \tag{4-15}$$

where all four gages have the same nominal resistance R.

It is evident from Eq. (4-15) that if gages R_2 and R_4 (Fig. 4-2) were subjected to strains of the same magnitude but opposite sign from that of R_1 and R_3,

$$E_0 = \frac{ER_G}{4(R + R_G)}\left(4\,\frac{\Delta R}{R}\right) = \frac{EF\epsilon R_G}{R + R_G} \tag{4-16}$$

This technique is commonly used in strain gage transducers as described in Chap. 11.

It can be noticed from the preceding equations that the output of the unbalanced bridge is proportional to the supply voltage. When the bridge is perfectly balanced, there is no output, that is, no voltage difference between points A and C in Fig. 4-1. Therefore, under balanced conditions, the bridge is absolutely unaffected by either battery voltage or galvanometer resistance. This is evident from Eq. (4-3), which involves nothing but the resistances of the four bridge legs. Because bridge performance is completely independent of the battery voltage when the bridge is balanced, the method of rebalancing the bridge for each strain reading is always used where highest accuracy is required.

Referring back to Eq. (4-8), it will be seen that whenever the bridge is unbalanced—when the factor $R_1R_4 - R_2R_3$ is *not* equal to zero—the bridge output in terms of galvanometer current is directly proportional to the battery voltage. This, of course, is a source of possible error when strains are being read directly from the galvanometer without rebalancing.

As indicated earlier, the output of the Wheatstone-bridge circuit is not a precisely linear function of the resistance change in any leg of the bridge. The nonlinearity is negligibly small, however, for strains no greater than several thousand micro-inches per inch. At post-yield strains of 1 per cent or greater, the nonlinearity may reach a significant magnitude. While the nonlinearity has no effect on the accuracy in null-balance operation of the Wheatstone bridge, it will distinctly limit the large-strain accuracy of a direct-reading instrument unless compensating circuitry is incorporated.

TEMPERATURE COMPENSATION IN THE WHEATSTONE BRIDGE

Up to this point little or nothing has been said about temperature compensation of strain gages. This is not meant to indicate, however, that the subject is of less than primary importance. Adequate temperature compensation is an absolute necessity for accurate measurement of static strains with all presently available bonded resistance strain gages. The need for temperature compensation of strain gages arises from two factors. First there is the fact that the resistance of most conductors changes with temperature. A second temperature effect occurs if the thermal coefficient of expansion of the strain gage filament is different from that of the structure to which it is bonded. Thus, even if the strain gage filament had a zero temperature coefficient of resistance, it would still be subject to false strain indications with temperature unless it had the proper coefficient of expansion. If such a gage were constructed so that it was completely free of temperature errors when bonded to steel, it would be greatly in error if bonded to aluminum or some other metal with a different thermal coefficient of expansion.

Temperature compensation can be easily accomplished by installing a second strain gage, often known as a "dummy" gage, on an unstrained piece of the same metal as that to which the active strain gage is bonded. If the two pieces of metal are subjected to the same temperatures during testing, both gages will experience identical thermal resistance changes. This is true whether resistance changes occur due to the temperature coefficient of resistance of the conductor in the gages or to the differential expansion existing between the gages and the metal to which they are bonded. The dummy gage can be connected in the Wheatstone bridge as R_2 in Fig. 4-1.

It will be recalled that when the bridge is balanced [Eq. (4-3)]

$$\frac{R_1}{R_4} = \frac{R_2}{R_3}$$

Since strain gages of the same type will be used for R_1 and R_2, they will have the same nominal resistance. If both gages experience the same small resistance change due to an increase in temperature, their final resistances are $R_1 + \Delta R_1$ and $R_2 + \Delta R_2$. It is apparent from the above considerations that if $R_1 \approx R_2$, then $R_1 + \Delta R_1 \approx R_2 + \Delta R_2$. Since both numerators in Eq. (4-3) are increased by like amounts, this is the same as multiplying both sides of the equation by the factor $(R + \Delta R)/R$ and does not destroy the equality of the expression. As long as this equality persists, there can be no galvanometer current, as was shown in Eq. (4-8), and the bridge remains balanced.

If the structure to which the active gage R_1 is bonded is simultaneously strained and exposed to an increased temperature and the dummy gage is exposed to the same temperature, the strain indication of the bridge will be unaffected by the temperature change.

The active and dummy gages could also be connected as R_1 and R_4 in Fig. 4-1 and result in equally effective compensation for all temperature changes. The same reasoning can apply here as in the previous case. If the bridge is initially balanced,

$$\frac{R_1}{R_4} = \frac{R_2}{R_3} \quad \text{and} \quad \frac{R_1 + \Delta R_1}{R_4 + \Delta R_4} = \frac{R_2}{R_3}$$

The ratio is undisturbed because the numerator and denominator of the left-hand member of the equation are both increased in the same proportion. It might be noticed at this time that while the dummy can be connected in the Wheatstone bridge as either R_2 or R_4, it *cannot* be connected as R_3. Putting the dummy in the R_3 position would double the effect of thermally caused resistance changes instead of compensating for them, as can be seen from the basic equation for the balanced bridge.

Up to this point the temperature-compensating strain gage has been used only in an inactive manner as a dummy. There is no reason, however, why in many cases the dummy gage cannot also be measuring strain. Consider, for example, a cantilever beam as in Fig. 4-4. With the beam loaded as indicated, gage R_1 will be strained in tension, while gage R_2 is strained in compression. It has already been shown that if the gages are connected in the circuit with R_1 as the active gage and R_2 as the compensating gage, all temperature effects will be canceled. Not so, however, with resistance changes caused by the strain from the beam load. Because the two gages are subjected to strains of equal magnitude and opposite signs, their resistance changes will also be of opposite signs. The resistance of gage R_1 will increase, while that of gage R_2 will decrease. The effect of straining either gage alone is to upset the bridge balance by an amount calculable from Eq. (4-8). The effect of straining both gages simultaneously to the same degree but in opposite directions is to double the bridge output. This method represents, therefore, a very effective device for significantly increasing the strain sensitivity and simultaneously securing complete temperature compensation.

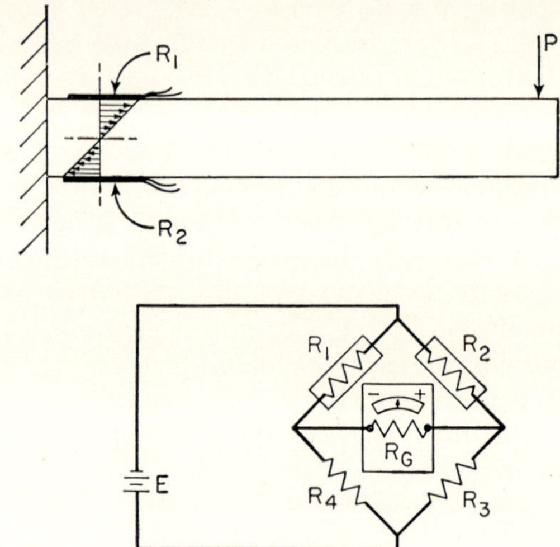

FIG. 4-4. Cantilever beam with strain gages mounted and connected to give augmented bridge output while maintaining temperature compensation.

In case the above beam were so arranged in a structure that the lower surface was inaccessible, temperature compensation could be accomplished by placing gage R_2 in the immediate vicinity of R_1 and at right angles to it as shown in Fig. 4-5. If gages R_1 and R_2 are connected in the Wheatstone-bridge circuit as shown in Fig. 4-5, complete temperature compensation will again result. In this arrangement, however, gage R_2, although in compression when gage R_1 is in tension, will not be subjected to so great a strain as R_1. The ratio of the strains (Poisson's ratio) varies between 0.25 and 0.35 for most metals. Thus, the bridge output in this case would be approximately 25 per cent greater than if the temperature compensation were obtained by merely cementing gage R_2 to an unstrained sample of the same metal. If this method is used, it will be necessary to obtain experimentally the exact ratio of the strains indicated by the gages.

When measuring strains in members subjected to pure tensile and compressive loads, this "Poisson arrangement" of strain gages is the only manner in which complete temperature compensation can be accomplished without the use of an unstrained dummy. For such a case, there is no equal strain of opposite sign as was true for the beam.

Torsional measurement with strain gages is readily adaptable to temperature compensation because of the fact that tensile and compressive

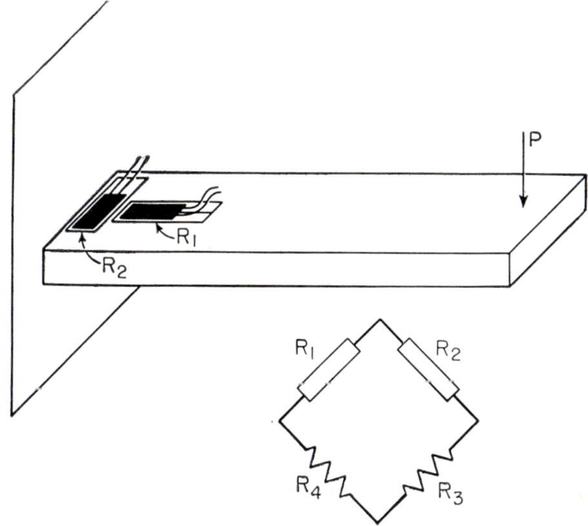

FIG. 4-5. Poisson arrangement of strain gages for temperature compensation and slightly increased output signal.

strains are always equal. The simplest arrangement is that illustrated in Fig. 4-6.

There is a general rule which can be used as a guide in selecting the arm of the bridge in which to connect temperature-compensating or output-augmenting strain gages. The rule is: The Wheatstone bridge will be unbalanced only in proportion to the algebraic *difference* of resistance changes in any two *adjacent* arms, or in proportion to the algebraic *sum* of the resistance changes in any two *opposite* arms. Thus, in Fig. 4-1 if R_1 is the active strain gage, R_2 or R_4 could be used for the compensating gage. Since the resistances of both gages change together with temperature, there is no difference and no unbalance of the bridge. Similarly, it was pointed out that if gage R_2 could be located on the same structure as R_1 in such a way that it would be subjected to an equal strain of *opposite* sign during loading, the bridge would be unbalanced in proportion to the algebraic difference resulting from the opposite signs. If R_2 were the active gage, the R_1 and R_3 positions would be eligible for use in temperature compensation.

To provide temperature compensation for the case in which two gages must be employed for purposes of eliminating the effect of bending strains, two separate dummies will be required. The crane hook discussed in Chap. 3 (Fig. 3-6) is an example of this situation. Another example would be the measurement of the compressive strains in a column while eliminating the effects of bending strains which generally exist due to slight eccentricity in load application. In this instance strain gages could be placed on opposite sides of the column at the base as shown in

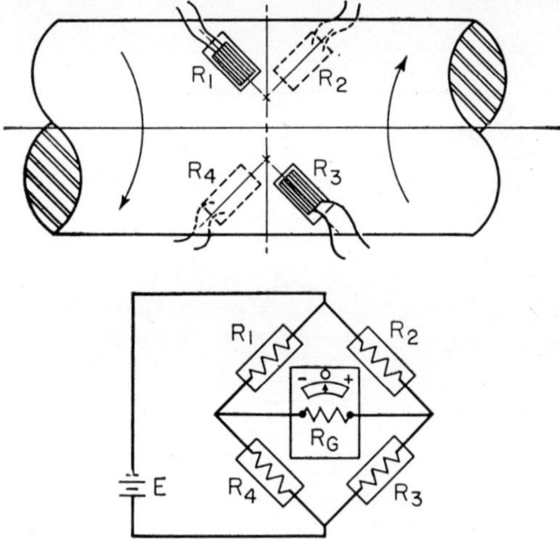

Fig. 4-6. Arrangement and connection of strain gages for measuring torsional strain with maximum output and optimum temperature compensation.

Fig. 4-7. All strains at the base which were alike in sign (from compressive forces) would, by the general rule, unbalance the bridge in proportion to the sum of the resistance changes. If the column had any tendency to bend, however, gages R_1 and R_3 would be strained equally in opposite directions and the resulting resistance changes would not affect the state of bridge balance. While this arrangement gives a double sensitivity to compressive strain, it is unfortunately doubly sensitive to temperature effects as well. Two additional dummy gages can be bonded to an unstrained piece of the column material, or to the column itself in the Poisson orientation, and placed in the R_2 and R_4 bridge legs.

The need for thorough temperature compensation becomes more acute as attempts are made to measure lower static stresses, because any thermally originated resistance changes are a greater portion of the total resistance change. In measuring dynamic strains, as will be discussed later, the necessity for temperature compensation is very much reduced, and such compensation may be totally unnecessary in instrumenting shock or impact strains.

It will be found that temperature compensation can be maintained over indefinitely long periods of time when proper installations are made. The active and compensating gages should be very nearly of the same resistance, have the same gage factor, and have the same resistance sensitivity to temperature. In general these conditions will be approximated in the case of commercial strain gages by the expedient of employing two gages from the same lot as received from the manufacturer. Under optimum circumstances, with both strain gages from the same lot, and with an arrangement such that the member on which the dummy gage is mounted is maintained stress-free and at the same temperature as the test piece, this method of temperature compensation represents the most accurate technique available. Temperature errors can be limited to a few micro-inches per inch over a very wide range of ambient temperatures. It is equally important that the two inactive arms of the bridge likewise be fully temperature-compensated; otherwise, the bridge could be unbalanced by the inactive arms alone. This factor should also be automatically taken care of in commercial bridges since the arms can be of the same kind of wire and can be located together in the instrument.

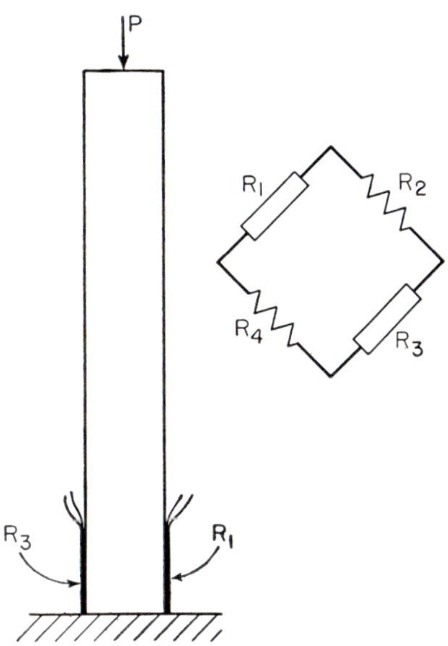

Fig. 4-7. Arrangement of strain gages for double sensitivity to axial compressive strain and cancellation of bending strains. The system as shown also exhibits double sensitivity to temperature effects.

It has been shown by Hines that when a strain gage is mounted on a sharply curved surface, a temperature error is produced in excess of that for mounting on a flat surface. In other words, complete temperature compensation will not be exhibited if the active gage is bonded to, say, a small-diameter shaft and the dummy gage to a flat metal specimen, or vice versa. Similarly, self-temperature-compensating strain gages will be in error under the same circumstances. The effect is due to the fact that the grid of the gage is a few thousandths of an inch above the surface of the member and is subject to a different strain under thermal expansion or contraction than the surface proper. The effect is negligible for surfaces with a radius of curvature greater than approximately ½ in.

THE SELF-TEMPERATURE-COMPENSATING STRAIN GAGE

In some strain gage installations where temperatures vary during the test, it is impossible to subject the dummy gage to the same temperature variations as the active gage. In this case the self-temperature-compensating strain gage is invaluable. This is a special type of gage which has an extremely low temperature sensitivity when cemented to the particular metal for which it is intended. The temperature sensitivity is commonly measured in terms of the "apparent strain" (indicated strain due to a temperature change without constraint or stress) per degree Fahrenheit. Self-temperature-compensating strain gages will produce apparent strains ranging from 0.1 to 1.0 micro-inch per in. per deg F, depending upon the gage type.

The self-temperature-compensating feature in strain gages can be achieved by several techniques. One of the simpler and more widely used methods involves incorporating in a single-element grid a special alloy, carefully selected and processed to exhibit predetermined thermal-response characteristics. Gages of this type are often referred to as "selected melt." The range of alloy and processing variations available is sufficient to permit the production of strain gages which will demonstrate apparent strains of 1 micro-inch per in. per deg F or less on materials with thermal coefficients of expansion from 5 to 15×10^{-6} in. per in. per deg F. Each self-temperature-compensating strain gage is intended for use on a material with a specific thermal coefficient of expansion. The gage manufacturer supplies a temperature-response curve with every package of self-temperature-compensating gages. This curve, as shown in Fig. 4-8, indicates the apparent strain from the gage as a function of temperature when it is bonded to the appropriate material.

A second type of self-temperature-compensating strain gage is produced by fabricating the filament from two different materials in series. The relative lengths of the two materials are proportioned so that the total increase in resistance with temperature (due to both thermal expansion and resistivity changes) of one material is very nearly canceled by a decrease in the resistance of the other. Gages of this type are available with apparent strains of 0.25 micro-inch per in. per deg F over a limited temperature range when bonded to the proper material. Figure 4-9 illustrates typical compensation characteristics for dual-material temperature-compensated strain gages.

Commercial strain indicating and recording instruments are often designed to accept either two or four of the legs of a Wheatstone bridge externally. These instruments are less frequently designed for a single external bridge leg. Whenever the instrument requires two legs of the bridge circuit externally, it is necessary to use a dummy gage for one of the legs even though the other leg is a temperature-compensated strain

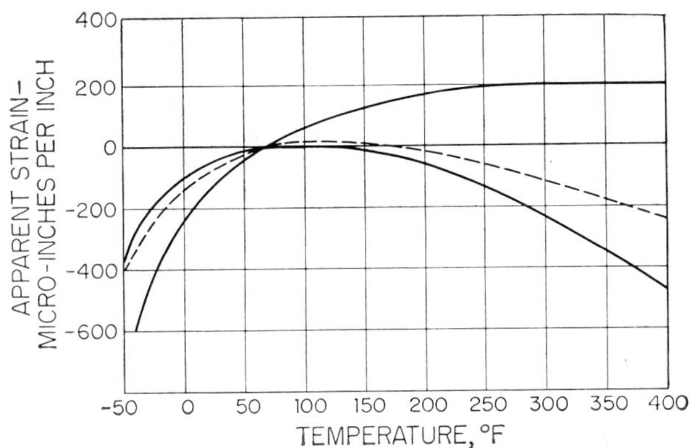

Fig. 4-8. Temperature-compensated characteristics of selected-melt strain gages showing tolerance band and typical performance (dashed line) of gage compensated for thermal expansion coefficient of 6×10^{-6} in. per in. per deg F when applied to mild steel. (*Courtesy of Baldwin-Lima-Hamilton Corporation.*)

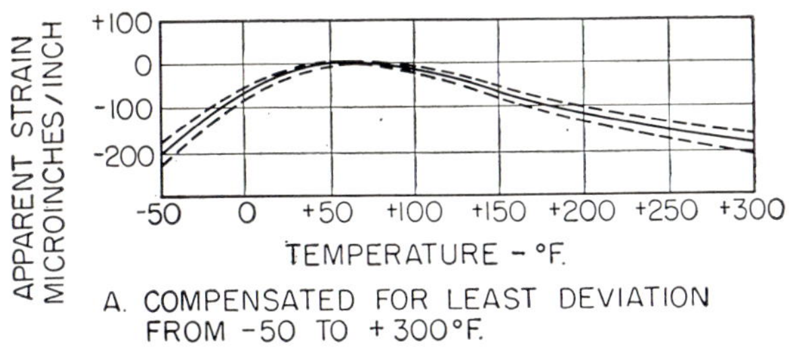

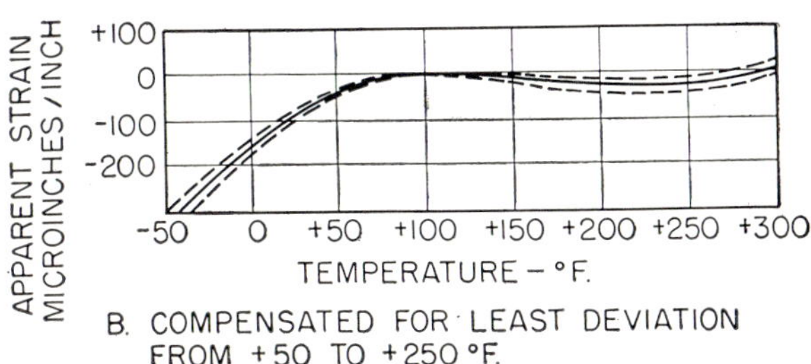

Fig. 4-9. Characteristics of temperature-compensated strain gages. (*Courtesy of Baldwin-Lima-Hamilton Corporation.*)

gage. For the dummy gage to be used in conjunction with a self-temperature-compensating installation, it is possible to employ any type of fixed resistance or mounted gage which is maintained at a constant temperature throughout the test. A second self-temperature-compensating gage can serve very satisfactorily as the dummy.

The use of the self-temperature-compensated gage introduces a new problem that is not usually encountered with conventional gages and that results from resistance changes in the lead wires due to temperature variations. With conventional gage installations, if lead wires of the active and dummy gages are subjected to identical temperature conditions, resistance changes in the leads are canceled out, since they appear

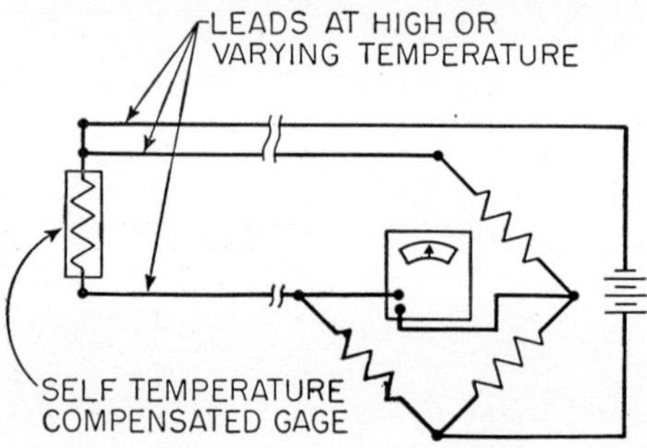

FIG. 4-10. Method of eliminating lead errors in employing a single self-temperature-compensated gage.

in adjacent legs of the bridge circuit. With the self-temperature-compensated gage, however, only one pair of lead wires is required, and since they are connected in one leg of the bridge, variations in their resistance will be indicated.

To show how serious this resistance change in the leads may be, let us assume that a 5-ft length of a pair of lead wires is subjected to an average temperature increase of 150°F. If the leads are No. 20 copper, their total resistance change will be 0.0206 ohm.

Substituting this value in the equation

$$\epsilon = \frac{\Delta R/R}{F}$$

we obtain for a 120-ohm gage, having a gage factor of 2, an equivalent strain

$$\epsilon = \frac{0.0206}{120 \times 2} = 80.6 \times 10^{-6}$$

This corresponds to a stress of 2,400 psi in steel. This example makes it apparent that some means must be provided to avoid this type of error when using the temperature-compensated strain gage.

The solution to this problem can be obtained quite simply through the procedure of placing one lead in one bridge leg and the other lead in the adjacent leg. How this is accomplished is demonstrated in Fig. 4-10. Note that temperature variations in the battery lead and its resultant resistance changes will not affect the balance of the bridge. Figure 4-11

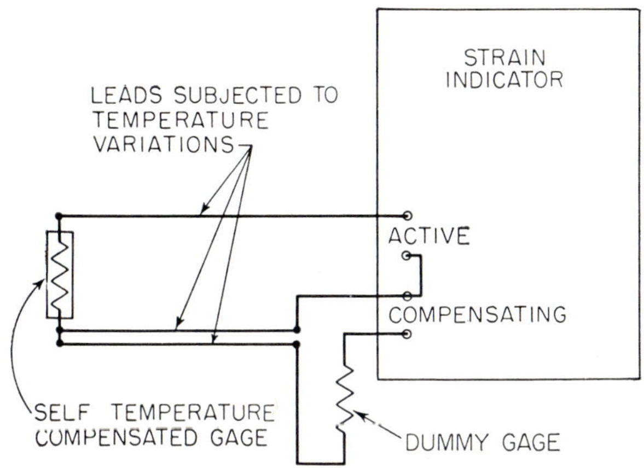

Fig. 4-11. Application of lead-wire correction circuit to a conventional strain indicator.

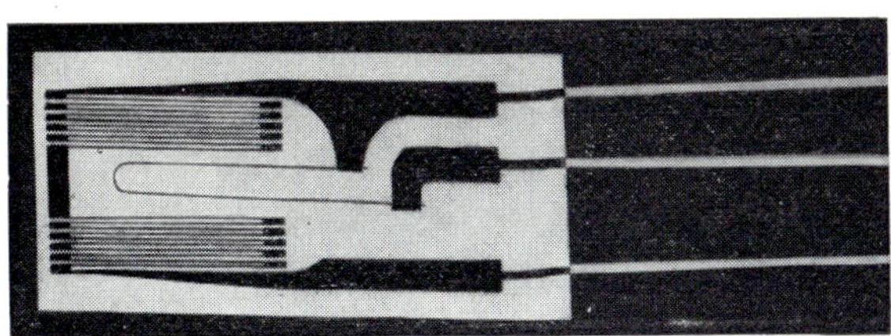

Fig. 4-12. Universally temperature-compensated strain gage. Foil grid supplemented by platinum wire compensating element. (*Courtesy of Baldwin-Lima-Hamilton Corporation.*)

shows how this principle can be applied when using a conventional strain indicator.

A novel variation of the self-temperature-compensating gage is the "universally temperature-compensated" gage (Fig. 4-12). This unit can be looked upon as a dual-element gage with a Nichrome strain-sensing filament and a platinum compensating element. As illustrated by Fig. 4-13, the platinum element actually serves as the dummy gage in the Wheatstone-bridge circuit. The circuit employs an adjustable ballast resistor in series with the low-resistance platinum element. The value

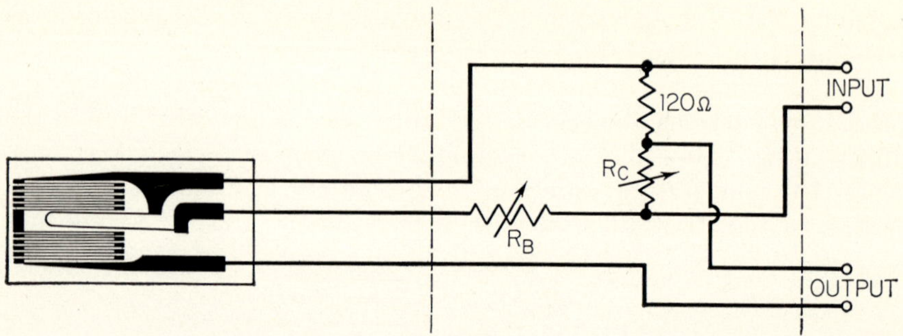

FIG. 4-13. Installation circuitry for universally temperature-compensated strain gage. The gage with its two elements constitutes one-half of the bridge circuit, with the remainder of the circuit supplied by a bridge-completion network. (*Courtesy of Baldwin-Lima-Hamilton Corporation.*)

of the ballast resistor is adjusted so that the per cent change in resistance of the platinum element caused by temperature change cancels the per cent change in resistance of the Nichrome strain-sensing element at a specific temperature on a particular test material. The ballast-resistor value can also be adjusted to provide minimum temperature sensitivity in the gage over a specified operating temperature range. In addition to the ballast resistor a balancing network is required to make up a complete Wheatstone bridge outside of the strain indicator. Specific instructions for calculating the value of the ballast resistor and for selecting the other bridge components are supplied by the manufacturer with the universally temperature-compensated strain gage. The manufacturer also supplies an encapsulated "bridge-completion network" (Fig. 4-14) embodying the ballast resistor and other external bridge components in convenient, incrementally variable form.

FIG. 4-14. Bridge-completion network for use with universally temperature-compensated strain gages. This encapsulated network can also be used as a fixed resistance dummy or to generally complete two-arm or four-arm Wheatstone bridges. (*Courtesy of Baldwin-Lima-Hamilton Corporation.*)

In addition to its capacity for compensating temperature effects on any material and at any particular temperature, the universally temperature-compensated strain gage is characterized by applicability over a very wide temperature range. It is available either on a phenolic backing for use between −320 and +500°F or on a strippable vinyl backing for use between −320 and +850°F. In the latter form, the filament is bonded to the test surface with a ceramic cement.

BIBLIOGRAPHY

Basic Wheatstone-bridge Description and Theory

Brewer, G.: Electric Strain Gage, *Metal Prog.*, vol. 48, pp. 91–96, 270–273, July–August, 1945.

Chandler, R. L., and E. J. Dent: Temperature Compensated Strain Gauges, *Electronic Eng.*, vol. 32, pp. 414–421, July, 1960.

Hamon, B. V.: Bridge Circuit for Wire Resistance Strain Gauges, *J. Sci. Instr.*, vol. 29, no. 2, pp. 53–54, February, 1952.

Hines, F.: Effect of Mounting Surface Curvature on the Temperature Coefficient of Bonded Resistance Strain Gages, *Baldwin-Lima-Hamilton Corporation Bull.*, Nov. 3, 1960.

Higson, G. R.: Resistance Strain Gauges of Low Temperature Sensitivity, *J. Sci. Instr.*, vol. 36, no. 4, pp. 157–159, April, 1959.

Kaufman, A. B.: Stress and Strain Determination, *Radio and Television News*, vol. 44, no. 5 (*Radio-Electronic Eng.*, vol. 15, no. 5), pp. 11A–14A, 29A, November, 1950.

Kern, R. E., and S. B. Williams: Stress Measurement by Electrical Means, *Elec. Eng.*, vol. 65, no. 3, Trans., pp. 100–107, March, 1946.

Mansfield, E. H.: Electrical Circuits for Adding Strain Gauge Signals, *Aircraft Eng.*, vol. 25, no. 290, pp. 108–114, April, 1953.

Rehling, K.: Ausschaltung der Temperatureinfluesse bei Setzdehnungsmessungen, *VDI Zeitschrift*, vol. 99, no. 11, p. 461–466, Apr. 11, 1957.

Ruge, A. C.: Elimination of Lead Wire Errors in the SR-4 Temperature Compensated Strain Gage, *Testing Topics* (Baldwin-Lima-Hamilton Corporation), vol. 6, no. 3, 1951.

Stein, P. K.: Strain Gage Bridge Sensitivity Control, *Product Eng.*, vol. 27, nos. 1, 3, pp. 200–204, January, 1956, pp. 196–198, March, 1956.

Stein, P. K.: Strain Gage Balancing Simplifies Multiple-bridge Measurements, *Product Eng.*, vol. 27, no. 6, pp. 161-163, June, 1956.

Stein, P. K.: Designing Strain Gage Circuits for Sensitivity and Linearity, *Product Eng.*, vol. 27, no. 7, pp. 144–149, July, 1956.

Strong, J. G.: Resistance-wire Strain Gauges, *J. Roy. Aeronaut. Soc.*, vol. 54, pp. 19–26, January, 1950.

Thomson, W. T.: Airframe Stress Analysis by the Electrical Strain Gage, *Aero Dig.*, vol. 42, no. 5, pp. 259, 261, 263, May, 1943.

Troke, R. W.: Direct-reading D-C Strain-gage Bridge, *Instruments*, vol. 24, nos. 4–5, pp. 400–401, 450–452, 454, 456, 458, April, 1951, pp. 535–536, 538, 540, 542, 544, May, 1951.

Wheatstone, Sir Charles: "Scientific Papers," Physical Society of London, London, 1879.

EXERCISES

4-1. Consider a length of Advance wire perfectly cemented to a piece of steel. If the temperature increases 57°F, what fractional change in resistance will be produced in the Advance wire? To what apparent or indicated strain in the steel does this correspond? Repeat the calculation for nickel wire cemented to dural.

4-2. Cement an Advance filament strain gage to a steel specimen and measure the apparent strain per degree Fahrenheit temperature change. Compare your results with Exercise 1.

4-3. Derive Eq. (4-8).

4-4. What location of the gages in Fig. 4-6 is necessary so that bending strains are canceled in the bridge circuit?

4-5. Derive Eq. (4-9).

4-6. Analyze the effect of a uniform axial temperature gradient in the shaft of Fig. 4-6 on the galvanometer indication.

4-7. A temperature-compensated strain gage indicates a strain of 397 micro-inches per in. at a temperature of -20°F (Fig. 4-9*B*). What is the true strain?

4-8. Derive Eq. (4-15).

4-9. Calculate the output voltage for a Wheatstone bridge consisting of four 120-ohm strain gages supplied by a 6-volt battery. Galvanometer resistance is 500 ohms. One gage is subjected to a strain of 1,350 micro-inches per in.

4-10. Derive Eq. (4-9) for the case in which R_3 and R_4 are each n times R_1 and R_2, and R_1 equals R_2.

4-11. Perform an experiment to determine the temperature-compensation effectiveness of the following three arrangements (for the conduct of this test set up a steel beam supported at the third points and loaded by equal weights at the overhanging ends—see figure below): (1) Apply a temperature-compensated gage to the central

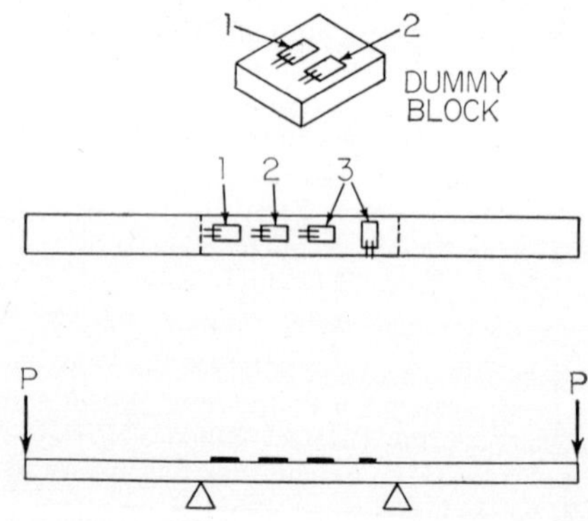

portion of the beam and a matching dummy to an unstressed block of the same material as shown in the accompanying figure. (2) Apply a similar but not temperature-compensated gage to the beam and to the unstressed dummy block. (3) Apply two similar gages, not temperature-compensated, to the beam, the second at right angles to the maximum stress direction. The transverse gage is to be used as the dummy. Obtain indicated stresses before and after subjecting the beam to at least a 50°F uniform temperature change. Compare the results obtained by the three techniques.

5 INSTRUMENTATION

INSTRUMENTS FOR STATIC STRAIN MEASUREMENT

Early Wheatstone bridges for static strain indication employed direct current to power the bridge circuit. The simplest of these bridges was composed of little more than four strain gages, a battery, and a galvanometer. Since in most strain gage installations a pair of gages (active and dummy) is used, only two more resistors, at least one of which must be variable, are required to complete the bridge circuit. Two additional strain gages can be adapted to serve this function quite satisfactorily. If R_1 is taken as the active gage and R_4 the dummy or compensating gage, R_2 and R_3 can then be bonded to opposite sides of a thin cantilever beam for the purpose of balancing the bridge. This beam is constructed so that it can be deflected to cause resistance changes in R_2 and R_3 which will counteract that in R_1 as the latter is strained. The Wheatstone-bridge circuit, as illustrated in Fig. 5-1, is completely conventional. The battery, galvanometer, and cantilever beam with a means of deflection are all built into the instrument. R_1 and R_4 are, of course, connected to this bridge when taking strain measurements.

With strain gages R_1 and R_4 bonded to some test surface and connected to the instrument as shown, the bridge can be initially balanced by deflecting the cantilever beam until a null indication is obtained on the galvanometer. It will be noticed that the free end of the beam is spring-loaded from one side with a low rate spring so that deflections in either direction can be obtained without backlash. This provision is necessary for establishing an initial balance, as well as for measuring either compressive or tensile strains without reversing the electrical connections. As R_1 is strained due to load application on the test member, the bridge will be unbalanced as indicated by the galvanometer needle. Balance can be restored by changing the deflection of the cantilever beam. The beam deflection or balancing control can be calibrated directly in micro-inches per inch of strain. This calibration will be a function of the gage factors of all four gages used, and if any gage were replaced by one of a different gage factor, the calibration constant would be altered.

The principal limitation of this instrument stems from the use of direct current to power the bridge circuit. As was pointed out earlier, the electrical-resistance change accompanying typical strains is very small, and in order to detect strain accurately, an extremely sensitive galvanometer is required. With a galvanometer of such high sensitivity (and long period) in the circuit, bridge balancing is apt to be a rather slow and tedious operation. If the bridge output could be amplified before presentation to a meter for indication, a less delicate and sensitive meter

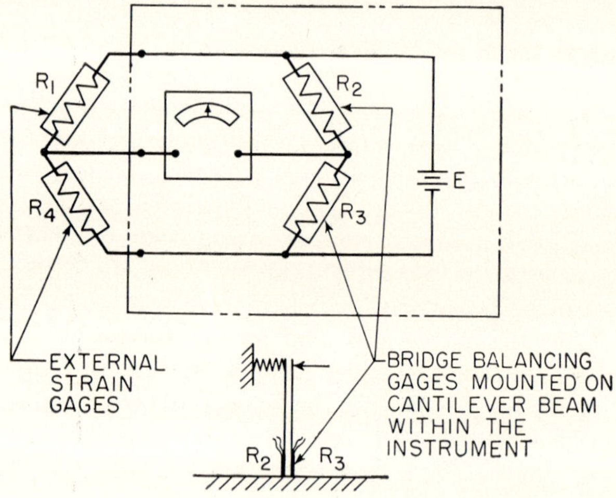

Fig. 5-1. Schematic drawing of a basic Wheatstone bridge for static strain measurement.

could be employed, resulting in much more rapid balancing of the bridge. At the time when wire resistance strain gages were first coming into use, devices for amplifying direct-current intelligence or signals had not reached a satisfactory degree of development. As a result it was general practice to power the Wheatstone bridge with alternating current. The bridge output from such a system could then be amplified with a conventional audio-frequency amplifier, rectified and indicated on a microammeter or milliammeter. This type of system is employed in most contemporary static strain indicators and makes a sensitive, stable, and convenient instrument. A typical strain indicator may be composed of an audio-frequency oscillator (from 60 to 4,000 cps) to supply the bridge circuit, an amplifier (several stages for an amplification on the order of 1,000 times), a detection circuit, and an indicating meter. The detection circuit is composed basically of a rectifier and filter. The action of a detector is indicated diagrammatically in Fig. 5-2. The detector first cuts off the bottom halves of all the carrier waves in the process known as rectification (Fig. 5-2*B*). The resultant waveform is then sent through a filter which will pass only relatively low frequencies and comes out

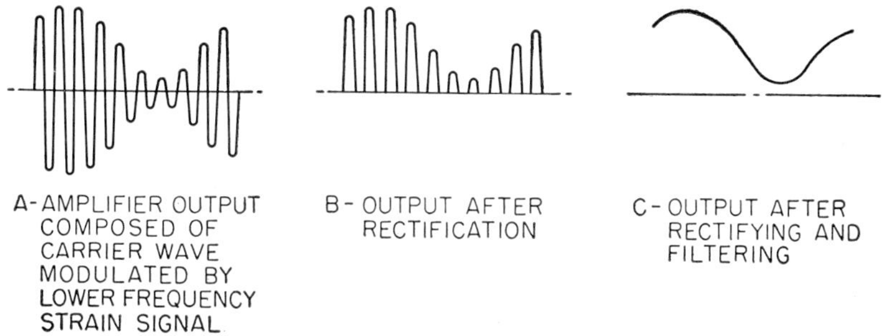

FIG. 5-2. Simplified representation of the detection process.

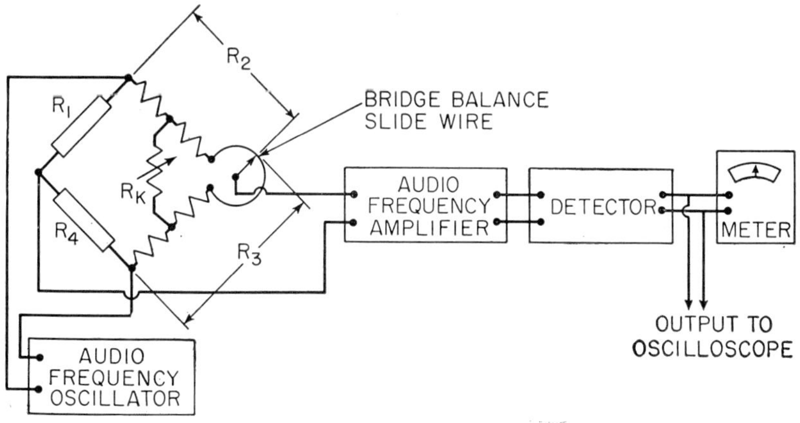

FIG. 5-3. Functional block diagram of a typical commercial static strain amplifier-indicator system.

looking like Fig. 5-2*C*. This is the voltage waveform applied to the galvanometer or other indicating or recording device and represents a slowly varying strain.

Figure 5-3 is a functional block diagram of a widely used static strain indicator. The circuit in Fig. 5-3 shows a variable resistor not indicated in any of the previous bridge circuits. This is the gage-factor adjustment R_k. The dial calibrations on the strain indicator are exact only so long as strain gages of a certain gage factor are employed. If strain gages of a higher gage factor are used, the strain indicator, unless corrected, will show a higher strain than actually exists. R_k is calibrated so that strain gages of a range of gage factors can be used without lessening the accuracy of the balancing-control dial. Actually the same result could be obtained by correcting all strain-indicator readings by the ratio of the gage factor at which the indicator was calibrated to the gage factor of the strain gages being used. For instance, if the strain-indicator dial readings were calibrated for a gage factor of 1.2, and the strain gage being employed had a gage factor of 3.6, the correction would be made as follows:

$$\text{True strain} = \text{indicated strain} \times \frac{1.2}{3.6}$$

Within a limited range this is the function performed by R_k. For strain gages of extremely high or low gage factor it may still be necessary to make this correction mathematically. It will be noticed in Fig. 5-3 that R_2 and R_3 have been made adjustable for bridge balancing. The coarse adjustment is usually incorporated in a multiple point switch, each step corresponding to a definite amount of strain. The fine adjustment is likely to be in the form of a slide wire, the slide for which is directly connected to a dial indicating strain in micro-inches per inch.

There is one other feature of the alternating-current type of bridge illustrated in Fig. 5-3 which is different from the direct-current bridge. In the ordinary d-c bridge of Fig. 4-1 the direction of current through the galvanometer depends only upon whether the voltage is higher at A or at C. The magnitude of the galvanometer current varies directly with the amount of this unbalance. In the alternating-current bridge the output voltage due to unbalance will be proportional to the voltage difference across the indicator system; but the sense of direction (compressive or tensile strain) is not so clearly retained. In order to keep track of the sign of the strain affecting the bridge, it is necessary to build a phase-sensitive detector into the rectifying circuit.

In an a-c Wheatstone-bridge circuit in which all legs are pure ohmic resistances, the bridge output voltage will be either in phase with the supply voltage or 180° out of phase, according to whether the resistance of the active gage is made greater or less than the value corresponding to balance. Commerical strain indicators take advantage of this fact by employing a bridge-type rectifier circuit for meter indication, the sign of which corresponds to the phase of the bridge output voltage. With this arrangement the movement of the meter needle in a given direction can always be associated with a particular sign of strain in the active gage.

Figure 5-4 illustrates two commerical static strain indicators which operate on the principle illustrated in Fig. 5-3. Both these instruments are transistorized and operate on the null-balance principle. The primary difference between the two strain indicators is in the form of the

(*B*)

FIG. 5-4. Portable static strain indicators: (*A*) analog read-out; (*B*) digital read-out. (*Courtesy of Baldwin-Lima-Hamilton Corporation.*)

"read-out"—one is analog, and the other digital. The instruments have self-contained batteries for portable operation. The use of batteries in static strain indicators, while convenient in terms of portability, results in limitations which should be recognized. One of these is that the bridge supply voltage is essentially fixed; thus, using multiple or high-resistance gages in the legs of the bridge circuit will not increase the output, as might be presumed. In order to increase the output of the

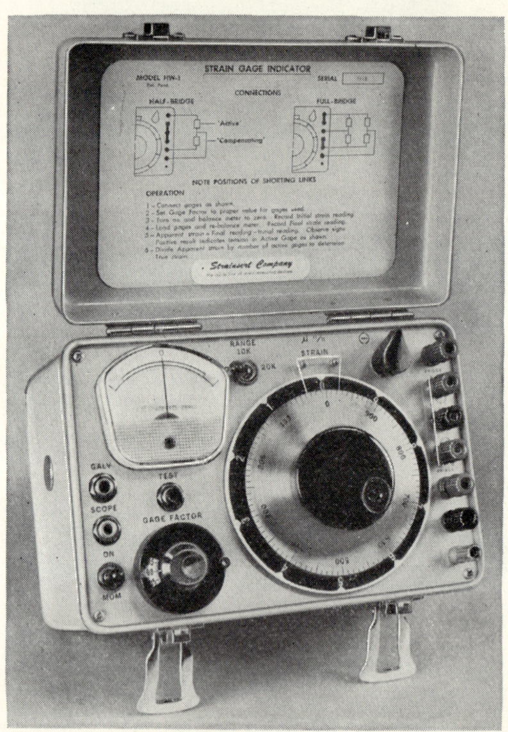

FIG. 5-5. Strainsert strain indicator, employing square-wave bridge supply voltage to eliminate capacitive unbalance effects. (*Courtesy of Strainsert Company.*)

Wheatstone bridge through using higher resistance in the individual legs, the bridge supply voltage must be increased in the same ratio as the resistance so that the nominal current through the strain gage remains the same. A potentially serious disadvantage of battery-supplied static strain indicators arises from the possibility of long-time drift or instability in the instrument as the batteries approach the end of their useful life. Specific methods of maintaining indicator stability are dealt with in a later chapter.

Static strain indicators employing alternating current to power the bridge circuit are also sensitive to the effects of reactive unbalance in the external circuit. A problem commonly occurs in attempting to measure strains from remotely located strain gages connected to the instrument through long lead wires. The capacitive unbalance created by the lead wires appears as a signal to the instrument amplifier, and is amplified along with the strain signal. The result can be a serious reduction in the sensitivity of the instrument. This problem is largely overcome in the Strainsert strain indicator (Fig. 5-5) through the use of a

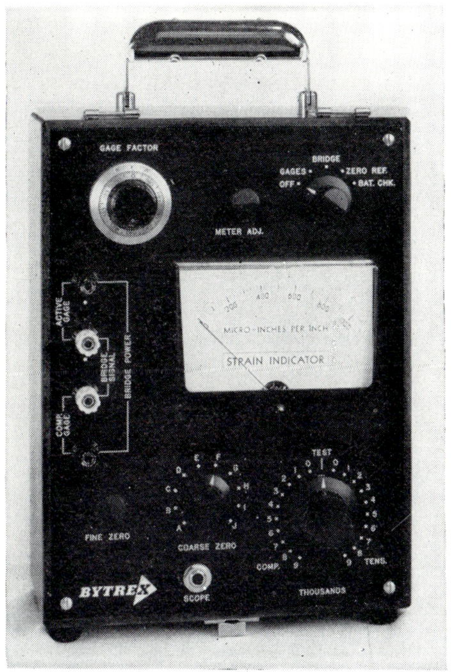

Fig. 5-6. Direct-reading portable static strain indicator. (*Courtesy of Bytrex Corporation.*)

square-wave voltage to supply the bridge circuit. The square-wave voltage allows the amplifier to discriminate between strain and reactive signals and reject the latter. The Strainsert instrument is claimed to tolerate up to 0.01 micro-farad of distributed capacity without a measurable loss of sensitivity and 0.1 micro-farad with a 1 per cent measurement error. Reactive unbalance, and techniques for eliminating it in conventional static strain indicators, are described in Chap. 12.

Static strain indicators are also available as direct-reading instruments. In this type of instrument, after an initial balance, the strain is read directly from a sensitive meter without rebalancing the bridge. Figure 5-6 shows a direct-reading strain indicator which is based upon a circuit similar to that in Fig. 5-3. This instrument features transistorized circuits, adjustable sensitivity, and automatic polarity reversal. It is powered by four standard flashlight batteries.

DYNAMIC STRAIN

The term "dynamic strain" is used to describe strain which varies appreciably in magnitude over a short time interval. It is obvious that if the strain in some structures were varying at more than several cycles per minute, it would be difficult or actually impossible to determine the strain by the process of balancing the bridge. Because the null-balance technique cannot be employed in measuring dynamic strain, such measurements are inherently less accurate than those for static strain. There are numerous other factors which contribute to the difficulty of accurately determining dynamic strains. Most of these are related to the fact that generally no two successive dynamic tests or cycles will produce identical results. A further limitation to the accuracy of dynamic strain instrumentation is the device employed for indicating or recording the strain. All mechanical, optical, and optical-mechanical oscillographs are limited by inertia, lack of record definition, or both. The strain gage itself is capable of responding to strains of extremely high frequency—50,000 cps or higher—but indicating or recording such strains is a little difficult. Because of the short time interval during which most dynamic and transient strains are measured, it is seldom necessary to use temperature compensation.

Figure 5-7*A* represents static strain which varies slowly or not at all with time. Figure 5-7*B* shows a pure oscillatory dynamic strain. In this case the strain is varying from positive (tension) to negative (compression) values of equal magnitude. This could be a representation of the strain in a spring under forced vibration. If the curves of Fig. 5-7*A* and *B* are superimposed, Fig. 5-7*C* results. The latter curve represents a static strain which is modulated by a dynamic component. Figure 5-7*D* shows a more extreme case of combined static and dynamic strain in which the dynamic component is of considerably greater magnitude than the static. These are, of course, simplified sketches. In actual practice both the frequency and magnitude, as well as the wave shape, of the dynamic fluctuations may vary with time.

CIRCUITS FOR SENSING DYNAMIC STRAIN

Either of two basic circuits can be employed in measuring dynamic strains. These are the Wheatstone-bridge and potentiometer circuits. The standard Wheatstone bridge as described earlier will respond satisfactorily to dynamic strains, but it is necessary to apply the output voltage of the bridge to an oscillograph or cathode-ray oscilloscope for indication. This is the same in principle as reading strains directly from the galvanometer without rebalancing, except that the galvanometer has

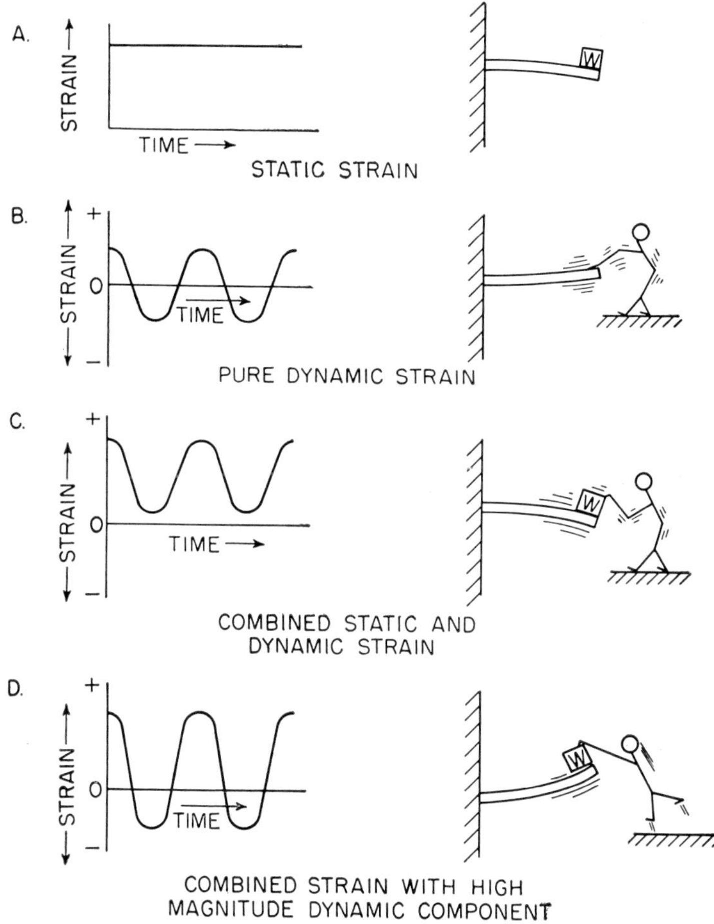

FIG. 5-7. Idealized types of static and dynamic strain.

been replaced by an indicator capable of following very high frequency changes. For a system of this type, the Wheatstone bridge itself can be powered with either alternating or direct current. Because the electrical output of the strain gage and the bridge circuit is comparatively small, considerable amplification will be required in order to drive the commonly used high-frequency indicators. If a direct-current bridge supply and a condenser-coupled audio-frequency amplifier are used, the direct-current component of the bridge output signal, corresponding to the static component of strain, will be blocked out. Thus it will be possible to indicate only a pure dynamic strain or the dynamic component of a combined strain with the above arrangement. Figure 5-8 is a functional block diagram indicating the necessary electrical components for

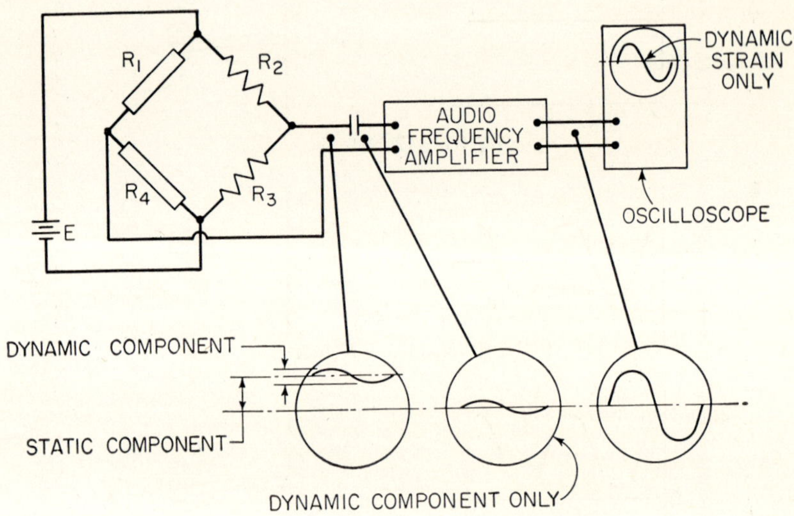

FIG. 5-8. Functional block diagram of a system for indicating pure dynamic strain (or the dynamic component of a combined strain) on an oscilloscope.

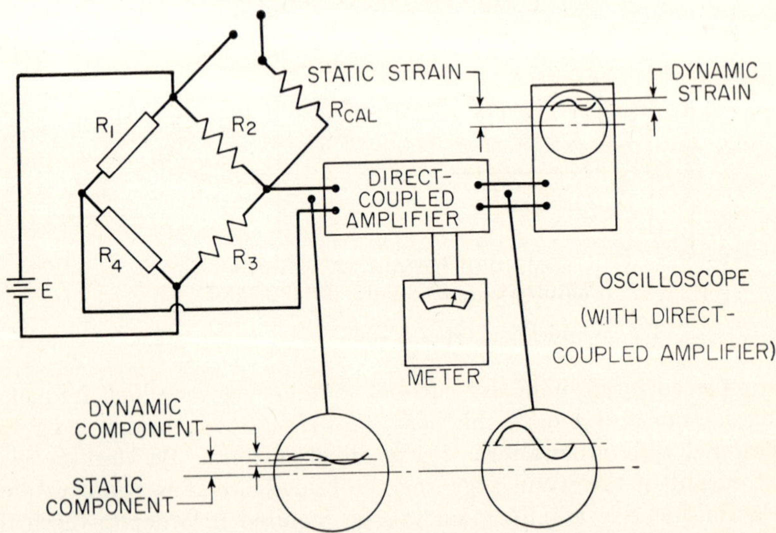

FIG. 5-9. Functional block diagram of a system for indicating static, dynamic, or combined strain with a direct-coupled (d.c.) amplifier.

measuring dynamic strains with the oscilloscope. The amplifier employed should have a flat (constant) gain or amplification factor over the complete frequency range to be expected from the strain gage.

If it is desired to indicate simultaneously the static and dynamic strain components, a direct-coupled, or d.c., amplifier must be used. In the early days of strain gage instrumentation d.c. amplifiers acquired a reputation for instability. As a result of subsequent development, however, d.c. amplifiers have achieved acceptable status, and are often used for

Fig. 5-10. Ellis BAM-1 strain amplifier based upon the system shown in Fig. 5-9. (*Courtesy of Ellis Associates.*)

measurements with strain gages, although somewhat less frequently than a-c amplifier systems. Figure 5-9 shows the manner in which a d.c. amplifier can be used in conjunction with a direct-current bridge supply and oscilloscope to indicate both static and dynamic strains. For those oscilloscopes which contain only a-c amplifiers, it will be necessary to apply the output voltage of the external d.c. amplifier directly to the deflection plates. Figure 5-10 illustrates the Ellis BAM-1 strain-amplifying unit which operates on the principle shown in Fig. 5-9. This instrument is flat in frequency response from direct current to 20,000 cps, falling off gradually to about 50 per cent at 70,000 cps, and thus covers the spectrum encountered in most mechanical problems.

In order to take advantage of the stability and gain available in a-c amplifiers, several other systems have been devised. One method of securing both the static and dynamic strain components is to use what is known as a "chopper." The chopper is in reality a high-speed switching unit which alternately passes the bridge output voltage and cuts it off as illustrated in Fig. 5-11. With a d-c-powered Wheatstone bridge and a static strain, a constant d-c voltage will be applied to the chopper. The output of the chopper, however, will be a continuous series of square waves. Square waves of this type can be amplified suitably with an a-c amplifier which has a sufficiently flat frequency response; that is, the degree of amplification should be constant over a broad range of input

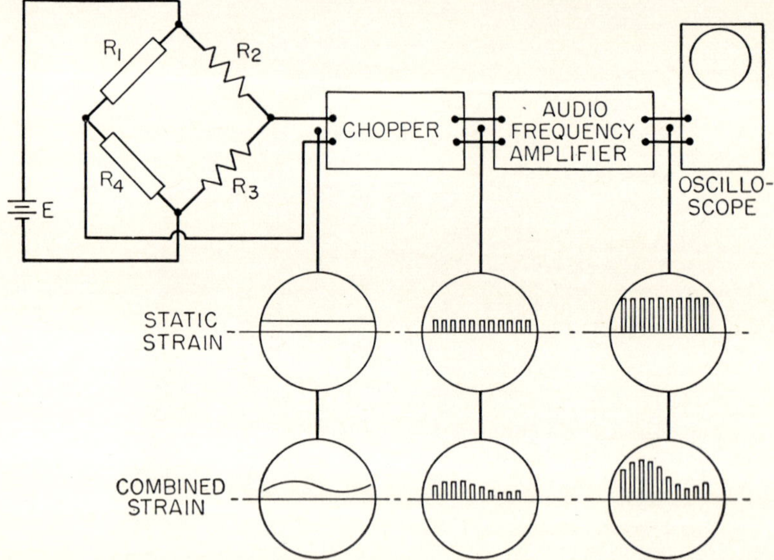

FIG. 5-11. Chopper system for indicating static, dynamic, and combined strains.

frequencies. If combined static and dynamic strain is being studied, the voltage applied to the chopper will be a modulated d-c signal as shown in Fig. 5-11. The chopper output will consist of a series of pulses of varying height. The average height corresponds to the static strain, while the variations in height correspond to the dynamic strain.

An advantage of the chopper system is that steadily repeated signals of all frequencies, both above and below the chopping frequency, will be displayed well on the oscilloscope face as long as the sweep is in phase with the signal frequency. Persistence of vision causes the signal to appear stationary while the chopped-in zero line passes through it. An ordinary automotive-ignition-type circuit breaker will perform very well as a chopper. There is available, however, a small self-contained electro-mechanical vibrator, similar in principle to a doorbell buzzer, designed specifically as a d-c chopper. There are also electronic devices for performing the same function. These are known as electronic inverters, switches, or choppers and operate to alternately pass and cut off the signal (make alternating current from direct current) by virtue of vacuum-tube characteristics. The electronic inverter is particularly advantageous in studying a high-frequency dynamic strain superimposed upon a static strain. For this purpose a very high chopping frequency may be required.

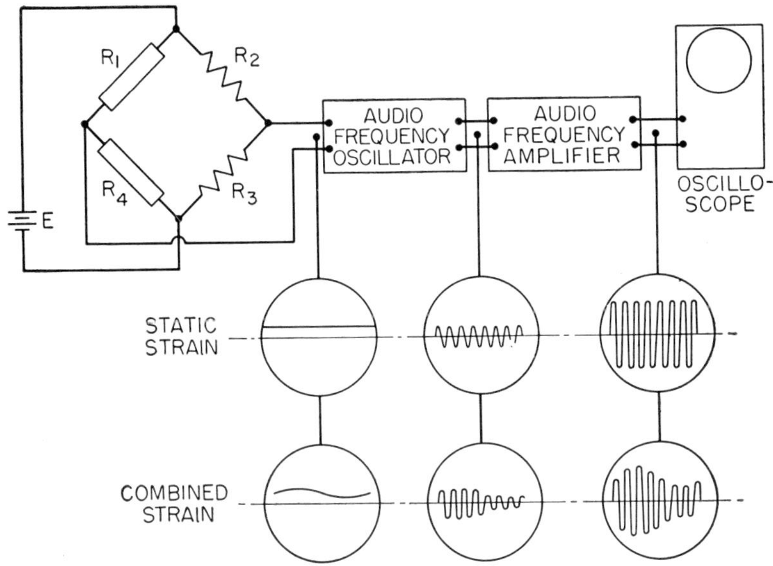

FIG. 5-12. Strain-indicating system in which a carrier wave is modulated by the bridge output.

A method similar in effect to the chopper is the *carrier-wave* system. Instead of following the bridge with a chopper which creates a square-wave signal to modulate the bridge output, an audio-frequency electronic oscillator can be substituted. The oscillator output can be modulated by the strain signal from the bridge circuit. Once an alternating voltage exists, it can be amplified in a conventional amplifier and presented for indication or recording. An arrangement of this type is illustrated functionally in Fig. 5-12. It will be noticed that the bridge supply is still direct current. Such a system can be simplified as shown in Fig. 5-13 by moving the oscillator ahead of the bridge circuit so that the bridge is powered by alternating current and the modulation takes place in the bridge circuit itself. The over-all results are the same in both cases.

The oscillator frequencies in these indicating systems should be at least ten times the highest strain frequency to be measured.

One problem which occurs with any modulated a-c strain-indicating equipment is that of differentiating between tensile strain and compressive strain. In the case of the chopper and the a-c-powered bridge systems, if the bridge is initially balanced, there will be no output signal to the indicator. Application of a static strain, whether tensile or compressive, would cause the carrier wave to show on an oscilloscope screen as

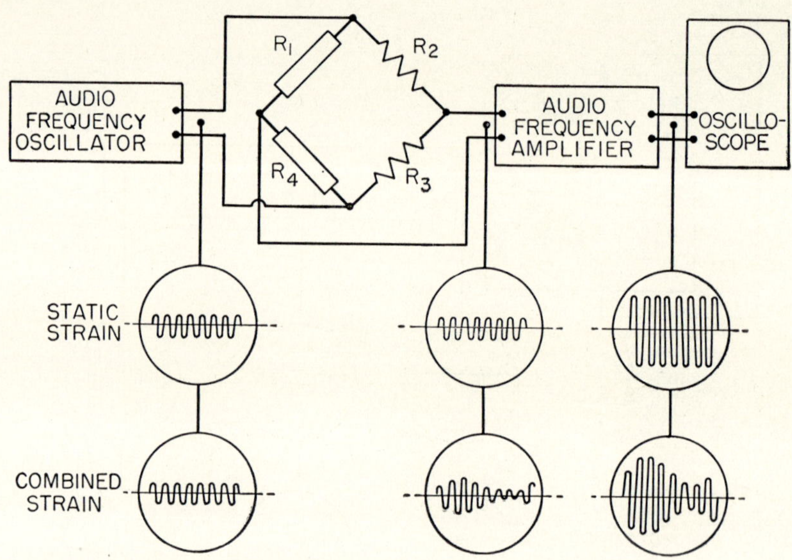

FIG. 5-13. An a-c-powered bridge system for indicating any combination of static and dynamic strains within the frequency limitations of the electronic components.

a continuous wave. Both tensile and compressive indications will, however, be identical. This can be remedied by initially unbalancing the bridge, say, in the tension direction. A continuous carrier wave will then be indicated on the oscilloscope when there is zero applied strain. If tension is applied to the strain gage, the amplitude of the carrier will increase. If compression is applied, it will decrease.

With the type of carrier-wave system in which the oscillator follows the bridge, the continuous carrier can be presented on the oscilloscope screen without initial unbalancing, and differentiation is accomplished in the above manner. Most commercial static-dynamic strain amplifiers employ a-c amplifiers and a chopper or oscillator. These instruments commonly include an output jack for connection to an oscilloscope, providing means for the observation and recording of low-frequency strains. The maximum frequency will ordinarily be limited to approximately 10 per cent of the carrier or chopper frequency. A versatile commercial unit employing the chopping principle is the Ellis BA-12 amplifier pictured in Fig. 5-14. This strain amplifier is essentially a d-c bridge supply, chopper, and a-c amplifier, with internal provisions for calibration. The Ellis amplifier is unusual in the range of frequencies which can be amplified. The amplifier response is flat up to 25,000 cps. This is very important when amplifying transient strains with steep wavefronts such as would occur because of shock or explosion. Another feature of the

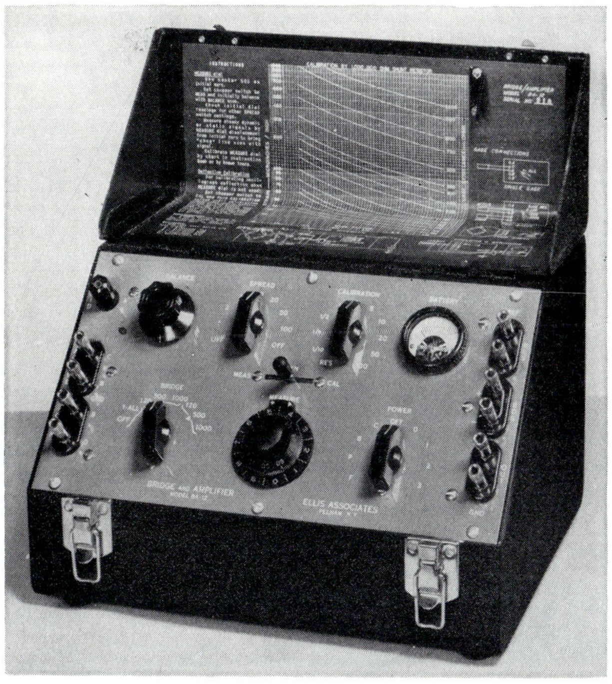

FIG. 5-14. Ellis BA-12 strain amplifier. (*Courtesy of Ellis Associates.*)

Ellis BA-12 is its system of using the chopper and an oscilloscope to indicate momentary null balance of any part of a steadily repeated strain signal, yielding the equivalent of balanced-bridge operation for dynamic strains. This attribute makes the unit very convenient for monitoring fatigue and other repetitive tests.

CALIBRATION

Since the final output of the strain amplifiers is an electrical signal whose magnitude depends on the strain to which the gage is subjected, the strain appears as nothing more than a wave or series of waves on an oscilloscope screen, and some means of judging its absolute magnitude must be provided. This calibration can be accomplished quite easily electrically by the technique indicated in Fig. 5-15. The strain gage resistance in one leg of the Wheatstone-bridge circuit is shunted by an open-circuited resistor of considerably higher value. When this resistor circuit is closed, a definite bridge unbalance will result. This bridge unbalance can be looked upon as a synthetic, controlled strain, and as such it will appear on the oscilloscope screen. Noting the height of the

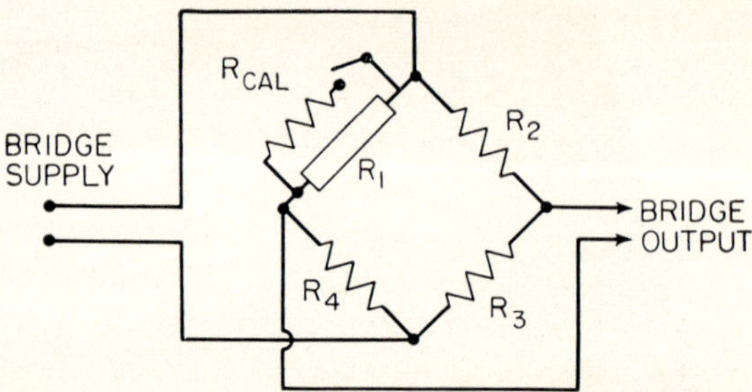

FIG. 5-15. Calibration technique for use in measuring dynamic strain.

wave or pulse from the synthetic or calibrating strain makes it possible to determine the factor relating strain to displacement of the oscilloscope electron beam.

The size of the calibration resistor R_c is selected so that the resistance change obtained by shunting the gage is equal to that produced by a particular strain.

The change in resistance of a strain gage (with known initial resistance R_g and gage factor F) for any assumed strain ϵ is

$$\Delta R = F\epsilon R_g$$

Similarly, the change in resistance of the parallel combination of the strain gage and the calibration resistor is

$$\Delta R = R_g - \frac{R_g R_c}{R_g + R_c}$$

Equating the above two expressions and solving for R_c yields

$$R_c = \frac{R_g(1 - F\epsilon)}{F\epsilon} \qquad (5\text{-}1)$$

Since the term $F\epsilon$ is commonly smaller than 0.005 for conventional metal-

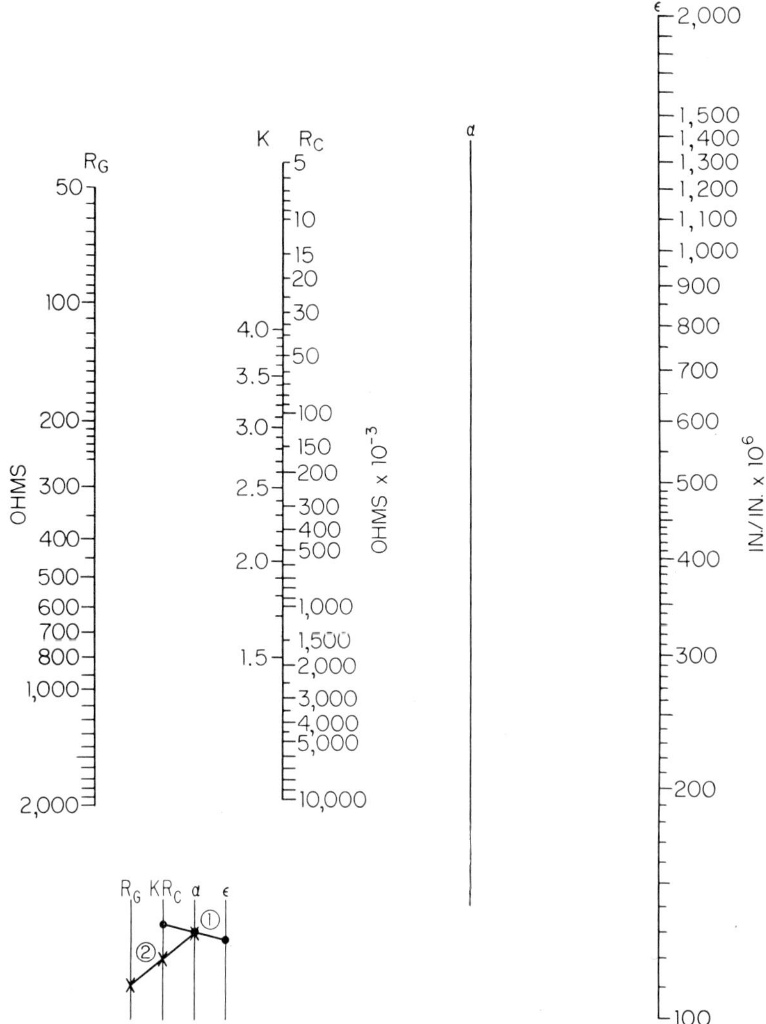

FIG. 5-16. Nomograph for determining calibration-resistor size, or for the synthetic strain signal resulting from a particular calibration resistor. To find calibration-resistor size, construct a line joining the desired synthetic strain signal on the ϵ scale and the gage factor on the K scale. Construct a second line from the strain gage resistance on the R_G scale to the intersection of the first line with the index line α. The second line crosses the R_C scale at the proper value of the calibration resistance. To find the synthetic strain signal from a particular calibration resistance, construct a line from the gage resistance on the R_G scale to the resistance of the calibration resistor on the R_C scale. Project this line to the index line α. A second line, constructed from the gage factor on the K scale through the intersection of the first line with the index line α to the ϵ scale, yields the magnitude of the synthetic strain signal. *(C. M. Harris and C. E. Crede, eds., "Shock and Vibration Handbook," vol. 1, p. 17-22, McGraw-Hill Book Company, Inc., New York, 1961.)*

lic resistance strain gages, Eq. (5-1) reduces to the following close approximation:

$$R_c = \frac{R_g}{F\epsilon} \tag{5-2}$$

If, for example, it were desired to display a calibrating pulse equivalent to a stress of 15,000 psi in steel ($E = 30 \times 10^6$ psi), assuming a strain gage with a resistance of 120 ohms and a gage factor of 2.04,

$$\epsilon = \frac{\sigma}{E} = \frac{15{,}000}{30 \times 10^6} = 500 \times 10^{-6} \text{ in. per in.}$$

From Eq. (5-2),

$$R_c = \frac{120}{2.04 \times 500 \times 10^{-6}} = 117{,}647 \text{ ohms}$$

The exact value of the calibration resistor as calculated from Eq. (5-1) is 117,527 ohms, and the error in the height of the calibration pulse is approximately 0.1 per cent.

A nomograph, based upon Eq. (5-2), is provided in Fig. 5-16 for the rapid determination of calibration-resistor sizes. The same nomograph can be used to calculate the synthetic strain corresponding to a particular calibration-resistor size. It is apparent that any small electrical resistance due to the switch contact in the calibrating circuit of Fig. 5-15 would be insignificant compared with the resistance of the calibrating resistor and thus would have no effect on the accuracy of the calibration.

Amplifier output calibration can also be secured by semimechanical means. The technique consists in mounting a strain gage (or pair of

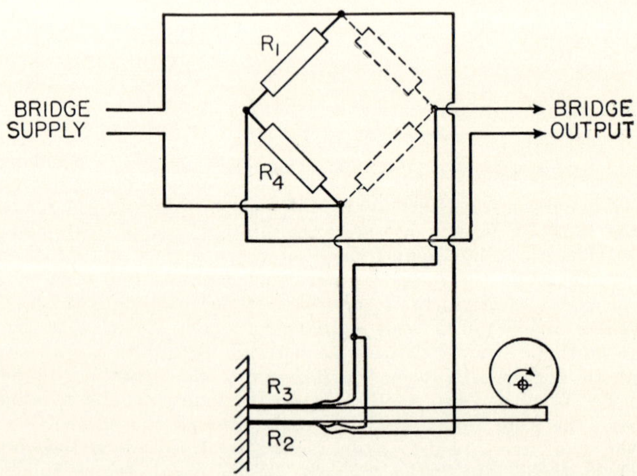

FIG. 5-17. Dynamic calibration with cam-deflected cantilever beam.

gages) on a cam-deflected cantilever beam as shown in Fig. 5-17. This strain gage is then connected as one leg of the Wheatstone bridge. Each time the cantilever suffers maximum deflection from the cam, the strain gage at its base will undergo a corresponding change in resistance. This change will unbalance the bridge and show on the oscilloscope as a calibrating pulse. The calibrating strain can be simply computed from the flexure formula.

THE POTENTIOMETER CIRCUIT

Another circuit commonly employed for indicating dynamic strain is the potentiometer circuit illustrated in Fig. 5-18. This circuit can be looked upon as the equivalent of half the Wheatstone bridge. The circuit, as shown in the figure, consists only of a battery, a ballast resistor R_b, the strain gage R_g, and a coupling condenser C_c. This arrangement will respond only to dynamic strains or the dynamic component of combined strains. The purpose of the coupling condenser is to prevent the passage of direct current. An analysis of this circuit can be made as follows:

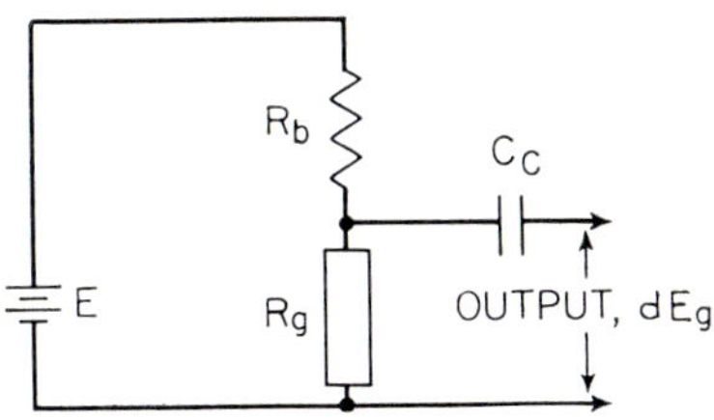

FIG. 5-18. Potentiometer circuit for sensing dynamic strain.

By Ohm's law, the instantaneous current in the circuit is

$$I_i = \frac{E}{R_b + R_g} \tag{5-3}$$

and

$$E_g = I_i R_g \tag{5-4}$$

Substituting Eq. (5-3) into Eq. (5-4), the voltage across the strain gage

$$E_g = \frac{E}{R_b + R_g} R_g = \frac{R_g}{R_b + R_g} E \tag{5-5}$$

Differentiating E_g with respect to R_g,

$$\frac{dE_g}{dR_g} = \frac{(R_b + R_g)E - R_g E}{(R_b + R_g)^2} = \frac{ER_b}{(R_b + R_g)^2} \tag{5-6}$$

or

$$dE_g = \frac{ER_b}{(R_b + R_g)^2} dR_g \tag{5-7}$$

Multiplying and dividing the right-hand side of the above equation by R_g does not destroy the equality; therefore,

$$dE_g = \frac{ER_b R_g}{(R_b + R_g)^2} \frac{dR_g}{R_g} \tag{5-8}$$

From the basic strain gage equation for $\Delta R/R$,

$$\frac{dR_g}{R_g} = F\frac{dL}{L}$$

and substituting this value in Eq. (5-8),

$$dE_g = E\frac{R_bR_g}{(R_b + R_g)^2}F\frac{dL}{L} \tag{5-9}$$

If, as in the full Wheatstone bridge, R_b is taken equal to R_g, Eq. (5-9) reduces to

$$dE_g = \frac{FE\,dL/L}{4} = \frac{FE\epsilon}{4} \tag{5-10}$$

Notice that this is of the same form as the expression [Eq. (4-12)] for the output of the Wheatstone bridge. The function of the ballast resistor in this type of system is to keep the current in the circuit from changing appreciably as the resistance of the strain gage varies. Any current variation which occurs due to a change in resistance of the strain gage will be of such a nature as to reduce the output of the gage. The ballast resistor, under these considerations, should be as large as possible but will be limited in actual practice to a value about twice that of the gage resistance because of the necessary increase in battery voltage to maintain rated current in the strain gage.

Another way of using the potentiometer circuit is to take the output from the ballast resistor. This method is often more expedient than the preceding one. If the latter system is analyzed mathematically, the output voltage dE_b is found to be the same (except for sign) as when the output is taken from the strain gage proper. That is,

$$dE_b = -E\frac{R_bR_g}{(R_b + R_g)^2}F\frac{dL}{L}$$

This is really self-evident when considered in the light of Kirchhoff's law. If the battery voltage is assumed to remain constant, any increase in E_g due to straining must be matched by an equal decrease in E_b in order that the voltages around the circuit add up to zero. Thus, the determining factor in selecting either the ballast resistor or the strain gage as the output member is largely one of impedance considerations. The impedance of the circuit component across which the measurements is being taken should match as closely as possible that of the circuit to which it is connected, to obtain a maximum response. The output of the potentiometer circuit will depend upon the ratio of the resistances R_b/R_g and the battery voltage E. In general, the output voltage of either arrangement will be increased (for a given strain) by using a large ballast resistor.

As the size of the ballast resistor is increased, however, it is necessary to increase the battery voltage if this gain is to be realized.

For any fixed battery voltage, the maximum output will occur when $R_b = R_g$ as shown in Fig. 5-19. It is evident from Fig. 5-20 that the circuit output can be increased markedly by increasing the size of the ballast resistor if the supply voltage is increased to maintain rated gage

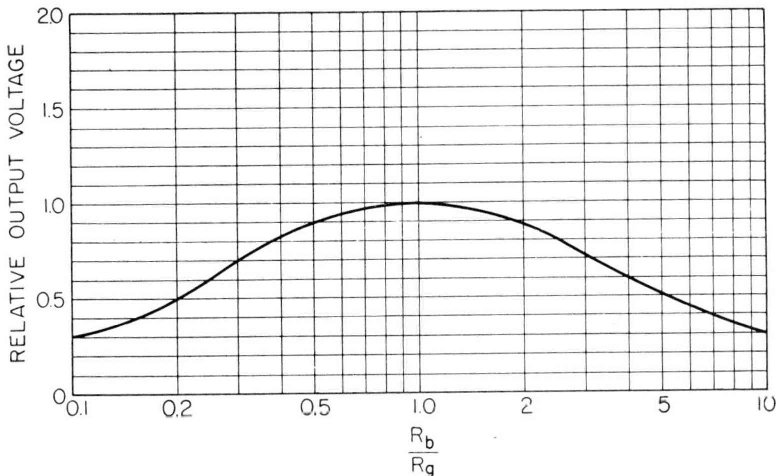

FIG. 5-19. Effect of ratio R_b/R_g on relative output voltage for a constant battery voltage.

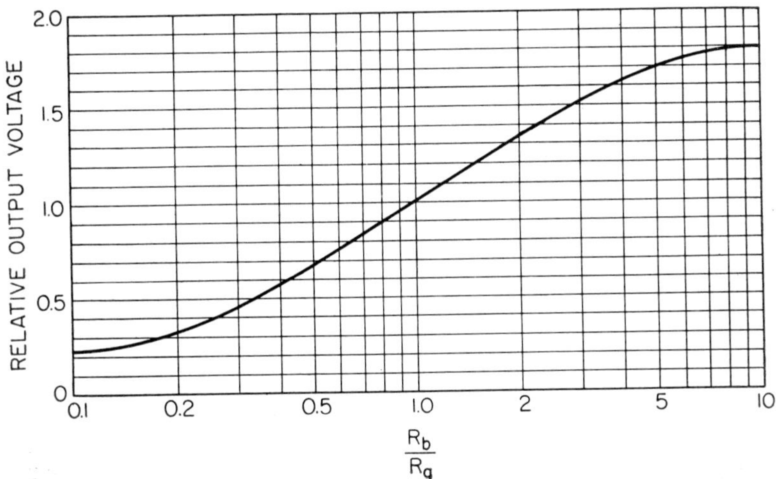

FIG. 5-20. Effect of ratio R_b/R_g on relative output voltage for a constant current $I = E/2R_g$.

current. Figure 5-21 indicates, however, that it rapidly becomes uneconomical to use a ballast resistor having more than twice the resistance of the strain gage.

Calibration for the potentiometer circuit is obtained in the same manner as in the Wheatstone-bridge circuit. Either the ballast or the strain gage is shunted by a large resistor so that the resultant parallel resistance is less than the original by an amount corresponding to the desired calibration strain. When the strain gage in the potentiometer circuit is

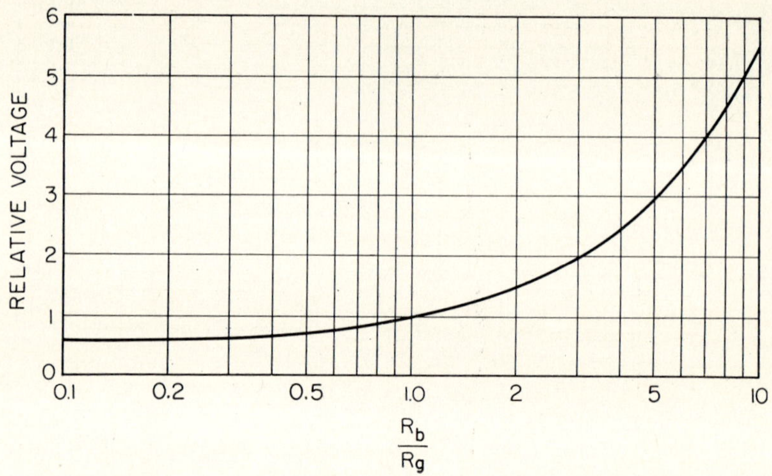

FIG. 5-21. Supply voltage corresponding to constant current $I = E/2R_g$.

to be shunted by the calibration resistor, Eqs. (5-1) and (5-2) for the Wheatstone bridge apply directly, as does the nomograph in Fig. 5-16. If calibration is to be accomplished by shunting the ballast resistor, the size of the calibration resistor can be calculated from

$$R_c = \frac{R_b(R_b - F\epsilon R_g)}{F\epsilon R_g} \tag{5-11}$$

And since $F\epsilon$ is small with respect to unity, and $R_g \leqq R_b$,

$$R_c = \frac{R_b^2}{F\epsilon R_g} = \left(\frac{R_b}{R_g}\right)^2 \frac{R_g}{F\epsilon} \tag{5-12}$$

Equation (5-12) differs from Eq. (5-2) by only the factor $(R_b/R_g)^2$, and thus the nomograph in Fig. 5-16 can still be used for this case if the result is multiplied by $(R_b/R_g)^2$.

STRAIN RECORDING

Static strain measurements can be obtained to a rather high degree of accuracy by the null-balance methods already described. There are numerous cases in which it is convenient and expedient to employ one of the manually operated static strain indicators for this purpose. If continuous strain gage readings must be made over a long period of time, or if the simultaneous strains at a number of different points on a structure are required, an automatic recording system will be found necessary. Static strain recording can be accomplished by a number of techniques. One of these would be to record continuously the galvanometer current in a Wheatstone bridge after initial balance at the beginning of the test.

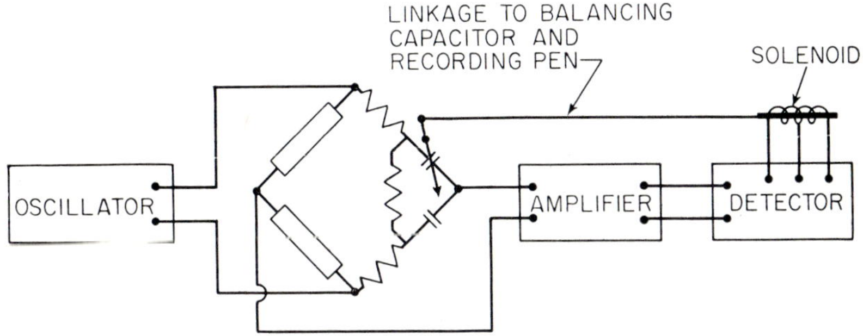

Fig. 5-22. Basic block diagram of a self-balancing bridge and amplifier system for recording static or near-static strain.

In this case some provision must be made for amplifying a d-c signal (corresponding to static strain) by using either a d.c. amplifier or a carrier-wave or chopper system and an a-c amplifier. The amplified signal would be used to drive an oscillographic pen motor to record the strain. Over long periods of time, however, even the best of commercial strain amplifiers would be expected to exhibit intolerable drift. Because of this consideration, the technique of continuously recording galvanometer current without rebalancing the bridge is ordinarily impracticable.

A better approach, and one much more commonly employed, is that of the self-balancing bridge. This system is based on the servo principle by which the unbalance signal from the Wheatstone-bridge circuit is used to control a motor for rebalancing the bridge. The balancing motor is mechanically connected to a recording stylus as well as to a device for varying the impedance of one leg of the bridge. Figure 5-22 is a functional block diagram of such a strain recorder. In this particular recorder, since an a-c bridge is being employed, bridge balancing is accomplished by adjusting a balancing capacitor with a solenoid acting as a servo. The capacitor has several advantages over a variable resistor in this application because the capacitor is not subject to wear, is essentially frictionless, and is generally very easy to control. Linked to the solenoid and capacitor mechanism is a pen or other stylus for recording the amount of impedance change necessary to keep the bridge in balance. The impedance change is, of course, directly related to the strain of the active gage in the bridge circuit. There are adjustments built into the instrument for initially balancing the bridge and for compensating for a range of gage factors. Other automatic strain recorders use a motor-controlled slide wire for bridge balancing, but the general system of operation is the same.

Another method of obtaining automatic balancing employs two strain gages mounted at the root of a cantilever beam, the free end of which rides on a motor-rotated cam. Any unbalance signal from the bridge is amplified and used to control motor rotation until the cam deflects the beam enough to rebalance the bridge. This cuts off the unbalance signal and stops the motor. The recording stylus is linked to the motor shaft and undergoes a displacement proportional to the strain in the active strain gage or gages. In both the strain recorders just described, tensile strains are differentiated from compressive strains by phase discrimination so that a given direction of displacement of the recording stylus can easily be associated with a corresponding sign of strain. Phase discrimination and other electronic-circuit details are beyond the scope of this book, and the interested reader is referred to "The Handbook for Experimental Stress Analysis," edited by Hetenyi.

If pen-and-ink records are to be obtained from a number of strain gages simultaneously, an equal number of recording amplifiers and pen systems will be required. Such an arrangement is known as a multichannel system, and, as might be presumed, the cost is very nearly proportional to the number of channels. If the situation is such that the strain gage recording can be done sequentially instead of simultaneously, a scanning recorder can be used. This type of recorder automatically selects the strain gages one at a time, connects them into a bridge circuit, balances the bridge, and records the amount of impedance change necessary to restore balance. The recorder goes from gage to gage until all have been recorded and then repeats the cycle. This arrangement works very well for recording multiple strains in comparatively static structures such as buildings. The recorders may handle as many as 48 strain gages and scan all of them in 60 to 90 sec. Scanning-type recorders are manufactured by several firms in this country including the Baldwin-Lima-Hamilton Corporation, Brown Instrument Company, and Leeds and Northrup Company.

INDICATING AND RECORDING DYNAMIC STRAINS

Dynamic strain recording requires a sensing circuit (potentiometer or bridge) involving one or more strain gages, an amplifier, and some form of recorder. The sensing circuits have already been discussed in some detail. Amplifiers specifically designed for strain measurement are available commercially and can be selected according to their applicability and merit. Recording techniques employed in dynamic strain analysis vary considerably. Widely used systems have included pen-and-ink writing, an electrically heated stylus marking waxed paper, and various light-beam and mirror galvanometer arrangements combined with photosensitive recording paper.

In general, the recorders employing mechanical styli are limited in frequency response to approximately 100 cps or less. There is also a distinct practical limit on the number of separate channels which can be combined in one instrument, since the styli cannot ordinarily cross one another. Thus, an N-channel instrument is apt to be at least N times as wide as the full-scale stylus movement for one channel. Because of this, mechanical stylus strain recorders are commonly two-, four-, or six-channel instruments. These instruments, because they have been made commercially available in comparatively compact, portable form, with convenient associated strain amplifiers intended specifically for use with strain gage Wheatstone bridges, and because they provide a directly readable record, have found broad application within the limitations of their frequency response and number of channels in one instrument. A 100-cps frequency response is adequate for recording many mechanical phenomena, although consideration should be given to the fact that with a basic event frequency of much less than 100 cps, the waveshape of the signal may require a considerably higher frequency response if it is to be recorded faithfully. This is particularly true for waveshapes involving steep leading or trailing edges, as, for example, square waves. Figure 5-23 illustrates a representative mechanical stylus-type strain-recording system, including amplifiers.

The mirror galvanometer oscillographs can respond to frequencies high enough to include virtually all mechanical phenomena (up to 30,000 cps, if necessary), and the crossing of recording traces from individual channels creates no problems more severe than identifying the traces. The latter can be accomplished, incidentally, by modulating the light-beam intensity differently for each trace. Since the crossing of traces allows combining channels into a small space, these units are commonly employed where a large number of channels (24, 48, etc.) is required. Mirror galvanometer oscillographs may record on film (requiring subsequent chemical processing) or on a special photosensitive paper providing a directly readable record. A direct-writing mirror galvanometer recorder is shown in Fig. 5-24.

Any dynamic strain recording system is really a device for plotting strain magnitude versus time. The scale value of the strain coordinate is obtainable by the calibration methods described earlier in this chapter. Calibration of the time coordinate can also be accomplished quite simply. In oscillographic (galvanometric) recording there are two basic methods

Fig. 5-23. Portable two-channel amplifier and direct-writing oscillograph based upon heated stylus principle. This system is applicable for frequencies up to 100 cps. (*Courtesy of Sanborn Company.*)

of time calibration. In one technique the time scale is furnished by knowledge of the paper speed and of the distance between adjacent grid lines printed on the paper. The second technique involves the use of an external signal of known frequency to mark the paper or film at regular time intervals. The direct-writing type of oscillograph may use an extra pen mounted near the edge of the paper for this purpose, while mirror galvanometer oscillographs use an auxiliary lamp to record timing pulses.

In some recording problems the actual time intervals may not be so important as the occurrence of certain functional events. Thus, in studying the rotating elements of an engine or pump, it may be desirable to have event marks on the record corresponding to the beginning of each cycle, critical occurrences in the cycle, or merely angular increments. The same technique is used as for time-interval marking except that the timing pulses originate from the device being studied.

An entirely different type of recording is accomplished with the cathode-ray oscilloscope.[1] The cathode-ray tube acts as an inertialess galvanometer with a weightless electron beam as an indicating pointer. The

FIG. 5-24. Direct-writing eight-channel mirror galvanometer oscillograph for high-frequency recording. (*Courtesy of Minneapolis Honeywell Regulator Company.*)

oscilloscope can respond to a wide range of frequencies with equal ease. The instrument itself is rugged compared with any instrument embodying a galvanometer. Mild shock or vibration will not distort the output in the least, and the instrument is not particularly susceptible to damage in the handling and transportation which are often involved in making field measurements.

[1] Because of the general confusion in the use of the terms *oscilloscope* and *oscillograph,* the convention has been adopted in this book of defining them, respectively, as instruments primarily intended for *viewing* dynamic phenomena and for *recording* dynamic phenomena. This leads to the description of all cathode-ray-tube instruments as oscilloscopes, while the instruments employing galvanometers are termed oscillographs, since they are more suited to recording electrical signals.

Most oscilloscopes are single-channel instruments, since the cathode-ray tube ordinarily contains only one electron gun. Special cathode-ray tubes with two, four, and higher numbers of electron guns are available for multichannel applications. Each electron gun requires its own channel of amplification and auxiliary circuits. A multichannel effect can be obtained from a single-channel oscilloscope by the use of an *electronic switch* to apply sequentially two signals to the oscilloscope input. The electronic switch contains no moving or vibrating parts but switches by purely electronic means from one signal source to the other at a rate too fast to be detected by the eye. As a result, the screen of the oscilloscope gives the appearance that both signal traces are present simultaneously. The electronic switch also contains biasing controls so that the relative positions of the two traces can be varied at will. Since a single-channel oscilloscope has but one synchronizing circuit, the two signals must be of the same frequency (or integral multiples thereof) if both traces are to remain stationary on the screen. It should be noted that the maximum frequency of the signal or signals being observed is limited to approximately one-tenth of the switching rate of these devices, as would be true, for instance, of any carrier-wave or chopper system.

To obtain a permanent record from the screen of the cathode-ray oscilloscope requires photographic means. There are several common techniques, the choice depending somewhat upon the nature of the phenomenon being recorded.

For recurrent phenomena, if the trace can be made to appear as a standing wave on the oscilloscope screen, a conventional still camera can be employed. This type of work does not require a camera with a particularly fast lens since exposure time can be regulated to give a satisfactory picture. The exposures will depend upon the type of cathode-ray tube being used. The screens of cathode-ray tubes vary in persistence and spectral distribution. In general, the most satisfactory tube for photographic work is one having a medium or short persistent phosphor high in actinic light output. Actually, any type of tube can be employed for photographically recording recurrent phenomena so long as the light output for a given phenomenon is sufficient. For nonrepeating strain signals such as those which would occur from shock or impact, it will be necessary to set the camera with the shutter open, let the event initiate or trigger the oscilloscope sweep, and close the camera shutter. To obtain good recordings by this method requires considerable experience and a fast lens (*f*2.8 or better). Eastman Kodak Royal-X Linagraph film is the fastest film (ASA rating 1,250–1,600) presently available for oscilloscope recording. Kodak Linagraph Ortho and Linagraph Pan films are also recommended for high-speed recording with green- and blue-phosphor oscilloscope screens, respectively. Specific recommendations on film type, camera settings, and other critical data for effectively photographing cathode-ray oscilloscope screens can usually be obtained from the oscilloscope manufacturer.[1]

It may be found in the above procedure that the initial portion of the wave is obscured by the beginning of the oscilloscope trace or lost altogether. In such instances the oscilloscope sweep should be triggered first and then followed, after a delay corresponding to approximately one-tenth of the sweep period, by the appearance of the signal to be recorded. This can be accomplished with most oscilloscopes by setting the "synch" switch to the "external" position, connecting the event signal to the "synch input" terminal of the oscilloscope for sweep-triggering purposes, and conducting the same signal, after passing it through a delay line, to the vertical axis input terminal of the oscilloscope. Commercial delay lines and delay generators are available for this and similar purposes, with delays ranging from fractional microseconds to several seconds.

For many oscilloscope recording tasks, the Polaroid Land camera can be used very conveniently. This camera provides a finished print for viewing within from 10 sec to 1 min after the picture is taken. Films available include a "10,000" extra-fast film adequate for most oscilloscope work and a special film for making positive transparencies directly. One of the commercially available oscilloscope cameras operating on the Land principle is shown in Fig. 5-25. This unit, which mounts directly on any standard 5-in. oscilloscope, allows simultaneous binocular viewing and recording of the oscilloscope trace. The camera mechanism also provides for the recording of as many as nine traces on the same film by merely shifting the camera relative to its mount between exposures. With the faster film, writing rates are limited to 20 to 40 in. per micro-second, depending upon the type of lens employed. The Land camera system is also available for use with various mirror galvanometer oscillographs.

Another common device for recording various transient phenomena is a shutterless motion-picture camera in conjunction with the oscilloscope. The camera is constructed so that film motion is continuous instead of intermittent as in conventional motion-picture cameras. The oscilloscope sweep is cut off so that if the screen is viewed with the eye, a straight vertical trace is seen. If the film is caused to travel past the oscilloscope screen in a horizontal plane, the result will be a continuous recording of strain versus time. The film motion, of course, furnishes the time base. A commercial shutterless motion-picture camera for use with oscilloscopes is shown in Fig. 5-26.

[1] Among the best of these is a paper entitled Techniques of Photo-recording by H. P. Mansberg, to be found in the April–June, 1950, *Oscillographer*, a Du Mont house publication. Other references will be found in the Bibliography at the end of this chapter.

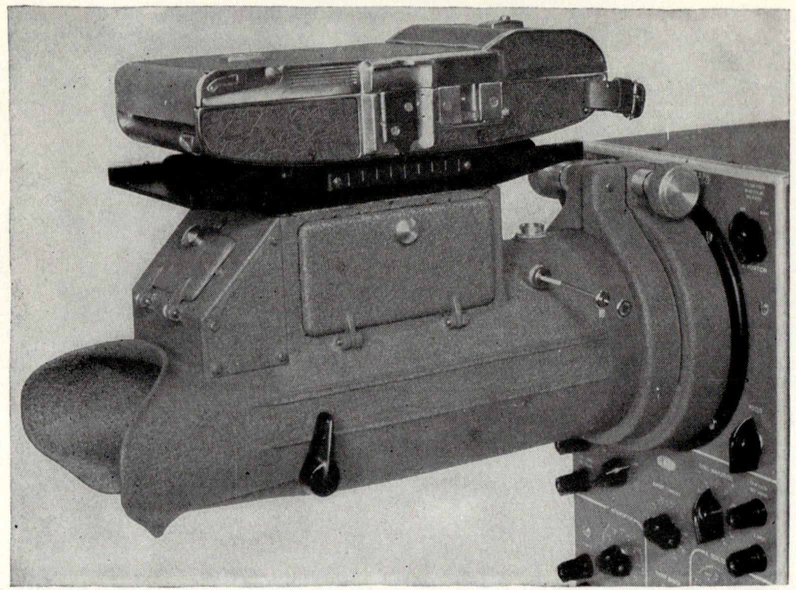

Fig. 5-25. Du Mont oscilloscope camera operating on the Polaroid Land principle and capable of producing a finished print within 10 sec to 1 min after exposure (*Courtesy of Allen B. Du Mont Laboratories, Inc.*)

Fig. 5-26. Du Mont motion-picture camera for recording transient signals on an oscilloscope. Film speed is variable from 0.8 to 10,800 in. per min. (*Courtesy of Allen B. Du Mont Laboratories, Inc.*)

Quantitative calibration of the time coordinate in recording with an oscilloscope and camera can be obtained by techniques similar to those used with oscillographs. When a still camera is being used to record either repetitive or transient phenomena, it is possible to accomplish time calibration by making a double exposure. An exposure of the signal being studied is first made in the normal manner. Without changing the oscilloscope sweep controls, a wave of known frequency is then substituted for the signal and a second exposure made. In another technique a timing wave is superimposed directly on the amplitude of the signal as a series of small pips. This method has the disadvantage of occasionally obscuring details of the primary trace. As an alternative, the voltage from the timing source can be applied to the intensity circuit of the cathode-ray tube (or z axis) and will result in a series of either blank spots or extraordinarily bright spots, depending upon the polarity of the timing voltage. An electronic switch can also, under certain circumstances, be used to present a timing wave on the oscilloscope. A dual-beam (two-channel) oscilloscope is ideal for recording time calibration, especially in making motion-picture records of transient phenomena. In this case the test signal is applied to one trace and the timing signal to the other. This system gives complete flexibility in the choice of camera and timing source.

STRAIN GAGE INSTRUMENTATION CHART

Although the bonded wire strain gage has been extolled as an extremely versatile, simple, and inexpensive device, it should be evident at this point that the instruments required to amplify and translate its strain signals into engineering numbers are often both complex and costly. The complexity should be no deterrent to the use of these instruments. Fortunately, one need not know all the electronic intricacies involved in the design of the instruments in order to use them successfully, any more than one does to operate a television set. The strain analyst should know, though, the functions which a given instrument is capable of performing and, conversely, what instruments to select for performing desired functions. Above all, he must be familiar with the limitations of any equipment he plans to use.

There is presently available a rather formidable array of instruments for use with strain gages. Some are complete in themselves; that is, they are capable, when connected to a strain gage, of producing a finished record of strain directly. Others are designed to perform specialized duties and must be used in conjunction with supplementary instruments. Still others are restricted in their use to indicating or recording only certain types of strain. All the instruments have limiting characteristics which will determine their comparative suitability for any given strain-measuring task. The experienced stress analyst may have acquired a thorough acquaintance with all the applicable instruments, their limitations, advantages, and disadvantages. The novice stress analyst or the individual who only occasionally becomes involved with the practical techniques of experimental stress analysis may, however, find himself a little bewildered by all of this.

A method employed by experts and amateurs alike for understanding the operation of complex devices involves subdividing the device into a number of elementary functional components. All instruments can be broken down into a series of these simple, understandable component sections. Each section has a function or operation to perform, and the overall transformation effected by the entire instrument is the cumulative result of that taking place in the individual sections. Thus, by understanding the functions performed by a few basic electronic circuits (not requiring much specific knowledge as to *how* the circuits perform these functions), it is possible to extrapolate our understanding until it encompasses an entire complex instrument. It is common practice to represent the instrument elements as blocks on a diagram, as has been done throughout this chapter. Lines can then be drawn connecting the blocks or elements so that a sequence of operations is indicated. Such a diagram is known as a functional block diagram. This technique will be found quite useful in helping to understand, select, and apply strain gage instruments.

A number of variables enter into the selection of strain gage instruments and instrument components for any one strain-measuring problem. The following list includes the primary factors which must be considered in making such a selection:

1. Type of strain to be measured (static or dynamic).
2. Form of strain indication or record which is desired.
3. Accuracy requirements.
4. Number of simultaneous strain measurements to be made.
5. Availability of equipment, and budget restrictions.

It may be possible to arrive at the desired results by any of several different instruments or combinations of instrument components. The method used will generally represent some compromise of the above factors. One very important factor to be kept in mind during the selection process is that the instruments or components which are to be combined must be *electrically compatible*. Each instrument has certain electrical characteristics, such as frequency response, input and output impedances, and voltage or current limitations. It is imperative for satisfactory results that each element involved in a complete sequence have characteristics which properly match those of the associated elements in that sequence. The matching is generally most critical between any two consecutive elements, but for some properties the sequence of elements acts like a chain. The characteristics of the entire instrument may be limited by those of one of the components. As a practical example of this, it is apparently foolish to purchase an expensive phonograph amplifier with a frequency response of 20 to 20,000 cps if the loudspeaker to be used with the amplifier has a response of only, say, 200 to 10,000 cps.

Because of the general complexity of strain gage instruments and the factors involved in their selection and use, the accompanying diagram (Fig. 5-27) has been constructed. This diagram is meant to clarify, and display with some degree of perspective, the greater portion of the strain gage instrumentation field. (Telemetering, or wireless transmission of strain data, is among the omissions.) The manner of presentation employed is that of the functional block diagram. Most of the commonly used instrument elements are shown as blocks, with connecting lines between elements indicating allowable paths for the flow of strain intelligence between compatible blocks. In general, indication or recording of strain can be accomplished by following with the arrows any continuous path from left to right. By using the chart in this manner, it is comparatively easy to realize or explain the instrument selection limitations imposed upon the stress analyst by the variables already mentioned. Commercially available strain gage instruments may, of course, embody any one or almost any combination of the functional blocks shown on the diagram.

It should be kept in mind that the strain gage instrumentation diagram is a generalization. As such, it has characteristics common to most generalizations. Any attempt to portray a relatively large field of activity in a compact diagram necessarily results in considerable loss of detail, as well as the omission of much valuable information. For instance, the voltage, current, and impedance levels given for each block indicate merely orders of magnitude, and not the magnitudes themselves. The waveforms shown are only representative of certain typical cases. There are also differences in the relative practicability of the various strain intelligence paths.

TELEMETERING

The subject of strain indication and recording should not be dismissed without a brief description of the process known as telemetering. This is the name given the technique of transmitting data from strain gages and other transducers over comparatively long distances by radio and television methods. There are numerous applications in aircraft, missile, and rocket research in which the probability of obtaining records from recording instruments mounted on the device itself is questionable, or actually zero. An experimental vehicle is an expensive piece of test equipment and, whether good or bad, should be made to yield the maximum amount of data.

Basically, the process consists in mounting radio transmitters in the vehicle which, instead of transmitting vocal or coded verbal intelligence, transmit radio-frequency carrier waves upon which strain or other physical data have been impressed. There are matching radio receivers at some ground station which pick up the carrier waves, detect the strain information, and present it for indication or recording by the conventional

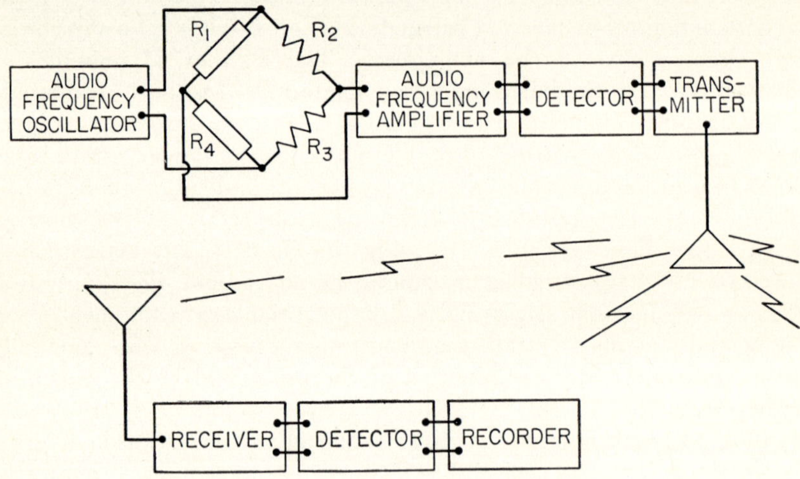

FIG. 5-28. Greatly simplified block diagram of a single-channel radio telemetering system.

methods already described. Figure 5-28 is a greatly simplified functional block diagram of a basic telemetering system. It is apparent that a great variety of strain, load, and other physical data can be obtained and recorded with a multiple-channel installation of such a system. It is also apparent that the number of channels necessary for transmission of data from the many significant points on, for example, an aircraft could easily reach near-astronomical proportions. One rather obvious technique for getting around this difficulty is the use of television. Many of the phenomena being studied during a flight test do not vary at a high frequency. These might include airspeed, altitude, engine speed or thrust, and similar physical variables, as well as a number of slowly varying strains. The common practice is to group the indicators for all these variables into a single panel which can be photographed by one television camera. The television camera mounted in the airplane then transmits a continuous picture of this instrument group to earth. A corresponding television receiver at a ground station picks up the picture. This can then be recorded by taking a continuous motion picture of the television screen.

A novel application of telemetering over very short distances was made by W. R. Campbell at the National Bureau of Standards. He chose to eliminate the problem of slip-ring interference in a strain gage shaft torque meter by mounting a small FM transmitter and antenna directly on the shaft with the strain gages. The Wheatstone-bridge output from the gages on the shaft was amplified on the spot and broadcast from the transmitter and antenna to a stationary receiving set in the same room. It is evident that the same methods of telemetering can be applied in a variety of circumstances—in nuclear installations, engine test cells, rocket launch pads—wherever it is hazardous, inconvenient, or impossible to have the final recording instruments and the operator in the same environment as the strain gages.

BIBLIOGRAPHY

Aughtie, F.: Electrical Resistance Wire Strain Gauges, with Particular Reference to Possible Errors in Their Use for Static and Dynamic Measurements, *Trans. Inst. Marine Engrs.*, vol. 58, no. 4, pp. 59–66, May, 1946.

Ball, L. M.: Strain Gage Technique, *Proc. SESA*, vol. 3, no. 1, pp. 1–22, 1945.

Bowman, C. E., and W. J. Craig: Modification of Portable Strain Indicator for Use with Closed External Bridge Circuit, *Instruments*, vol. 24, no. 5, p. 533, May, 1951.

Branson, N. G.: Strain Gage Amplifier, *Gen. Elec. Rev.*, vol. 48, no. 4, pp. 55–58, April, 1945.

Christian, D.: "BL-310" Strain Analyzer, *Proc. SESA*, vol. 7, no. 1, pp. 21–29, 1949.

Dohrenwend, C. O., and W. R. Mehaffey: Electrical-resistance Gages and Circuit Theory, "Handbook of Experimental Stress Analysis," p. 160, John Wiley & Sons, Inc., New York, 1950.

Dohrenwend, C. O., and W. R. Mehaffey: Measurement of Dynamic Strain, *Trans. ASME* (*J. Appl. Mechanics*), vol. 65, pp. A-85 to A-92, June, 1943.

Dowell, T. M., and J. A. Mackinnon: Measurement of Cyclic Strain, *J. Sci. Instr.*, vol. 37, pp. 138–140, April, 1960.

Enslein, K.: High-speed Low Level Scanner, *Inst. Radio Engrs., Trans. on Indus. Electronics*, *PGIE*-8, pp. 17–24, January, 1959.

Fick, N. C., and N. A. Crites: Fifty-point Bridge Balance Unit for Use with a Baldwin SR-4 Strain Indicator, *Instruments*, vol. 21, no. 4, pp. 329–330, April, 1948.

Foster, W. H.: Strain Gage Oscillator for Flight Testing, *Electronics*, vol. 31, pp. 40–42, Jan. 31, 1958.

Frederick, C. L.: Aircraft Instruments for Radio-telemetering and Television-telemetering, *Proc. SESA*, vol. 4, no. 2, pp. 103–121, 1947.

Geschelin, J.: Mobile Electronometer Records Stresses in Vehicle Road Test by Electric Strain Gage Method, *Automotive and Aviation Inds.*, vol. 95, pp. 28–31+, Oct. 15, 1946.

Gunning, W. F., and E. G. Van Leeuwen: Resistance Wire Strain Gage Equipment for Static and Dynamic Testing, *Product Eng.*, vol. 16, no. 9, pp. 608–613, September, 1945.

Haakana, C. H.: Shunt Bridge Balancing in Strain-gage Indicators, *Electronics*, vol. 32, no. 30, pp. 50–51, July 24, 1959.

Halio, M.: Dynamic Strain Calibrator, *Electronic Ind.*, vol. 18, no. 12, pp. 104–109, December, 1959.

Halling, J.: Modification for Use with Wire Resistance Strain Gage Circuits, *J. Sci. Instr.*, vol. 35, p. 72, February, 1958.

Hamner, B. B., and H. Sommer: Modified SR-4 Indicator to Measure Dynamic Strains, *Product Eng.*, vol. 20, pp. 143–145, September, 1949.

Hathaway, C. M., and K. C. Rock: Dynamic Strain Measurement, *Elec. Eng.*, vol. 70, no. 8, pp. 675–678, August, 1951.

Kammer, E. W.: Constant Time Interval Reference Potential Indicator for Use with R-C Coupled Amplifiers, *Rev. Sci. Instr.*, vol. 17, pp. 102–106, March, 1946.

Kaufman, A. B.: Carrier Strain Gauge System, *Radio and Television News*, vol. 46, no. 1 (Radio-Electronic Eng.), pp. 7–9, July, 1951.

Kaufman, A. B.: Oscillographic Strain Gauge Recording, *Radio and Television News*, vol. 44, no. 3 (*Radio-Electronic Eng.*, vol. 15, no. 3), pp. 15A–18A, 27A, September, 1950.

Kaufman, A. B.: Phase Sensitive Strain Gauge System, *Radio and Television News*, vol. 45, no. 1 (*Radio-Electronic Eng.*, vol. 16, no. 1), pp. 3A–6A, 27A, January, 1951.

Kaufman, A. B.: Self-balancing Strain Gauge Equipment, *Radio and Television News*, vol. 46, no. 2 (*Radio-Electronic Eng.*), pp. 12–14, August, 1951.

Loubser, R. S., and W. W. Schroeder: Measuring Repeated Strains with a Modified Null-balancing Strain Indicator, *Experimental Mechanics*, vol. 1, no. 4, p. 136, April, 1961.

Mehaffey, W. R., J. N. Van Scoyoc, and D. C. Schover: A Direct Coupled Amplifier for Recording Dynamic Strain, *Proc. SESA*, vol. 6, no. 1, pp. 44–54, 1948.

Meier, J. H.: Recording Unit for Strain and Timing Functions, *Electronics*, vol. 16, no. 4, pp. 79–83+, April, 1943.

Meyer, R. D.: A Note on Indicating and Recording Instruments, *Instrument Notes* (Statham Laboratories), August–September, 1948, 10 pp.

Parina, J., Jr.: Mobile Laboratory Measures Stresses in Steel Trailers under Road Conditions, *Steel*, vol. 120, pp. 88–89+, Mar. 10, 1947.

Rauch, L. L.: Electronic Commutation of Strain Gages for Telemetering, *Proc. SESA*, vol. 5, no. 1, pp. 111–121, 1947.

Roberts, H. C.: Carrier-type Amplifier for Electric Gages, *Electronics*, vol. 20, no. 5, pp. 92–95, May, 1947.

Roberts, H. C.: "Mechanical Measurements by Electrical Methods," Instruments Publishing Co., Inc., Pittsburgh, 1946.

Senior, D. A.: Recording Signals from Resistance Strain Gauges. I—Introduction and Galvanometer Design. II—Operation of Wire Resistance Strain Gauges at High Power Dissipation, *Engineer*, vol. 197, Mar. 19, 26, 1954, pp. 410, 446.

Tatnall, F. G., and C. H. Gibbons: Static and Dynamic Testing of Structures, *Soc. Naval Architects Marine Engrs., Trans.*, vol. 52, pp. 114–124, 1944.

Widdis, F. C.: Direct Reading Electrical Strain Meter, *J. Sci. Instr.*, vol. 24, no. 11, pp. 302–303, November, 1947.

Worley, W. J.: Simplified Dynamic Strain Equipment, *Instruments*, vol. 21, no. 4, pp. 330–332, April, 1948.

Yates, J. G., D. H. Lucas, and D. L. Johnston: Multi-channel Measurement of Physical Effects by Confluent Pulse Technique with Particular Reference to Analysis of Strain, *Proc. Inst. Elec. Engrs.* (London), vol. 98, pt. 2 (*Power Eng.*), no. 62, pp. 109–119, 120–124 (discussion), April, 1951.

Yates, J. G., D. H. Lucas, and D. L. Johnston: Pulse-excitation of Resistance Strain Gauges for Dynamic Multi-channel Observation, *Proc. SESA*, vol. 11, no. 1, p. 35, 1954.

Phase-indicating Null Indicator for Bridges, *Electronics*, vol. 17, no. 8, pp. 242+, August, 1944.

Symposium on Dynamic Stress Determination, *ASTM, Spec. Tech. Pub.* 104 (4 papers), October, 1949.

EXERCISES

5-1. Build a strain indicator similar to that shown in Fig. 5-1. A suggested source for an inexpensive meter is the movement from a light meter.

5-2. *A*. Calculate the size of the resistor for placing in shunt with a 120-ohm strain gage to produce a synthetic strain indication on the meter of the static strain indicator of 1,000 micro-inches per in. when the gage-factor setting is 1.85.

B. Using the procedure in *A*, calibrate a static strain indicator; i.e., balance the indicator with two dummy gages mounted on a small block of metal, shunt one of the gages with the above resistor, and balance the meter to determine the error in strain indication.

C. Modify the setup of *B* by placing 200 ft of No. 18 wire in series with one of the strain gages. Recalibrate the static strain indicator under this condition. Test the effect on the calibration of tightly coiling the 200 ft of wire with and without an iron core. Explain the results obtained.

5-3. Calibrate the course balance control and the range extender of the strain indicator.

5-4. The strain reading obtained in a given test is 518 micro-inches per in. The gage-factor setting of the instrument was 1.76 when this reading was obtained. The gage factor of the gage used was 1.96. Determine the true strain.

5-5. Mount two strain gages axially and on opposite sides of a steel tensile specimen. Mount two more strain gages on a dummy block. Record strains while loading the specimen incrementally to a maximum strain of approximately 1,000 micro-inches per in., taking data on both increasing and decreasing loads. Draw the best line through the data and calculate the modulus of elasticity of the steel. Repeat the experiment with cast iron or magnesium.

5-6. Repeat Exercise 5 with strain gages mounted transversely to the axis of the test specimen. After correcting the latter data for transverse sensitivity effects as described in Chap. 7, calculate Poisson's ratio for the test material from the data obtained here and in Exercise 5.

5-7. Apply an impact load to a steel specimen on which a strain gage has been mounted, recording the strain on a moving-pen-type galvanometer. Repeat the test, obtaining the strain recording on a cathode-ray oscilloscope. Compare the results obtained.

5-8. Using a cathode-ray oscilloscope with a d.c. amplifier, trace the signal through the circuits of a commercial static strain indicator with the bridge first balanced and then unbalanced. Record the waveforms at each point and draw a schematic diagram of the indicator circuitry with the waveforms shown.

5-9. A transient signal having frequencies up to 350 cps is to be observed. Draw the block diagram of the practical instrumentation system to record the signal sensed by the strain gage.

6 STRAINS AND STRESSES

The proper use of strain gages depends not only upon such mundane factors as cementing, wiring, and instrumentation but also, and very critically, upon certain subtleties involved in the manner in which stress is related to strain. The strain gage applications described up to this point have been of the very simplest nature. It should be recognized that most of the examples given are so elementary that the stresses could be calculated quite accurately from knowledge of the loads and dimensions. For such cases, the strain gage is unnecessary except for use as a transducer to measure load or displacement. Unfortunate as it may be, practical cases of stress analysis are seldom as simple as the examples given in the previous chapters. The strain gage is commonly used where it is impossible to calculate the stresses, generally because of the complexity of the structure being tested. To interpret strain gage information correctly requires a basic knowledge of the natural laws of elasticity. This chapter attempts to supply in an understandable form the background information necessary for competent use of strain gages. By making a few geometric approximations which do not affect the accuracy of the over-all results, it is possible to demonstrate the complex interrelationships between elastic stress and strain with nothing more profound than a few algebraic and trigonometric manipulations.

The limitations of materials in their ability to carry loads or withstand forces have always been expressed in terms of stresses. This is true for both the maximum load-carrying capacity and working loads. The characteristics of materials in general, such as proportional limit, yield point, and ultimate and breaking strength, are all expressed as stresses. Stress however, is not a fundamental, but rather a derived quantity. Stress as such is impossible to measure. It must be computed, either from the applied force and area involved, as in tension and compression members, or from a consideration of the strains and their distribution, as in members subjected to bending and torsion. Normal strain, on the other hand, is a change in dimension, and therefore a fundamental quantity subject to direct measurement. Shearing strain is a change in angle and can also be measured, but not so readily as normal strain.

Since stress is universally used in describing the strength of materials, it is necessary to translate the strains which can be measured into the stresses which can be understood. This process of translating strains into stresses is complicated by the Poisson effect. When a primary strain is produced in the x direction by a force in that direction, secondary, or Poisson, strains are simultaneously produced in the y and z directions normal to the primary strain. These Poisson strains are, however, unaccompanied by stresses in the y and z directions. This point is frequently overlooked in strain measurement.

For the case of uniaxial stress which would be represented by a simple tension or compression member (Fig. 6-1) the primary strain is related to the stress by Hooke's law of proportionality. In this instance the stress in the direction of the applied force is equal to the product of the modulus of elasticity and the primary strain, provided that the proportional limit of the material is not exceeded. In every other direction this relationship does not apply because of the Poisson effect. In the more complex case of biaxial stress (Fig. 6-2), where primary strains exist in both the x and y directions, the above simple relationship between stress and strain is not valid in any direction. This is because Poisson strains now exist in all directions.

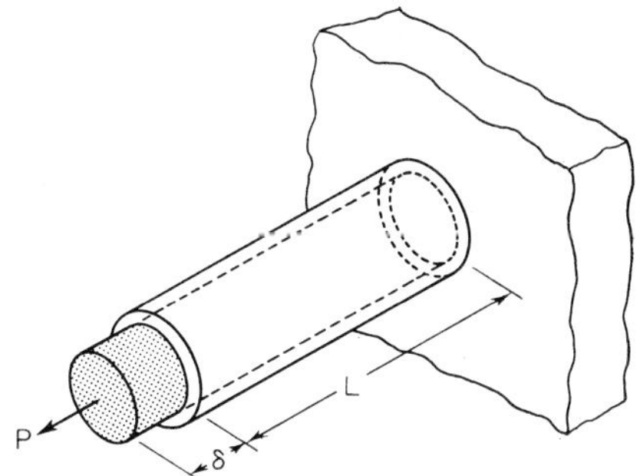

Fig. 6-1. Exaggerated deformation produced by uniaxial stress in a simple tension member.

Figure 6-3 illustrates the variation in strain about a point for the case of a primary strain in one direction only. The stress variation about the same point has also been plotted on the figure. The radial scales for strain and stress have been selected to result in equal vectorial lengths in the direction of the applied load. It is evident from this figure that the relationship between stress and strain varies with the angle of measurement. The figure shows that if the relationship $\sigma = E\epsilon$ is true in the direction of the applied load, it cannot be true in any other direction. At an angle of about 60° from the y axis the stress has an appreciable magnitude, but the strain is zero. At right angles to the direction of the primary strain, where the stress is zero, the strain has the value $-\mu\epsilon$, in which μ is Poisson's ratio. Figure 6-3 further illustrates why in general

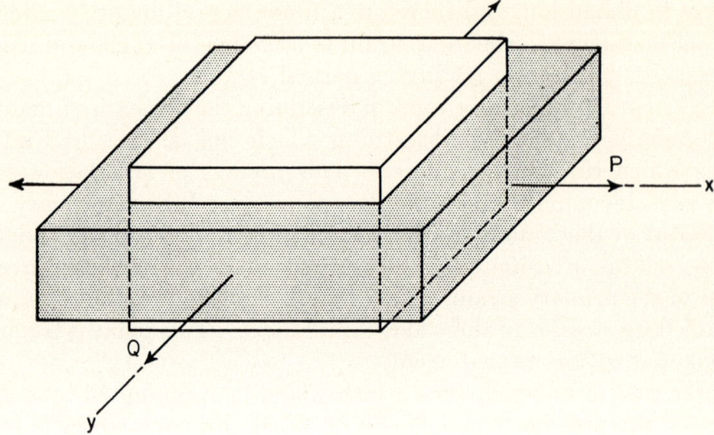

Fig. 6-2. Exaggerated deformations in an element of matter subjected to a biaxial stress condition.

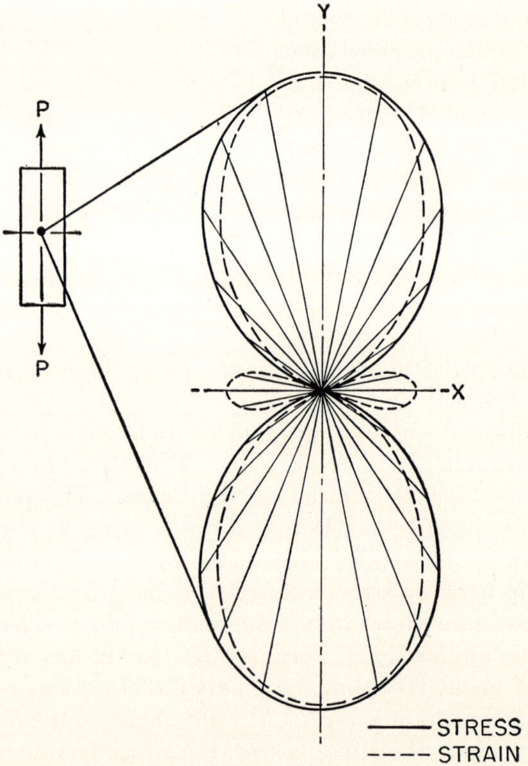

Fig. 6-3. Stress and strain magnitudes about a point in a plane uniaxial stress field.

it is not possible simply to multiply the strain as measured in any arbitrary direction by the modulus of elasticity E and obtain the stress in the direction of the applied strain gage. Before the stress can be determined, it will be necessary to have some additional information.

The total strain in any direction can be considered to consist of three separate parts: first, the strain due to temperature change, the effect of

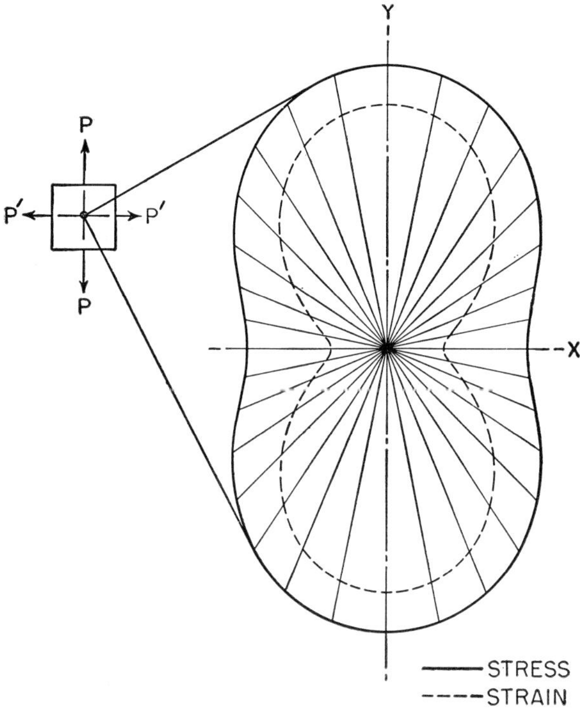

FIG. 6-4. Stress and strain magnitudes about a point in a plane biaxial stress field. The stress and strain scales are the same as those in Fig. 6-3.

which we have previously learned to eliminate when taking measurements with the strain gage; second, the strain due to the Poisson effect which is unaccompanied by stress; and third, the primary strain that is directly related to stress by Hooke's law. The problem, then, is to obtain a relationship between the measured strain and the corresponding stress.

Examining the more complicated condition of biaxial stress leads to the relationship between stress and strain shown in Fig. 6-4. The stress-strain scale ratio in this case is the same as in Fig. 6-3. It is apparent that the maximum and minimum values of stress lie along mutually perpendicular directions. This will always be true for any condition of loading; namely, *the maximum and minimum values of stress will always be found at right angles to each other.* These stresses are called *principal stresses,* and the planes on which they act are *principal planes.* Since one of the principal stresses is always the greatest stress acting at a point, its magnitude and direction are usually of primary significance. It is to be noted that the minimum stress represents compression if its sign becomes negative, and it may actually be numerically larger than the maximum value. It is further seen from Fig. 6-4 that the relationship

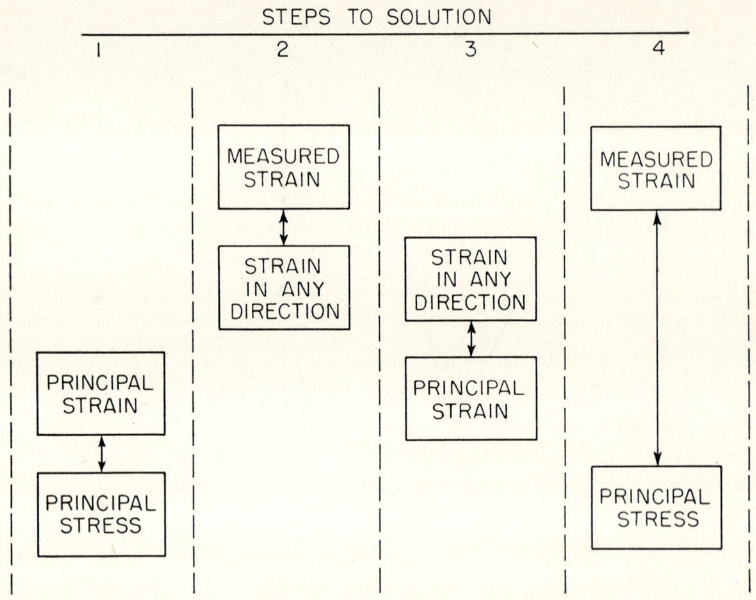

Fig. 6-5. Development of the relationships between measured strain and principal stress.

existing for stresses also applies to the strains. The principal strains are the maximum and minimum values about a point and are mutually perpendicular. The directions of the principal strains coincide with those of the principal stresses, and the planes on which they act are, of course, the principal planes. Another distinguishing feature of principal planes is that no shearing stresses or strains act on them.

Figures 6-3 and 6-4 demonstrate conclusively that, except in the single special case mentioned earlier, there is no simple proportional relationship between stress and strain. Since the principal stresses are usually required, the next problem is to set up a relationship between the measured strains and the corresponding principal stresses. This must be accomplished in several steps, as indicated diagrammatically in Fig. 6-5.

The first step is to obtain the relationship between the principal stresses and their accompanying principal strains. These equations will be directly useful only if the principal stress directions are known so that the strains can be measured in these directions. In the general case, however, this information is not available, and it will be necessary to determine the orientation of the principal planes. The second step requires writing the general relationship between the strain measured in any direction and the strains that exist in any other direction. It is then possible to find the direction in which the strain has a maximum value. With this information the principal stresses can be computed from strain measurements made in any direction.

Proceeding with the first step to determine the relationship between the principal stresses and their accompanying principal strains, picture the deformations occurring in a unit cube of material subjected to a tensile force in the x direction only (Fig. 6-6). In this case the strain in the x direction is σ_x/E and in the y and z directions, $-\mu(\sigma_x/E)$ Repeating the experiment with the force applied only in the y direction results in ϵ_y equal to σ_y/E and ϵ_z and ϵ_x equal to $-\mu(\sigma_y/E)$. Similarly, for a force applied only in the z direction the strain in the same direction is then σ_z/E, and in the x and y directions it is $-\mu(\sigma_z/E)$. If all three forces are applied simultaneously, the strains in any direction can be found by simply adding algebraically the values obtained with each force acting separately. Thus,

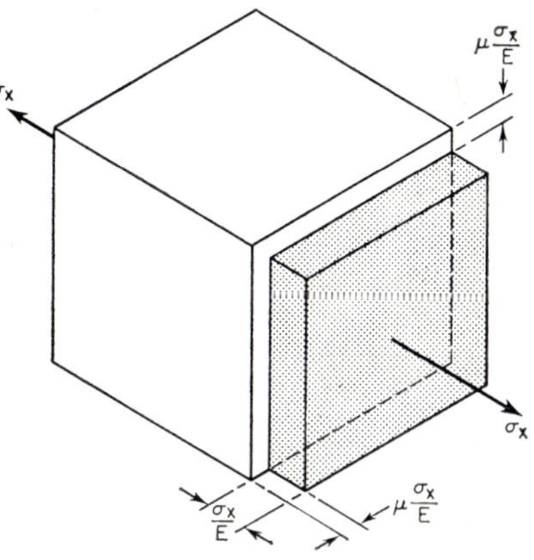

FIG. 6-6. Strains produced in a unit cube by a uniaxial stress.

$$\epsilon_x = \frac{\sigma_x}{E} - \frac{\mu\sigma_y}{E} - \frac{\mu\sigma_z}{E}$$

$$\epsilon_y = \frac{\sigma_y}{E} - \frac{\mu\sigma_z}{E} - \frac{\mu\sigma_x}{E} \qquad (6\text{-}1)$$

$$\epsilon_z = \frac{\sigma_z}{E} - \frac{\mu\sigma_x}{E} - \frac{\mu\sigma_y}{E}$$

If no shearing stresses act on the x, y, and z selected planes, the stresses and strains will be principal stresses and strains. For the case of plane, or two-dimensional, stress, σ_z becomes zero in the above equations. Then rewriting the equations to obtain the principal stresses in terms of the principal strains,

$$\sigma_x = \frac{E}{1 - \mu^2} (\epsilon_x + \mu\epsilon_y)$$
$$\sigma_y = \frac{E}{1 - \mu^2} (\epsilon_y + \mu\epsilon_x) \tag{6-2}$$

These equations demonstrate that σ_x is a function of both ϵ_y and ϵ_x. The same conditions holds for σ_y. Thus, even if the principal stress directions are known so that the principal strains can be measured in these directions, both of the strains must be measured to determine either one or both of the principal stresses.

FIG. 6-7. Punch press instrumented for stress analysis. Note that rosette-type strain gages are used, since the directions of the principal axes cannot be readily inferred by analytical means. (*Courtesy of Given Brewer.*)

Very frequently, however, the principal stress directions are unknown. For example, in the press shown in Fig. 6-7 the orientation of the principal planes is not evident at the point where the gages are located. Therefore, some means must be found for expressing the principal strains in terms of the strains in any direction. This is done by examining the geometric relationships existing between the principal strain and the strain in any arbitrary direction.

Figure 6-8 shows a gage applied on the line OB at an angle φ with the x axis, along which a strain ϵ_x exists. The Poisson strain in the y direction is not introduced, since only the geometry of the problem is being considered at this point.

After applying the strain in the x direction, the line OA of length x has been stretched by the amount δ_x to OA'; and the gage, whose original

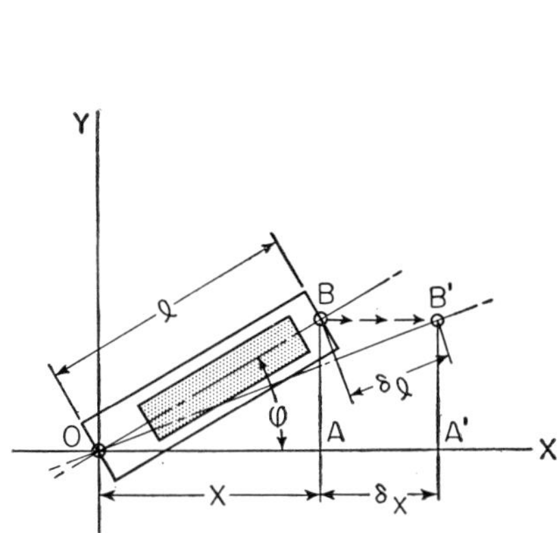

FIG. 6-8. Geometrical representation of strain gage deformation due to a strain in the x direction.

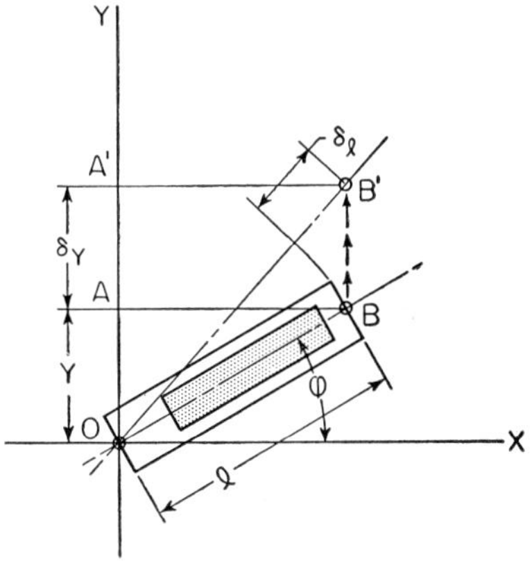

FIG. 6-9. Geometrical representation of strain gage deformation due to a strain in the y direction.

length was l, now lies along the line OB' and is stretched by the amount δ_l. The strain in the x direction is then

$$\epsilon_x = \frac{\delta_x}{x}$$

The strain measured by the gage is

$$\epsilon_\varphi = \frac{\delta_l}{l}$$

Since

$$l = \frac{x}{\cos \varphi}$$

and

$$\delta_l = \delta_x \cos \varphi$$

then

$$\epsilon_\varphi = \frac{\delta_x \cos^2 \varphi}{x} = \epsilon_x \cos^2 \varphi \tag{6-3}$$

Next, by applying a strain in the y direction (Fig. 6-9) the analogous geometrical relationship between ϵ_y and the strain ϵ_φ as measured by the strain gage can be obtained. From the figure it is seen that the angle involved is $90 - \varphi$ with all other conditions identical to those used in obtaining the relation between ϵ_x and ϵ_φ. Substituting $90 - \varphi$ in place of φ, and ϵ_y in place of ϵ_x in Eq. (6-3),

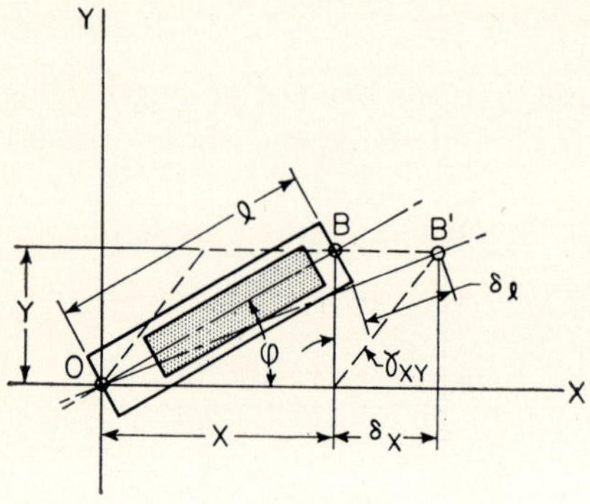

FIG. 6-10. Geometrical representation of strain gage deformation due to a shearing strain.

$$\epsilon_\varphi = \epsilon_y \cos^2 (90 - \varphi) = \epsilon_y \sin^2 \varphi \tag{6-4}$$

As a final step, a study must be made to determine what strain the gage would indicate if a shearing strain γ_{xy} were applied to the plate on which the gage is mounted. As shown in Fig. 6-10, after applying the shearing strain γ_{xy}, the gage lies along the line OB' and has lengthened by the amount δ_l. The strain recorded by the gage is

$$\epsilon_\varphi = \frac{\delta_l}{l}$$

But

$$l = \frac{y}{\sin \varphi}$$

and

$$\delta_l = \delta_x \cos \varphi \qquad \text{where} \qquad \delta_x = y \tan \gamma_{xy} \approx y\gamma_{xy}$$

Then

$$\delta_l = y\gamma_{xy} \cos \varphi$$

and

$$\epsilon_\varphi = \frac{y\gamma_{xy} \cos \varphi}{y/(\sin \varphi)} = \gamma_{xy} \sin \varphi \cos \varphi \tag{6-5}$$

Now if strains ϵ_x, ϵ_y, and γ_{xy} act simultaneously, the gage will record the algebraic sum of the strains, or

$$\epsilon_\varphi = \epsilon_x \cos^2 \varphi + \epsilon_y \sin^2 \varphi + \gamma_{xy} \sin \varphi \cos \varphi \tag{6-6}$$

This equation shows that the strain ϵ_φ measured by a strain gage is a function of the shearing strain γ_{xy}, as well as the normal strains ϵ_x and ϵ_y. Writing Eq. (6-6) in terms of the double angle 2φ,

$$\epsilon_\varphi = \frac{\epsilon_x + \epsilon_y}{2} + \frac{\epsilon_x - \epsilon_y}{2} \cos 2\varphi + \frac{\gamma_{xy}}{2} \sin 2\varphi \tag{6-7}$$

Since ϵ_φ can be measured with a strain gage, the strains in any selected x and y directions can be determined. In Eq. (6-7) above there are three unknowns, ϵ_x, ϵ_y, and γ_{xy}; and therefore three strains, ϵ_1, ϵ_2, and ϵ_3, are required. The latter strains can be measured along any three lines making angles φ_1, φ_2, and φ_3 with the chosen x axis. Then

$$\begin{aligned} \epsilon_1 &= \frac{\epsilon_x + \epsilon_y}{2} + \frac{\epsilon_x - \epsilon_y}{2} \cos 2\varphi_1 + \frac{\gamma_{xy}}{2} \sin 2\varphi_1 \\ \epsilon_2 &= \frac{\epsilon_x + \epsilon_y}{2} + \frac{\epsilon_x - \epsilon_y}{2} \cos 2\varphi_2 + \frac{\gamma_{xy}}{2} \sin 2\varphi_2 \\ \epsilon_3 &= \frac{\epsilon_x + \epsilon_y}{2} + \frac{\epsilon_x - \epsilon_y}{2} \cos 2\varphi_3 + \frac{\gamma_{xy}}{2} \sin 2\varphi_3 \end{aligned} \tag{6-8}$$

Having three unknowns and three equations, ϵ_x, ϵ_y, and γ_{xy} can now be evaluated.

ILLUSTRATIVE EXAMPLE

To illustrate the use of these equations, let us consider a specific example. Suppose three strain gages are applied to an area in such a manner that gage 2 makes a positive angle of 30° with gage 1, and gage 3 makes a positive angle of 45° with gage 2 (Fig. 6-17*A*). The strain readings obtained are as follows:

Gage Number	*Strain, In. per In.*
1	123×10^{-6}
2	-57×10^{-6}
3	244×10^{-6}

Selecting the x axis in the direction of gage 1,

$$\begin{aligned} \varphi_1 &= 0° \\ \varphi_2 &= 30° \\ \varphi_3 &= 75° \end{aligned}$$

Then substituting in Eqs. (6-8)

$$\begin{aligned} 123 \times 10^{-6} &= \frac{\epsilon_x + \epsilon_y}{2} + \frac{\epsilon_x - \epsilon_y}{2} = \epsilon_x \\ -57 \times 10^{-6} &= \frac{\epsilon_x + \epsilon_y}{2} + \frac{\epsilon_x - \epsilon_y}{2} 0.5 + \frac{\gamma_{xy}}{2} 0.866 \\ 244 \times 10^{-6} &= \frac{\epsilon_x + \epsilon_y}{2} - \frac{\epsilon_x - \epsilon_y}{2} 0.866 + \frac{\gamma_{xy}}{2} 0.5 \end{aligned}$$

The first equation gives $\epsilon_x = 123 \times 10^{-6}$ in. per in. as it should, since ϵ_1 was measured in that direction. Substituting this value in the second and third equations and solving them simultaneously gives

$$\begin{aligned} \epsilon_y &= 409 \times 10^{-6} \\ \gamma_{xy} &= -588 \times 10^{-6} \end{aligned}$$

It still remains necessary to determine the relation between ϵ_x, ϵ_y, and γ_{xy} and the principal strains existing at the point. Since by definition the principal strains are the maximum and minimum values existing at a point, the general expression for ϵ_φ can be differentiated with respect to φ to obtain the angle φ_p giving the direction of the principal strains.

$$\epsilon_\varphi = \frac{\epsilon_x + \epsilon_y}{2} + \frac{\epsilon_x - \epsilon_y}{2} \cos 2\varphi + \frac{\gamma_{xy}}{2} \sin 2\varphi$$

$$\frac{d\epsilon_\varphi}{d\varphi} = \frac{-2(\epsilon_x - \epsilon_y)}{2} \sin 2\varphi_p + \frac{2\gamma_{xy}}{2} \cos 2\varphi_p = 0$$

$$\frac{\sin 2\varphi_p}{\cos 2\varphi_p} = \tan 2\varphi_p = \frac{\gamma_{xy}}{\epsilon_x - \epsilon_y} \qquad (6\text{-}9)$$

The expression for the magnitude of the principal strain, $\epsilon_{\max}$, is now obtained by substituting the value of $2\varphi_p$ in the general expression for ϵ_φ in Eq. (6-7). The easiest method for obtaining the trigonometric

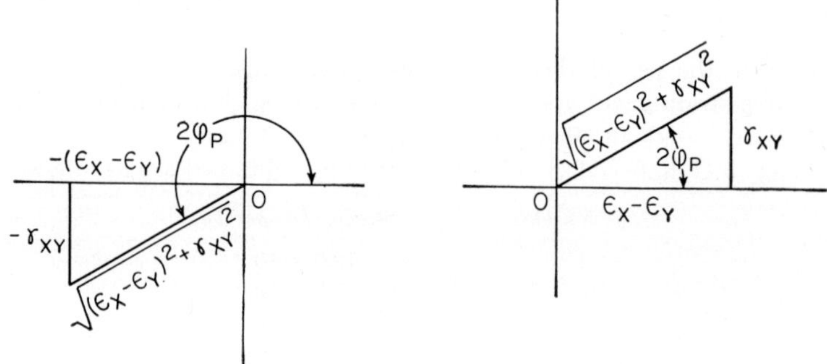

FIG. 6-11. Trigonometric representation of strain relationships.

functions of the angle $2\varphi_p$ is to construct an angle whose tangent is $\gamma_{xy}/(\epsilon_x - \epsilon_y)$. From Fig. 6-11 it is seen that

$$\sin 2\varphi_p = \pm \frac{\gamma_{xy}}{\sqrt{(\epsilon_x - \epsilon_y)^2 + \gamma_{xy}^2}}$$

and

$$\cos 2\varphi_p = \pm \frac{\epsilon_x - \epsilon_y}{\sqrt{(\epsilon_x - \epsilon_y)^2 + \gamma_{xy}^2}}$$

Then substituting the positive values of $\sin 2\varphi_p$ and $\cos 2\varphi_p$ in Eq. (6-7), the maximum principal strain

$$\epsilon_{\max} = \frac{\epsilon_x + \epsilon_y}{2} + \frac{\epsilon_x - \epsilon_y}{2} \frac{\epsilon_x - \epsilon_y}{\sqrt{(\epsilon_x - \epsilon_y)^2 + \gamma_{xy}^2}} + \frac{\gamma_{xy}}{2} \frac{\gamma_{xy}}{\sqrt{(\epsilon_x - \epsilon_y)^2 + \gamma_{xy}^2}}$$

$$\epsilon_{\max} = \frac{\epsilon_x + \epsilon_y}{2} + \frac{1}{2} \frac{(\epsilon_x - \epsilon_y)^2 + \gamma_{xy}^2}{\sqrt{(\epsilon_x - \epsilon_y)^2 + \gamma_{xy}^2}}$$

$$\epsilon_{\max} = \frac{\epsilon_x + \epsilon_y}{2} + \frac{\sqrt{(\epsilon_x - \epsilon_y)^2 + \gamma_{xy}^2}}{2} \qquad (6\text{-}10)$$

Using the negative values, the minimum principal strain

$$\epsilon_{min} = \frac{\epsilon_x + \epsilon_y}{2} - \frac{\sqrt{(\epsilon_x - \epsilon_y)^2 + \gamma_{xy}{}^2}}{2} \tag{6-11}$$

Continuing the numerical example by substituting the previously obtained values of ϵ_x, ϵ_y, and γ_{xy} in the equation for maximum principal strain,

$$\epsilon_{max} = \left[\frac{123 + 409}{2} + \frac{\sqrt{(123 - 409)^2 + 588^2}}{2}\right] \times 10^{-6}$$

$$\epsilon_{max} = 593 \times 10^{-6}$$

Similarly

$$\epsilon_{min} = -61 \times 10^{-6}$$

The angle to the maximum principal stress direction as measured from the x axis will be obtained by substituting in the equation

$$\tan 2\varphi_p = \frac{\gamma_{xy}}{\epsilon_x - \epsilon_y}$$

$$\tan 2\varphi_p = \frac{-588 \times 10^{-6}}{(123 - 409) \times 10^{-6}} = 2.06$$

$$2\varphi_p = 244°04'$$

$$\varphi_p = 122°02'$$

Note that the angle $2\varphi_p$ in this case is in the third quadrant since the tangent is the ratio of negative quantities.

MOHR'S CIRCLE FOR STRAIN

It is possible to employ a graphical method to show the relationship that exists between normal and shearing strains in any direction at a point. This construction is called Mohr's circle for strain. It uses ϵ and $\gamma/2$ as the axes of a coordinate system, so a single point can be used to represent the state of strain on some plane in a strained body. Figure 6-12 shows how a normal strain of, say, 500×10^{-6} and a shearing strain of 400×10^{-6} are represented by point A in this coordinate system. Notice particularly that the positive $\gamma/2$ axis is chosen downward.

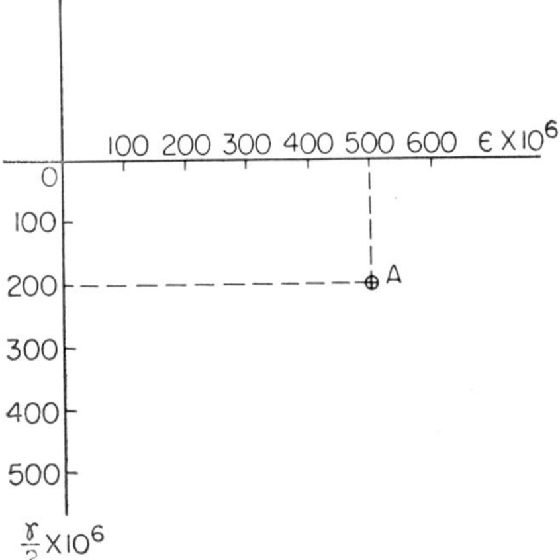

FIG. 6-12. Strain magnitude plotted on ϵ, $\gamma/2$ coordinates. Point A represents a normal strain of 500×10^{-6} in. per in. and a shearing strain of 400×10^{-6} radian.

Mohr's circle can be employed to obtain the solution of the problem under consideration. The strain gage readings ϵ_1, ϵ_2, and ϵ_3, when substituted in Eq. (6-8), give values of ϵ_x, ϵ_y, and γ_{xy} which can be plotted in the ϵ, $\gamma/2$ coordinate system. ϵ_x and $\gamma_{xy}/2$ are represented by a single point A (Fig. 6-13). ϵ_y and $\gamma_{yx}/2$ (which must always be equal in magnitude and opposite in sign to $\gamma_{xy}/2$) are also represented by a single point B. The line joining points A and B is the diameter of Mohr's circle of strain, which can now be drawn. All points on the circumference of the circle represent the strain conditions on some plane at the point being considered. The principal strains occur where the circle crosses the ϵ axis, since the shearing strains are zero at these points.

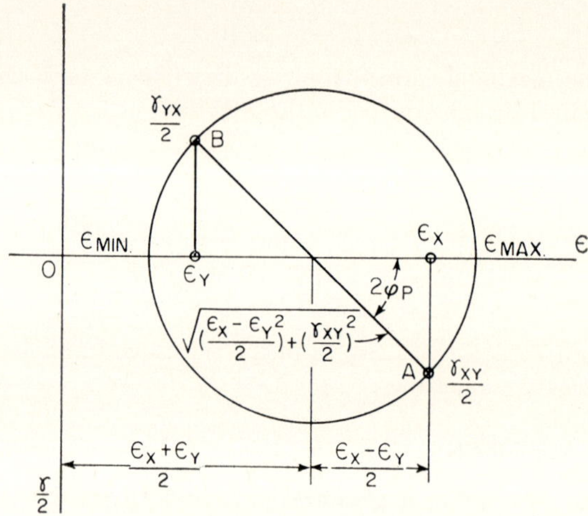

FIG. 6-13. Mohr's circle for strain.

From Fig. 6-13 it can be seen that the distance from the center of the circle to the point representing ϵ_x on the ϵ axis is $(\epsilon_x - \epsilon_y)/2$, and the distance between the origin and the center of the circle is $(\epsilon_x + \epsilon_y)/2$. The right triangle in the circle having the sides $(\epsilon_x - \epsilon_y)/2$ and $\gamma_{xy}/2$ will have for its hypotenuse (and the radius of the circle)

$$\frac{\sqrt{(\epsilon_x - \epsilon_y)^2 + \gamma_{xy}^2}}{2}$$

If the angle between this hypotenuse and the ϵ axis is called $2\varphi_p$, $\tan 2\varphi_p = \gamma_{xy}/(\epsilon_x - \epsilon_y)$, which is the same as the value obtained algebraically.

From Fig. 6-13

$$\epsilon_{\max} = \frac{\epsilon_x + \epsilon_y}{2} + \frac{\sqrt{(\epsilon_x - \epsilon_y)^2 + \gamma_{xy}^2}}{2}$$

$$\epsilon_{\min} = \frac{\epsilon_x + \epsilon_y}{2} - \frac{\sqrt{(\epsilon_x - \epsilon_y)^2 + \gamma_{xy}^2}}{2}$$

These equations are found to be identical with Eqs. (6-10) and (6-11).

From the same figure it is apparent that the angles measured around the circumference of Mohr's circle are twice as great as those measured in the x, y coordinate system. For example, point A, which represents the strains along and perpendicular to the x plane, is 180° from point B, which represents the strains along and perpendicular to the y plane; but the x and y planes are, of course, only 90° apart. The maximum principal strains will be found in a direction making a counterclockwise angle φ_p with the x axis.

Figure 6-14 represents the solution of the illustrative example by means of Mohr's circle for strain.

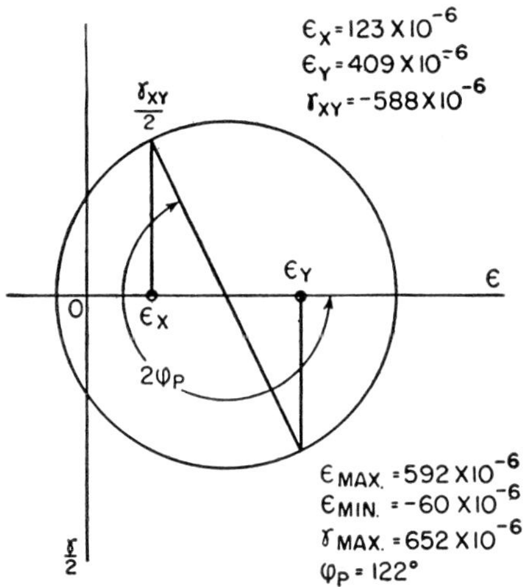

FIG. 6-14. Solution of the illustrative example by Mohr's circle for strain.

It is suggested that the principal use of the circle is not to obtain a graphical solution of the problem but rather to use the freehand construction of the circle as a means of obtaining the algebraic solution from the geometry involved, and so avoid the necessity for remembering the complex equations defining ϵ_{max}, ϵ_{min}, and φ_p.

Since the principal strains can now be determined from either the equations or Mohr's circle, it is at last possible to calculate the principal stresses from the three measured strains ϵ_1, ϵ_2, and ϵ_3 by substituting the computed values of ϵ_{max} and ϵ_{min} into the previously derived Eqs. (6-2).

$$\sigma_{max} = \frac{E}{1 - \mu^2} (\epsilon_{max} + \mu\epsilon_{min})$$

$$\sigma_{min} = \frac{E}{1 - \mu^2} (\epsilon_{min} + \mu\epsilon_{max})$$

If the numerical example were applied to steel having $E = 30 \times 10^6$ psi and $\mu = 0.3$, the following results would be obtained:

$$\sigma_{\max} = \frac{30 \times 10^6}{1 - 0.3^2}(593 - 0.3 \times 61) \times 10^{-6}$$
$$\sigma_{\max} = 18{,}930 \text{ psi}$$
$$\sigma_{\min} = \frac{30 \times 10^6}{1 - 0.3^2}(-61 + 0.3 \times 593) \times 10^{-6}$$
$$\sigma_{\min} = 3{,}850 \text{ psi}$$

To summarize, the steps required to determine the maximum and minimum stresses existing at a point are as follows:

1. An x axis is selected and magnitudes of strain are determined in three directions, making angles of φ_1, φ_2, and φ_3 with the chosen axis. φ_1 is usually made equal to zero for convenience; that is, the first strain is measured along the x axis.

2. The three strains obtained are substituted in Eqs. (6-8), which are solved simultaneously for ϵ_x, ϵ_y, and γ_{xy}.

3. The values of ϵ_x, ϵ_y, and γ_{xy} obtained in the second step are substituted in Eqs. (6-10) and (6-11) to obtain the principal strains $\epsilon_{\max}$ and $\epsilon_{\min}$. In place of these equations, Mohr's circle for strain can be substituted to obtain the principal strains graphically or algebraically.

4. If the directions of the principal strains and stresses are required, the values of ϵ_x, ϵ_y, and γ_{xy} must be substituted in Eq. (6-9) to determine the angle φ_p which the maximum principal strain (and stress) makes with the originally selected x axis. φ_p can also be obtained from Mohr's circle for strain.

5. The maximum and minimum principal stresses are now obtained by substituting $\epsilon_{\max}$ and $\epsilon_{\min}$ in Eqs. (6-2).

Since this algebraic procedure is quite lengthy, involving as it does four separate steps, a graphical procedure has been developed by means of which the principal strains and their directions can be obtained more rapidly. This eliminates step 2 required in the algebraic method.

The problem requires that a Mohr's circle for strain be constructed directly from the three initially measured normal strains. These three strains must lie on the circumference of the circle. The angles between these strains on the circle must also be double the angles between the axes along which the strains were measured; that is, the distance from ϵ_1 to ϵ_2 as measured around the circle must be $2\varphi'$, and the distance from ϵ_2 to ϵ_3 must be $2\varphi''$.

The first step of this solution may require extension through the origin of one or two of the axes along which the strains are measured. This is usually necessary since, to obtain a solution by this method, the strain of intermediate magnitude must lie between the axes of the greater and lesser strains. The total included angle must always be less than 180°. Such a transformation will be possible in all cases. Suppose the three measured strains are

$$\epsilon_1 = 200 \times 10^{-6} \text{ in. per in.}$$
$$\epsilon_2 = 300 \times 10^{-6} \text{ in. per in.}$$
$$\epsilon_3 = -50 \times 10^{-6} \text{ in. per in.}$$

and the angles

$$\varphi' = 40°$$
$$\varphi'' = 80°$$

as shown in Fig. 6-15*A*. In this case the intermediate strain, in terms of position (ϵ_2), is not intermediate in magnitude. Since ϵ_1 is the intermediate strain in magnitude, a rearrangement must be made to place it between ϵ_2 and ϵ_3. This is accomplished by extending the axes of ϵ_1 and ϵ_2 through the point of their intersection as shown in Fig. 6-15*B*. Now the strain of intermediate magnitude lies between the position of the

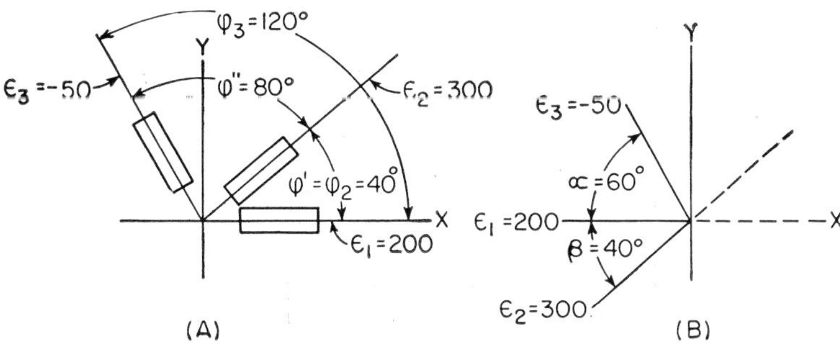

FIG. 6-15. Method of transferring axes for graphical solution.

maximum and minimum strains, and the total angle between these two latter strains still remains less than 180°.

The next step after this preliminary orientation is to lay off the three strains ϵ_1, ϵ_2, and ϵ_3 from the vertical axis $\gamma/2$, positive values to the right and negative values to the left as shown in Fig. 6-16. Vertical lines parallel to the $\gamma/2$ axis are then drawn through the points representing the strains. From an arbitrarily selected point A on the intermediate line, representing the strain in our example, a line making a clockwise angle α with the vertical is drawn to intersect the ϵ_3 vertical at B. α is the angle between the axes of ϵ_1 and ϵ_3 as shown in Fig. 6-15*B*. From the same point A another line is drawn, making a counterclockwise angle β with the vertical. This line intersects the ϵ_2 vertical at C, and β is the angle between the axes of ϵ_1 and ϵ_2. Points A, B, and C lie on the circumference of Mohr's circle, whose center lies at the intersection of the perpendicular bisectors of the lines AB and AC. The ϵ axis can now be drawn through this center.

The points defining the complete states of strain along the initially selected axes, that is, shearing as well as normal strain, may be either on the upper half or on the lower half of the circle. The correct position is determined from the fact that as one proceeds around the circumference of the circle in a counterclockwise direction, the angle from ϵ_3 to ϵ_1 must

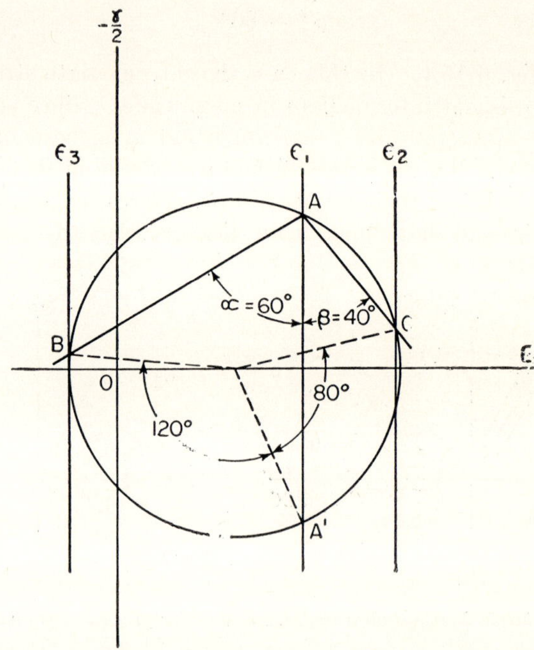

Fig. 6-16. Graphical solution for obtaining principal strains directly from measured strains.

be 2α, or 120°, and the angle from ϵ_1 to ϵ_2 must be 2β, or 80°. Assuming that point B represents the true total strain along ϵ_3 and proceeding counterclockwise around the circumference of the circle $2\alpha = 120°$, one arrives at point A', which must represent the total strain along the ϵ_1 axis. Continuing from A' counterclockwise through an angle of 2β, or 80°, point C is reached. This point must then represent the total strain along the ϵ_2 axis. The maximum and minimum principal strains occur where the circle crosses the ϵ axis, and their magnitudes and directions can be scaled directly from the figure. Figure 6-17 shows this type of graphical solution for our original problem. Figure 6-17A shows the gage axes as originally laid out, and Fig. 6-17B shows the modifications required to locate the gage line of intermediate magnitude between the other two.

The relationships between the stresses existing on any two mutually perpendicular planes and those on any other planes are of a similar nature

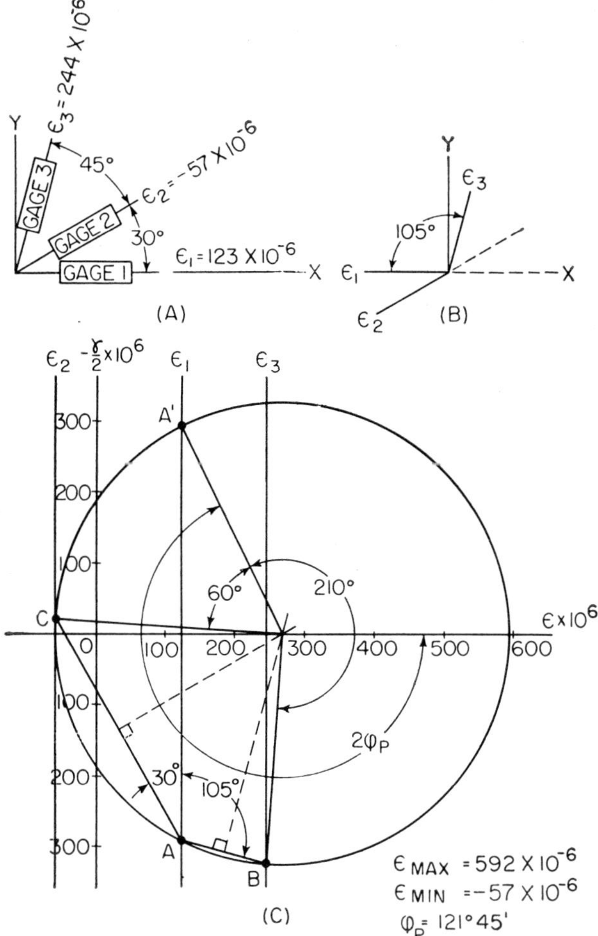

FIG. 6-17. Graphical solution for principal strains in the illustrative example.

to the relationships for strains. Beginning with an element of volume in which a general two-dimensional state of stress exists in the x and y directions, it is possible to write the expression for the stress conditions on a plane whose normal makes an angle φ with the x axis. First an element of volume is isolated as shown in Fig. 6-18, and the area of the slant face is labeled A. The area of the horizontal face will then be

A sin φ; of the vertical face, A cos φ. Summing up the forces perpendicular and parallel to the slant face,

$$\begin{aligned}
\sigma_\varphi A &= \sigma_x A \cos^2 \varphi + \sigma_y A \sin^2 \varphi - 2\tau_{xy} A \sin \varphi \cos \varphi \\
\sigma_\varphi &= \sigma_x \cos^2 \varphi + \sigma_y \sin^2 \varphi - 2\tau_{xy} \sin \varphi \cos \varphi \\
\tau_\varphi A &= \sigma_x A \sin \varphi \cos \varphi - \sigma_y A \sin \varphi \cos \varphi + \tau_{xy} A \cos^2 \varphi - \tau_{xy} A \sin^2 \varphi \\
\tau_\varphi &= (\sigma_x - \sigma_y) \sin \varphi \cos \varphi + \tau_{xy}(\cos^2 \varphi - \sin^2 \varphi)
\end{aligned}$$

These equations can be written

$$\sigma_\varphi = \frac{\sigma_x + \sigma_y}{2} + \frac{\sigma_x - \sigma_y}{2} \cos 2\varphi - \tau_{xy} \sin 2\varphi \tag{6-12}$$

$$\tau_\varphi = \frac{\sigma_x - \sigma_y}{2} \sin 2\varphi - \tau_{xy} \cos 2\varphi \tag{6-13}$$

If the equation for σ_φ is compared with Eq. (6-6) for ϵ_φ, it is apparent that they are of the same form, σ replacing ϵ and $-\tau$ replacing $\gamma/2$. The

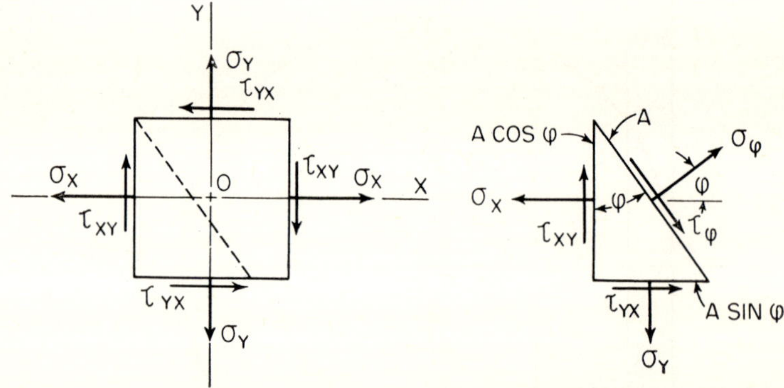

FIG. 6-18. Free body diagram of an element of mass subjected to a biaxial stress system.

expression for the angle at which the normal stress becomes a maximum can then be written as

$$\tan 2\varphi_p = \frac{2\tau_{xy}}{\sigma_x - \sigma_y}$$

Since the equations for stress are similar in form to those for strain, a Mohr's circle for stress can also be constructed by substitution of σ and τ for the coordinate axes, with the positive τ axis drawn in the opposite direction to the positive $\gamma/2$ axis. The general construction of Mohr's circle for stress is shown in Fig. 6-19. As long as the stress conditions are known on any two orthogonal planes, they can be plotted as points on the σ, τ coordinate system and the line joining the two points will be the diameter of Mohr's circle for stress. The circle having been constructed, the stress conditions on any plane can be determined directly.

The greatest utility of Mohr's circle for stress, as in the case for the strain circle, is not in the graphical construction but rather in the fact that an analytical solution is readily obtained from the geometry of a freehand construction, so that it is not necessary to remember the complex equations defining σ and τ. Similarly, if both the stress and strain

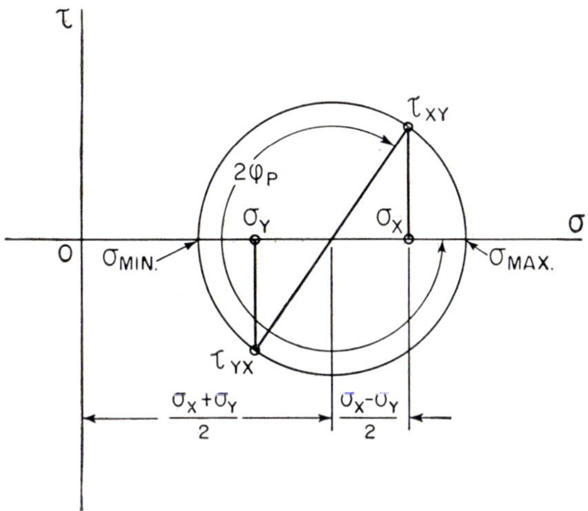

FIG. 6-19. Mohr's circle for stress.

circles are constructed on the same center, using the proper scale ratios as shown in Fig. 7-15, the relationships between stress and strain at any angle can be easily visualized.

BIBLIOGRAPHY

Frocht, M. M.: "Photoelasticity," vol. 1, pp. 1–46, John Wiley & Sons, Inc., New York, 1941.

Hoff, N. J.: A Graphic Solution of Strain, *Trans. ASME (J. Appl. Mechanics)*, vol. 67, pp. A-211 to A-216, December, 1945.

Marin, J.: Strain-rosette Analysis Is Effective Design Aid, *Machine Design*, vol. 15, no. 3, pp. 101–104, March, 1943.

McClintock, F. A.: On Determining Principal Strains from Strain Rosettes with Arbitrary Angles, *Proc. SESA*, vol. 9, no. 1, pp. 209–210, 1951.

Murphy, G.: A Graphical Method for the Evaluation of Principal Strains from Normal Strains, *Trans. ASME (J. Appl. Mechanics)*, vol. 67, pp. A-209 to A-210, December, 1945.

Rankin, A. N.: Orientation of Strain Gages in Stress Analysis, *Gen. Elec. Rev.*, vol. 50, no. 9, pp. 14–21, September, 1947.

Smith, T. F. W.: Uses of Mohr Circle Pole, *Engineer*, vol. 200, no. 5027, pp. 696–697, Nov. 11, 1955.

Thomson, W. T.: Analytical Expressions for Principal Strains, *Trans. ASME* (*J. Appl. Mechanics*), vol. 68, p. A-221, 1946.

Timoshenko, S.: "Theory of Elasticity," 1st ed., McGraw-Hill Book Company, Inc., New York, 1934.

Willis, A. H.: Analysis of Strain and Its Graphical Representation, *Engineering*, vol. 165, no. 4294, pp. 457–460, May 14, 1948.

Wise, J. A.: Circles of Strain, *J. Aeronaut. Sci.*, vol. 7, no. 10, pp. 438–440, August, 1940. (But notice typographical errors in Equation 13 of this reference.)

EXERCISES

6-1. Construct polar diagrams as shown in Figs. 6-3 and 6-4 from the concentric Mohr's circles of stress and strain for the uniaxial and biaxial stress cases, respectively. In the latter instance, take $\sigma_y = \sigma_x$.

6-2. On an appropriately sized solid or hollow cylindrical shaft, place three strain gages at arbitrary angles with respect to the shaft axis (say, 10°, 75°, and 120°). Subject the shaft to pure torsion and measure the strain in all three gages. Calculate the following: maximum principal strain, minimum principal strain, maximum principal stress, minimum principal stress, maximum shear stress, maximum shear strain, angle from the shaft axis to the principal axis.

6-3. Three strain gages mounted as shown in Fig. 6-15 produce the following strain readings: $\epsilon_1 = 925$ micro-inches per in.; $\epsilon_2 = -165$ micro-inches per in.; $\epsilon_3 = -475$ micro-inches per in. Compute the principal strains and stresses ($E = 30 \times 10^6$ psi, and $\mu = 0.285$). Check your solution graphically.

6-4. In Fig. 6-17 showing gage positions, the strain indicated by gage 1 is -865 micro-inches per in., gage 2 reads 217 micro-inches per in., and gage 3 reads -254 micro-inches per in. Determine the principal strains and stresses analytically and graphically. $E = 10 \times 10^6$ psi, and $\mu = 0.33$.

6-5. Calculate the possible error in strain indication due to gage misalignment as a function of the angle from the principal axis in a uniaxially stressed member.

6-6. Compute the strain reading indicated by a strain gage making an angle of 60° with the x axis when σ_x is 2,250 psi, σ_y is $-5{,}780$ psi, E is 30×10^6, and μ is 0.285.

6-7. Three strain gages surrounding a point on the surface of a test piece are oriented with respect to one another as follows, reading counterclockwise: gage 1, 0°; gage 2, 70°; gage 3, 150°. Observed strains are: $\epsilon_1 = 740$ micro-inches per in.; $\epsilon_2 = 1{,}210$ micro-inches per in.; $\epsilon_3 = 60$ micro-inches per in. Plot the polar diagrams for normal stress, normal strain, shear stress, and shear strain when $E = 30 \times 10^6$ and $\mu = 0.285$.

6-8. Draw concentric Mohr circles for stress and strain for the case where $\mu = 0$

7 STRAIN ROSETTES AND STRESS GAGES

If enough strain gages are mounted adjacent to or overlapping each other to obtain the principal strains in an area, the resulting configuration is termed a *strain rosette*. From the previous chapter we learned that for the general case of plane stress it is necessary that strains be measured in at least three directions in order to find the principal strains and their directions. Strain rosettes, therefore, commonly consist of three gages. If a strain reading is obtained in a fourth direction, this value could also be used either directly in the computations for principal strains or as a check on the accuracy of the results obtained from the other three gages. For the case in which the principal strain directions are known, two strain readings in these directions will suffice for the determination of the principal strains and stresses. So, for this special case, a two-gage rosette with the gages placed at right angles to each other will be adequate.

According to the previously developed theory, the principal strain can be determined from any three strain readings, no matter what the angles between their directions. Practically, however, it is apparent that if small angles exist between the directions in which the strains are measured, large errors in the magnitudes and directions of the computed principal strains could result. In addition to the advisability of making the angles relatively large, we find from examination of the fundamental equation

$$\epsilon_\varphi = \frac{\epsilon_x + \epsilon_y}{2} + \frac{\epsilon_x - \epsilon_y}{2} \cos 2\varphi + \frac{\gamma_{xy}}{2} \sin 2\varphi$$

that the selection of certain angles will simplify the solution appreciably. Since the equation involves the sine and cosine functions of 2φ, angles giving the simplest solution are as shown in Table 7-1. In order to satisfy the requirement that the angles between measured strain directions be fairly large, angles of 45° and greater should be selected.

Table 7-1. Angles Producing the Simplest Solution of the Fundamental Strain Equation

φ	sin 2φ	cos 2φ
0°	0	1
15°	½	$\frac{\sqrt{3}}{2}$
30°	$\frac{\sqrt{3}}{2}$	½
45°	1	0
60°	$\frac{\sqrt{3}}{2}$	−½
90°	0	−1
120°	$-\frac{\sqrt{3}}{2}$	−½

The most common rosettes available commercially are of two types: one uses gages oriented at 0, 45, and 90° and is called the *rectangular rosette;* the other, at 0, 60, and 120°, is called the *delta rosette*. The latter takes its name from the fact that its axes form the Greek letter Δ. A variation of the delta rosette, known as the *T-delta,* is available with a fourth gage perpendicular to one of the other three. The two-gage rosette with the gages at right angles to each other is also manufactured commercially. Figure 7-1 shows the orientation of the strain-sensitive filament in several types of commercially available rosettes, and Fig. 7-2 is a photograph of two foil rosettes.

When the directions of the principal strains are known approximately, use of the rectangular strain rosette is preferred since two gages can be oriented in the estimated direction of those principal strains. When the principal strain direction is completely unknown, the delta or T-delta rosette should be employed since this type has the maximum possible angle between gage axes.

A word of caution is necessary regarding the use of rosettes in a region of steep strain gradient, as in the neighborhood of a discontinuity or stress raiser. The relationships between the strains in any three directions and the principal strains and their directions apply only at a single point. Therefore, a correct result will be obtained from a rosette only if the strains in the area covered by the rosette are not varying. In a region in which a steep strain gradient exists, the results obtained from a rosette will be in error, and the larger the area covered by the rosette, the greater the error. If principal strains and their directions are required in such

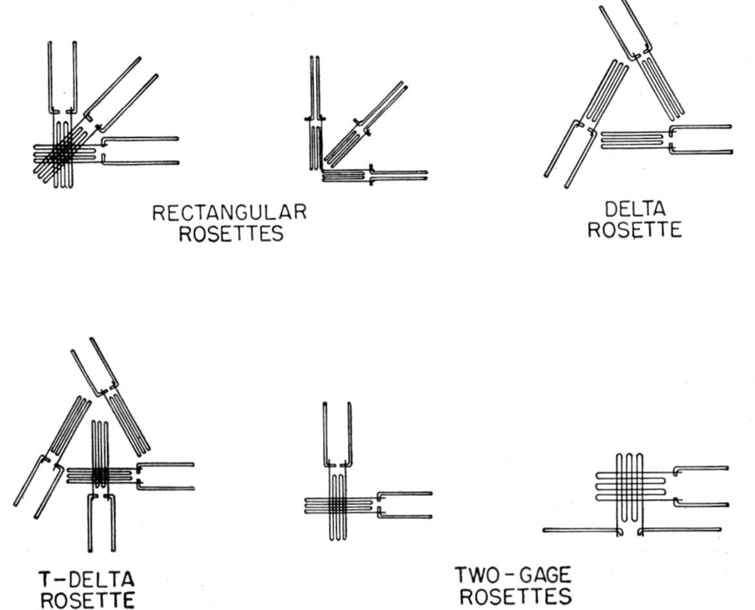

FIG. 7-1. Strain gage rosette configurations.

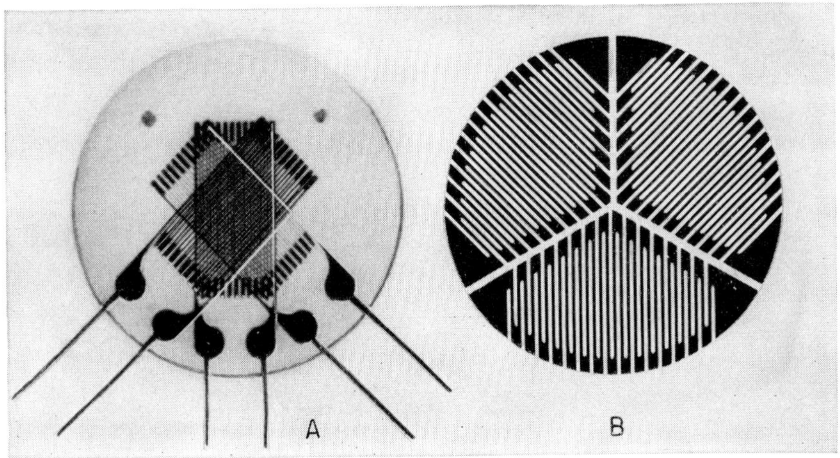

FIG. 7-2. Appearance of typical commercial foil strain gage rosettes: (*A*) rectangular rosette; (*B*) single-plane-delta rosette. (*Courtesy of Baldwin-Lima-Hamilton Corporation.*)

a region of high strain gradient, the rosette must be confined to the smallest possible area. This means that the stress analyst may have to make his own rosette by using individual gages, since commercial rosettes often use relatively long gage lengths. The majority of the manufactured rosettes use ⅛ in. or longer gages. In the neighborhood of a sharp notch or discontinuity it would be desirable to use $\frac{1}{16}$-in. or shorter gages in the rosette.

THE RECTANGULAR ROSETTE

The commercial rectangular rosette is available in the two forms shown in Fig. 7-1. The rosette in which one gage is mounted on top of another will cover a smaller area than that having all the gages in one plane and so would give more accurate results in a region in which the strains were varying. However, if this rosette were mounted on a member subjected to severe bending and the surface to which the gages were cemented were close to the neutral axis, a considerable error could be introduced since each gage is at a different distance from the neutral axis. The foil gage, because of its thinner construction, produces less error when the gages are overlapped in this manner. A very thin plate in bending is an example in which a steep stress gradient exists between the neutral axis and the surface of the plate to which a rosette might be cemented. For this case the use of the rosette having all the gages in one plane is preferable.

The equations defining the principal stresses in terms of the strains measured by the various types of rosette are given in Table 7-2. The derivation of these equations for the rectangular rosette follows. In this case $\varphi_1 = 0°$, $\varphi_2 = 45°$, and $\varphi_3 = 90°$. Substituting the numerical values of $\sin 2\varphi$ and $\cos 2\varphi$ into the fundamental equation (6-7),

$$\epsilon_\varphi = \frac{\epsilon_x + \epsilon_y}{2} + \frac{\epsilon_x - \epsilon_y}{2}\cos 2\varphi + \frac{\gamma_{xy}}{2}\sin 2\varphi$$

we obtain

$$\begin{aligned} \epsilon_1 &= \frac{\epsilon_x + \epsilon_y}{2} + \frac{\epsilon_x - \epsilon_y}{2} = \epsilon_x \\ \epsilon_2 &= \frac{\epsilon_x + \epsilon_y}{2} + \frac{\gamma_{xy}}{2} \\ \epsilon_3 &= \frac{\epsilon_x + \epsilon_y}{2} - \frac{\epsilon_x - \epsilon_y}{2} = \epsilon_y \end{aligned} \tag{7-1}$$

Solving for ϵ_x, ϵ_y, and γ_{xy},

$$\begin{aligned} \epsilon_x &= \epsilon_1 \\ \epsilon_y &= \epsilon_3 \\ \gamma_{xy} &= 2\epsilon_2 - (\epsilon_1 + \epsilon_3) \end{aligned} \tag{7-2}$$

From Eqs. (6-9), (6-10), and (6-11),

$$\begin{aligned}
\epsilon_{\max} &= \frac{\epsilon_x + \epsilon_y}{2} + \frac{1}{2}\sqrt{(\epsilon_x - \epsilon_y)^2 + \gamma_{xy}{}^2} \\
\epsilon_{\min} &= \frac{\epsilon_x + \epsilon_y}{2} - \frac{1}{2}\sqrt{(\epsilon_x - \epsilon_y)^2 + \gamma_{xy}{}^2} \\
\gamma_{\max} &= \sqrt{(\epsilon_x - \epsilon_y)^2 + \gamma_{xy}{}^2} \\
\varphi_p &= \frac{1}{2}\tan^{-1}\frac{\gamma_{xy}}{\epsilon_x - \epsilon_y}
\end{aligned}$$

where φ_p is the angle between the direction of the maximum principal strain and the x axis. Substituting Eqs. (7-2) into the above, we obtain the following:

$$\begin{aligned}
\epsilon_{\max} &= \tfrac{1}{2}(\epsilon_1 + \epsilon_3) + \tfrac{1}{2}\sqrt{(\epsilon_1 - \epsilon_3)^2 + [2\epsilon_2 - (\epsilon_1 + \epsilon_3)]^2} \\
\epsilon_{\min} &= \tfrac{1}{2}(\epsilon_1 + \epsilon_3) - \tfrac{1}{2}\sqrt{(\epsilon_1 - \epsilon_3)^2 + [2\epsilon_2 - (\epsilon_1 + \epsilon_3)]^2} \\
\gamma_{\max} &= \sqrt{(\epsilon_1 - \epsilon_3)^2 + [2\epsilon_2 - (\epsilon_1 + \epsilon_3)]^2} \qquad (7\text{-}3) \\
\varphi_p &= \frac{1}{2}\tan^{-1}\frac{2\epsilon_2 - (\epsilon_1 + \epsilon_3)}{\epsilon_1 - \epsilon_3}
\end{aligned}$$

Using the previously developed relationships

$$\begin{aligned}
\sigma_{\max} &= \frac{E}{1 - \mu^2}(\epsilon_{\max} + \mu\epsilon_{\min}) \\
\sigma_{\min} &= \frac{E}{1 - \mu^2}(\epsilon_{\min} + \mu\epsilon_{\max}) \\
\tau_{\max} &= \frac{E}{2(1 + \mu)}\gamma_{\max}
\end{aligned}$$

we obtain for the principal stresses and the maximum shearing stress

$$\begin{aligned}
\sigma_{\max} &= \frac{E}{2}\left[\frac{\epsilon_1 + \epsilon_3}{1 - \mu} + \frac{1}{1 + \mu}\sqrt{(\epsilon_1 - \epsilon_3)^2 + [2\epsilon_2 - (\epsilon_1 + \epsilon_3)]^2}\right] \\
\sigma_{\min} &= \frac{E}{2}\left[\frac{\epsilon_1 + \epsilon_3}{1 - \mu} - \frac{1}{1 + \mu}\sqrt{(\epsilon_1 - \epsilon_3)^2 + [2\epsilon_2 - (\epsilon_1 + \epsilon_3)]^2}\right] \qquad (7\text{-}4) \\
\tau_{\max} &= \frac{E}{2(1 + \mu)}\sqrt{(\epsilon_1 - \epsilon_3)^2 + [2\epsilon_2 - (\epsilon_1 + \epsilon_3)]^2}
\end{aligned}$$

As an example, suppose we make the following readings of strain on a rectangular strain rosette mounted on steel for which $E = 30 \times 10^6$ psi and $\mu = 0.3$:

$$\begin{aligned}
\epsilon_1 &= 285 \times 10^{-6} \text{ in. per in.} \\
\epsilon_2 &= 65 \times 10^{-6} \text{ in. per in.} \\
\epsilon_3 &= 102 \times 10^{-6} \text{ in. per in.}
\end{aligned}$$

Solving for principal stresses and their direction and for the maximum shearing stress, we have

$$\sigma_{\max} = \frac{30 \times 10^6}{2}\left[\frac{285 + 102}{1 - 0.3} + \frac{1}{1 + 0.3}\sqrt{(285 - 102)^2 + [2 \times 65 - (285 + 102)]^2}\right] \times 10^{-6}$$

$$\sigma_{\min} = \frac{30 \times 10^6}{2}\left[\frac{285 + 102}{1 - 0.3} - \frac{1}{1 + 0.3}\sqrt{(285 - 102)^2 + [2 \times 65 - (285 + 102)]^2}\right] \times 10^{-6}$$

$$\tau_{\max} = \frac{30 \times 10^6}{2(1 + 0.3)}\sqrt{(285 - 102)^2 + [2 \times 65 - (285 + 102)]^2} \times 10^{-6}$$

$$\varphi_p = \frac{1}{2}\tan^{-1}\frac{2 \times 65 - (285 + 102)}{285 - 102}$$

$$\sigma_{\max} = 11{,}930 \text{ psi}$$
$$\sigma_{\min} = 4{,}670 \text{ psi}$$
$$\tau_{\max} = 3{,}630 \text{ psi}$$
$$\varphi_p = -27°15'$$

GRAPHICAL SOLUTION OF THE RECTANGULAR ROSETTE

The graphical solution for obtaining principal strains from the values measured with the rectangular rosette is shown in Fig. 7-3. The points

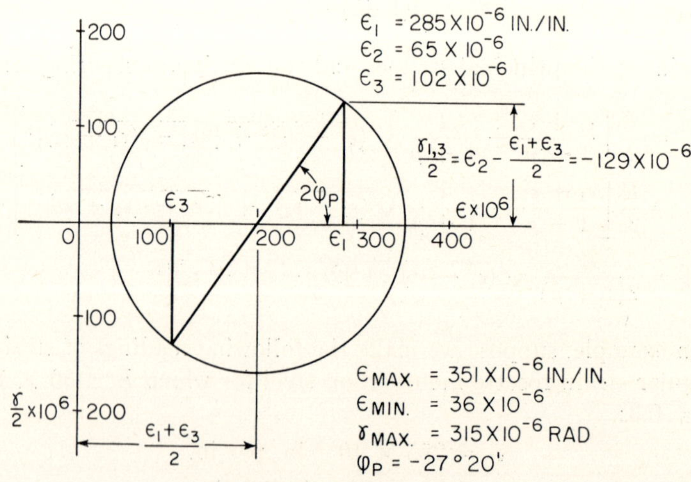

FIG. 7-3. Graphical solution of rectangular rosette example.

representing the strains along axes 1 and 3 must lie on the circumference of Mohr's circle for strain and be 180° apart, since axes 1 and 3 are 90° apart. Therefore, the line joining these points will be a diameter of the circle. These points will generally not occur at the intersection of the circle with the ϵ axis since shearing strains will usually be present. Their projections on the ϵ axis, however, will be equal to ϵ_1 and ϵ_3. The center of the circle must then occur midway between these projections, or at a distance $(\epsilon_1 + \epsilon_3)/2$ from the $\gamma/2$ axis.

In order to determine the magnitude of $\gamma_{1,3}$, we must refer back to Eq. (6-7), which can be written

$$\epsilon_2 = \frac{\epsilon_1 + \epsilon_3}{2} + \frac{\epsilon_1 - \epsilon_3}{2} \cos 2(45°) + \frac{\gamma_{1,3}}{2} \sin 2(45°)$$

Then, solving for $\gamma_{1,3}/2$, which is to be laid off from ϵ_1 parallel to the $\gamma/2$ axis, we obtain

$$\frac{\gamma_{1,3}}{2} = \epsilon_2 - \frac{\epsilon_1 + \epsilon_3}{2}$$

This construction is shown in Fig. 7-3 and establishes the point on the circumference of the circle representing the strain condition on the plane defined by axis 1. Connecting this point with the center of the circle gives the radius, from which the circle is readily constructed and the principal strains and their angles obtained.

While graphical solutions exist for obtaining the principal stresses and maximum shearing stress from this circle for strain, the simplest method is to substitute the principal strains into the equations

$$\sigma_{max} = \frac{E}{1 - \mu^2} (\epsilon_{max} + \mu\epsilon_{min})$$

$$\sigma_{min} = \frac{E}{1 - \mu^2} (\epsilon_{min} + \mu\epsilon_{max})$$

$$\tau_{max} = \frac{E}{2(1 + \mu)} \gamma_{max}$$

A numerical solution is also shown in Fig. 7-3 for the principal strains and the maximum shearing strain for our previous example, in which

$$\epsilon_1 = 285 \times 10^{-6} \text{ in. per in.}$$

$$\epsilon_2 = 65 \times 10^{-6} \text{ in. per in.}$$

$$\epsilon_3 = 102 \times 10^{-6} \text{ in. per in.}$$

This solution gives

$$\begin{aligned} \epsilon_{max} &= 351 \times 10^{-6} \text{ in. per in.} \\ \epsilon_{min} &= 36 \times 10^{-6} \text{ in. per in.} \\ \gamma_{max} &= 315 \times 10^{-6} \text{ radian} \\ \varphi_p &= -27°20' \end{aligned}$$

Substituting in the equations for principal stresses and maximum shearing stress, we have

$$\begin{aligned} \sigma_{max} &= 11{,}930 \text{ psi} \\ \sigma_{min} &= 4{,}660 \text{ psi} \\ \tau_{max} &= 3{,}640 \text{ psi} \end{aligned}$$

THE DELTA ROSETTE

The delta, or equiangular, rosette is commercially available in several configurations as shown in Figs. 7-1 and 7-2, and all the gages are in one plane and not arranged on top of one another. This rosette is preferred if the principal stress direction is unknown. For the delta rosette the angles φ_1, φ_2, and φ_3 are 0, 60, and 120°. We can develop the equations relating the strains measured by the rosette to the principal stresses, as shown in Table 7-2, by substituting the sines and cosines of these angles into the fundamental equation

$$\epsilon_\varphi = \frac{\epsilon_x + \epsilon_y}{2} + \frac{\epsilon_x - \epsilon_y}{2} \cos 2\varphi + \frac{\gamma_{xy}}{2} \sin 2\varphi$$

Then

$$\begin{aligned} \epsilon_1 &= \frac{\epsilon_x + \epsilon_y}{2} + \frac{\epsilon_x - \epsilon_y}{2} = \epsilon_x \\ \epsilon_2 &= \frac{\epsilon_x + \epsilon_y}{2} - \frac{\epsilon_x - \epsilon_y}{2}\frac{1}{2} + \frac{\gamma_{xy}}{2}\frac{\sqrt{3}}{2} \\ \epsilon_3 &= \frac{\epsilon_x + \epsilon_y}{2} - \frac{\epsilon_x - \epsilon_y}{2}\frac{1}{2} - \frac{\gamma_{xy}}{2}\frac{\sqrt{3}}{2} \end{aligned} \tag{7-5}$$

Solving for ϵ_x, ϵ_y, and γ_{xy},

$$\begin{aligned} \epsilon_x &= \epsilon_1 \\ \epsilon_y &= \frac{-\epsilon_1 + 2\epsilon_2 + 2\epsilon_3}{3} \\ \gamma_{xy} &= \frac{2(\epsilon_2 - \epsilon_3)}{\sqrt{3}} \end{aligned} \tag{7-6}$$

Substituting these values into the equations for ϵ_{max}, ϵ_{min}, γ_{max}, and φ_p,

$$
\begin{aligned}
\epsilon_{max} &= \frac{\epsilon_1 + \epsilon_2 + \epsilon_3}{3} + \sqrt{\left(\epsilon_1 - \frac{\epsilon_1 + \epsilon_2 + \epsilon_3}{3}\right)^2 + \left(\frac{\epsilon_2 - \epsilon_3}{\sqrt{3}}\right)^2} \\
\epsilon_{min} &= \frac{\epsilon_1 + \epsilon_2 + \epsilon_3}{3} - \sqrt{\left(\epsilon_1 - \frac{\epsilon_1 + \epsilon_2 + \epsilon_3}{3}\right)^2 + \left(\frac{2 - \epsilon_3}{\sqrt{3}}\right)^2} \\
\frac{\gamma_{max}}{2} &= \sqrt{\left(\epsilon_1 - \frac{\epsilon_1 + \epsilon_2 + \epsilon_3}{3}\right)^2 + \left(\frac{\epsilon_2 - \epsilon_3}{\sqrt{3}}\right)^2} \qquad (7\text{-}7) \\
\varphi_p &= \frac{1}{2} \tan^{-1} \frac{\frac{1}{\sqrt{3}}(\epsilon_2 - \epsilon_3)}{\epsilon_1 - \frac{\epsilon_1 + \epsilon_2 + \epsilon_3}{3}}
\end{aligned}
$$

Substituting these values into

$$
\begin{aligned}
\sigma_{max} &= \frac{E}{1 - \mu^2}(\epsilon_{max} + \mu\epsilon_{min}) \\
\sigma_{min} &= \frac{E}{1 - \mu^2}(\epsilon_{min} + \mu\epsilon_{max}) \\
\tau_{max} &= \frac{E}{2(1 + \mu)}\gamma_{max}
\end{aligned}
$$

we obtain

$$
\begin{aligned}
\sigma_{max} &= E\left[\frac{\epsilon_1 + \epsilon_2 + \epsilon_3}{3(1 - \mu)} + \frac{1}{1 + \mu}\sqrt{\left(\epsilon_1 - \frac{\epsilon_1 + \epsilon_2 + \epsilon_3}{3}\right)^2 + \left(\frac{\epsilon_2 - \epsilon_3}{\sqrt{3}}\right)^2}\,\right] \\
\sigma_{min} &= E\left[\frac{\epsilon_1 + \epsilon_2 + \epsilon_3}{3(1 - \mu)} - \frac{1}{1 + \mu}\sqrt{\left(\epsilon_1 - \frac{\epsilon_1 + \epsilon_2 + \epsilon_3}{3}\right)^2 + \left(\frac{\epsilon_2 - \epsilon_3}{\sqrt{3}}\right)^2}\,\right] \\
\tau_{max} &= \frac{E}{1 + \mu}\sqrt{\left(\epsilon_1 - \frac{\epsilon_1 + \epsilon_2 + \epsilon_3}{3}\right)^2 + \left(\frac{\epsilon_2 - \epsilon_3}{\sqrt{3}}\right)^2} \qquad (7\text{-}8)
\end{aligned}
$$

As a numerical example, assume that the following strains are measured with a delta rosette on steel, having E equal to 30×10^6 psi and μ equal to 0.3.

$$
\begin{aligned}
\epsilon_1 &= 374 \times 10^{-6} \text{ in. per in.} \\
\epsilon_2 &= -135 \times 10^{-6} \text{ in. per in.} \\
\epsilon_3 &= 227 \times 10^{-6} \text{ in. per in.}
\end{aligned}
$$

The principal stresses will then be

$$\sigma_{\min} = 30 \times 10^6 \left[\frac{374 - 135 + 227}{3(1 - 0.3)} + \frac{1}{1 + 0.3} \right.$$

$$\left. \sqrt{\left(374 - \frac{374 - 135 + 227}{3}\right)^2 + \left(\frac{-135 - 227}{\sqrt{3}}\right)^2} \right] \times 10^{-6}$$

$$\sigma_{\min} = 30 \times 10^6 \left[\frac{374 - 135 + 227}{3(1 - 0.3)} - \frac{1}{1 + 0.3} \right.$$

$$\left. \sqrt{\left(374 - \frac{374 - 135 + 227}{3}\right)^2 + \left(\frac{-135 - 227}{\sqrt{3}}\right)^2} \right] \times 10^{-6}$$

$$\sigma_{\max} = 13{,}600 \text{ psi}$$

$$\sigma_{\min} = -300 \text{ psi}$$

The angle to the maximum principal stress from axis 1

$$\varphi_p = \frac{1}{2} \tan^{-1} \frac{\dfrac{1}{\sqrt{3}}(-135 - 227)}{374 - \dfrac{374 - 135 + 227}{3}}$$

$$\varphi_p = -21°50'$$

The maximum shearing stress will be

$$\tau_{\max} = \frac{30 \times 10^6}{1 + 0.3}$$

$$\sqrt{\left(374 - \frac{374 - 135 + 227}{3}\right)^2 + \left(\frac{-135 - 227}{\sqrt{3}}\right)^2} \times 10^{-6}$$

$$\tau_{\max} = 6{,}960 \text{ psi}$$

GRAPHICAL SOLUTION OF THE DELTA ROSETTE

The graphical method of obtaining the principal strains and the maximum shearing strain from the three gage readings is shown in Fig. 7-4. Since the three measured strains are actually 60° apart, they will have to be 120° apart on Mohr's circle and lines connecting them will form an equilateral triangle.

On the ϵ, $\gamma/2$ coordinate system, we begin by laying off the numerical values of the three strains ϵ_1, ϵ_2, and ϵ_3, drawing lines through each point parallel to the $\gamma/2$ axis. From any arbitrarily selected point on the line farthest to the right, we draw two lines extending toward the left and making angles of plus and minus 30° with the horizontal. Four points of intersection are obtained where these lines cross the other two verticals. Two additional lines AC and BD can be drawn connecting these four points, as shown in Fig. 7-4, and one of these is the first side of the required equilateral triangle, whose vertex will lie on the vertical farthest to the right. The proper one to select will be that connecting the values of the strains in the order of gage mounting. Since the gages are mounted in the order φ_1, φ_2, and φ_3, measured counterclockwise, the vertices of the triangle should also read ϵ_1, ϵ_2, and ϵ_3 counterclockwise. In Fig. 7-4, the proper line to fulfill this condition is AC since we go from ϵ_1 to ϵ_2 to ϵ_3 in circling the vertices of the equilateral triangle in a counterclockwise

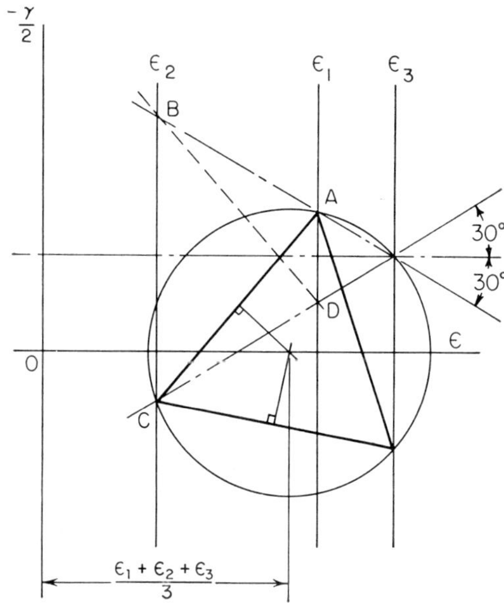

FIG. 7-4. Method of constructing Mohr's circle for strain from delta rosette data.

direction. After the proper base line of the triangle is selected, the triangle is completed with the vertex on the vertical farthest to the right. A circumscribing circle is then constructed about the triangle and the ϵ axis drawn through the center of the circle. Values of the principal strains and maximum shearing strain obtained from the circle can be substituted into

$$\sigma_{\max} = \frac{E}{1 - \mu^2} (\epsilon_{\max} + \mu\epsilon_{\min})$$

$$\sigma_{\min} = \frac{E}{1 - \mu^2} (\epsilon_{\min} + \mu\epsilon_{\max})$$

$$\tau_{\max} = \frac{E}{1 + \mu} \frac{\gamma_{\max}}{2}$$

to obtain principal stresses and maximum shearing stress.

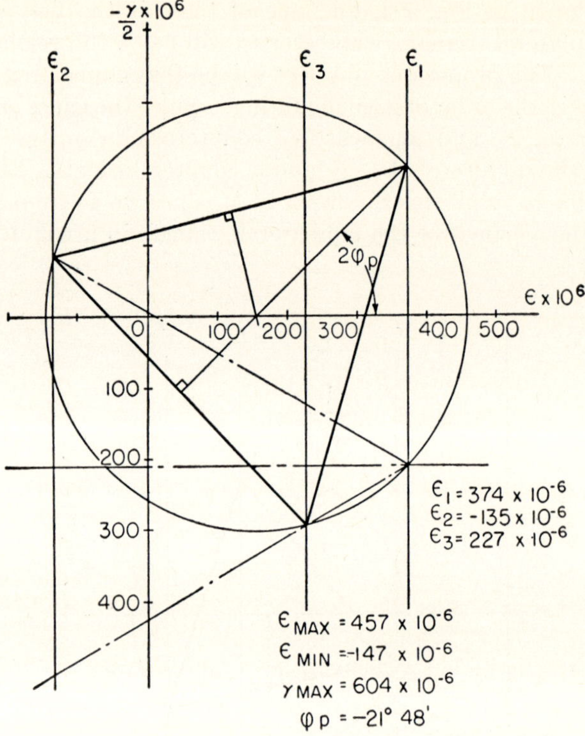

FIG. 7-5. Graphical solution of delta rosette example.

The graphical solution of the illustrative example gives values of

$$\epsilon_{max} = 457 \times 10^{-6} \text{ in. per in.}$$
$$\epsilon_{min} = -147 \times 10^{-6} \text{ in. per in.}$$
$$\frac{\gamma_{max}}{2} = 302 \times 10^{-6} \text{ radian}$$
$$\varphi_p = -21°48'$$

as shown in Fig. 7-5. From this we obtain

$$\sigma_{max} = 13{,}600 \text{ psi}$$
$$\sigma_{min} = -325 \text{ psi}$$
$$\tau_{max} = 6{,}970 \text{ psi}$$

THE T-DELTA ROSETTE

The T-delta rosette is identical with the delta rosette previously described, with the addition of a fourth gage mounted at right angles to and on top of one of the other gages. This fourth gage can be used to serve as a check on the results obtained from the other three gages; or strains obtained from all four gages can be substituted into the following equations to obtain principal strains and stresses:

$$\begin{aligned}
\epsilon_{max} &= \tfrac{1}{2}(\epsilon_1 + \epsilon_4) + \tfrac{1}{2}\sqrt{(\epsilon_1 - \epsilon_4)^2 + \tfrac{4}{3}(\epsilon_2 - \epsilon_3)^2} \\
\epsilon_{min} &= \tfrac{1}{2}(\epsilon_1 + \epsilon_4) - \tfrac{1}{2}\sqrt{(\epsilon_1 - \epsilon_4)^2 + \tfrac{4}{3}(\epsilon_2 - \epsilon_3)^2} \\
\varphi_p &= \frac{1}{2}\tan^{-1}\frac{2(\epsilon_2 - \epsilon_3)}{\sqrt{3}\,(\epsilon_1 - \epsilon_4)} \\
\gamma_{max} &= \sqrt{(\epsilon_1 - \epsilon_4)^2 + \tfrac{4}{3}(\epsilon_2 - \epsilon_3)^2}
\end{aligned} \tag{7-9}$$

Then

$$\begin{aligned}
\sigma_{max} &= \frac{E}{2}\left[\frac{\epsilon_1 + \epsilon_4}{1 - \mu} + \frac{1}{1 + \mu}\sqrt{(\epsilon_1 - \epsilon_4)^2 + \frac{4}{3}(\epsilon_2 - \epsilon_3)^2}\right] \\
\sigma_{min} &= \frac{E}{2}\left[\frac{\epsilon_1 + \epsilon_4}{1 - \mu} - \frac{1}{1 + \mu}\sqrt{(\epsilon_1 - \epsilon_4)^2 + \frac{4}{3}(\epsilon_2 - \epsilon_3)^2}\right] \\
\tau_{max} &= \frac{E}{2(1 + \mu)}\sqrt{(\epsilon_1 - \epsilon_4)^2 + \frac{4}{3}(\epsilon_2 - \epsilon_3)^2}
\end{aligned} \tag{7-10}$$

As a numerical example, assume the following strains measured in steel with $E = 30 \times 10^6$ psi and $\mu = 0.3$:

$$\begin{aligned}
\epsilon_1 &= 225 \times 10^{-6} \text{ in. per in.} \\
\epsilon_2 &= 305 \times 10^{-6} \text{ in. per in.} \\
\epsilon_3 &= -274 \times 10^{-6} \text{ in. per in.} \\
\epsilon_4 &= -65 \times 10^{-6} \text{ in. per in.}
\end{aligned}$$

Substituting into the equations for principal stresses and maximum shearing stress,

$$\sigma_{max} = \frac{30 \times 10^6}{2}\left[\frac{225 - 65}{1 - 0.3} + \frac{1}{1 + 0.3}\sqrt{(225 + 65)^2 + \frac{4}{3}(305 + 274)^2}\right] \times 10^{-6}$$

$$\sigma_{max} = 11{,}800 \text{ psi}$$

$$\sigma_{min} = \frac{30 \times 10^6}{2}\left[\frac{225 - 65}{1 - 0.3} - \frac{1}{1 + 0.3}\sqrt{(225 + 65)^2 + \frac{4}{3}(305 + 274)^2}\right] \times 10^{-6}$$

$$\sigma_{min} = -4{,}940 \text{ psi}$$

$$\varphi_p = \frac{1}{2}\tan^{-1}\frac{2}{\sqrt{3}}\frac{305 + 274}{225 + 65} = 33°35'$$

$$\tau_{max} = \frac{30 \times 10^6}{2(1 + 0.3)}\frac{1}{2}\sqrt{(225 + 65)^2 + \frac{4}{3}(305 + 274)^2} \times 10^{-6} = 8{,}380 \text{ psi}$$

The alternative solution with the delta-rosette equations (7-8) gives

$$\begin{aligned} \sigma_{\max} &= 12{,}000 \text{ psi} \\ \sigma_{\min} &= -4{,}650 \text{ psi} \\ \varphi_p &= 33°35' \\ \tau_{\max} &= 8{,}300 \text{ psi} \end{aligned}$$

which checks the above results.

The graphical solution for the T-delta rosette is identical with that for the delta rosette, the fourth gage reading simply serving as a check on the results obtained from the other three. The projection on the ϵ axes of the point on the circumference of the circle opposite to that representing the strain on the plane normal to axis 1 must be equal to ϵ_4 as shown in Fig. 7-6.

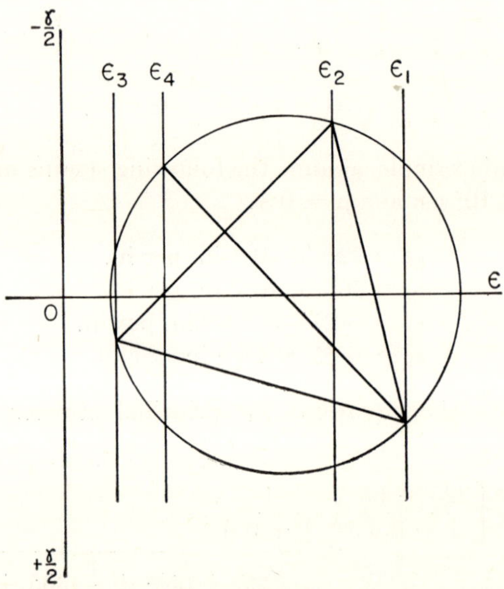

FIG. 7-6. Graphical check for the numerical value of ϵ_4 from the T-delta rosette.

Table 7-2 summarizes the equations required to find the principal stresses, the maximum shearing stress, and the angle to the principal stress direction for the various types of commercially available rosettes.

NOMOGRAPHIC SOLUTIONS FOR STRAIN ROSETTES

Since the solution of the rosette equations for stress is a tedious and time-consuming operation, particularly when large numbers of rosettes are in use, several automatic computers have been devised to perform

Table 7-2. Relations between Strain Rosette Readings and Principal Stresses

Required solution ↓ / Rosette types →	Two-gage	Rectangular	Delta	T-Delta
Maximum normal stress σ_{max}	$\frac{E}{1-\mu^2}(\epsilon_1 + \mu\epsilon_2)$	$\frac{E}{2}\left\{\frac{\epsilon_1+\epsilon_3}{1-\mu} + \frac{1}{1+\mu}\sqrt{(\epsilon_1-\epsilon_3)^2 + [2\epsilon_2 - (\epsilon_1+\epsilon_3)]^2}\right\}$	$E\left[\frac{\epsilon_1+\epsilon_2+\epsilon_3}{3(1-\mu)} + \frac{1}{1+\mu}\sqrt{\left(\epsilon_1 - \frac{\epsilon_1+\epsilon_2+\epsilon_3}{3}\right)^2 + \left(\frac{\epsilon_2-\epsilon_3}{\sqrt{3}}\right)^2}\right]$	$\frac{E}{2}\left[\frac{\epsilon_1+\epsilon_4}{1-\mu} + \frac{1}{1+\mu}\sqrt{(\epsilon_1-\epsilon_4)^2 + \frac{4}{3}(\epsilon_2-\epsilon_3)^2}\right]$
Minimum normal stress σ_{min}	$\frac{E}{1-\mu^2}(\epsilon_2 + \mu\epsilon_1)$	$\frac{E}{2}\left\{\frac{\epsilon_1+\epsilon_3}{1-\mu} - \frac{1}{1+\mu}\sqrt{(\epsilon_1-\epsilon_3)^2 + [2\epsilon_2 - (\epsilon_1+\epsilon_3)]^2}\right\}$	$E\left[\frac{\epsilon_1+\epsilon_2+\epsilon_3}{3(1-\mu)} - \frac{1}{1+\mu}\sqrt{\left(\epsilon_1 - \frac{\epsilon_1+\epsilon_2+\epsilon_3}{3}\right)^2 + \left(\frac{\epsilon_2-\epsilon_3}{\sqrt{3}}\right)^2}\right]$	$\frac{E}{2}\left[\frac{\epsilon_1+\epsilon_4}{1-\mu} - \frac{1}{1+\mu}\sqrt{(\epsilon_1-\epsilon_4)^2 + \frac{4}{3}(\epsilon_2-\epsilon_3)^2}\right]$
Maximum shearing stress τ_{max}	$\frac{E}{2(1+\mu)}(\epsilon_1 - \epsilon_2)$	$\frac{E}{2(1+\mu)}\sqrt{(\epsilon_1-\epsilon_3)^2 + [2\epsilon_2 - (\epsilon_1+\epsilon_3)]^2}$	$\frac{E}{1+\mu}\sqrt{\left(\epsilon_1 - \frac{\epsilon_1+\epsilon_2+\epsilon_3}{3}\right)^2 + \left(\frac{\epsilon_2-\epsilon_3}{\sqrt{3}}\right)^2}$	$\frac{E}{2(1+\mu)}\sqrt{(\epsilon_1-\epsilon_4)^2 + \frac{4}{3}(\epsilon_2-\epsilon_3)^2}$
Angle from gage 1 axis to maximum normal stress axis φ_P	0	$\frac{1}{2}\tan^{-1}\left[\frac{2\epsilon_2 - (\epsilon_1+\epsilon_3)}{\epsilon_1 - \epsilon_3}\right]$	$\frac{1}{2}\tan^{-1}\left[\frac{\frac{1}{\sqrt{3}}(\epsilon_2-\epsilon_3)}{\epsilon_1 - \frac{\epsilon_1+\epsilon_2+\epsilon_3}{3}}\right]$	$\frac{1}{2}\tan^{-1}\frac{2(\epsilon_2-\epsilon_3)}{\sqrt{3}(\epsilon_1-\epsilon_4)}$

this task. These computers operate on either mechanical or electronic principles, but the description of this type of apparatus is beyond the scope of this book. Those interested in this type of equipment may consult the references listed in the Bibliography at the end of the chapter.

Another approach to the rapid determination of principal stresses from the observed strains is by means of the nomograph, an example of which will be given for each of the rosettes discussed. First it is to be pointed out that the general forms of the equations defining the principal stresses, their directions, and the maximum shearing stress are the same for all three rosettes discussed. For each rosette the equations have the form

$$\begin{aligned} \sigma_{\max} &= \frac{E}{1-\mu} A + \frac{E}{1+\mu} \sqrt{B^2 + C^2} \\ \sigma_{\min} &= \frac{E}{1-\mu} A - \frac{E}{1+\mu} \sqrt{B^2 + C^2} \\ \varphi_p &= \frac{1}{2} \tan^{-1} \frac{C}{B} \\ \tau_{\max} &= \frac{E}{1+\mu} \sqrt{B^2 + C^2} \end{aligned} \tag{7-11}$$

The values A, B, and C for the different rosettes are given in Table 7-3.

TABLE 7-3. ALGEBRAIC EXPRESSIONS FOR ROSETTE STRAIN PARAMETERS

	Rectangular	Delta	T-Delta
A	$\dfrac{\epsilon_1 + \epsilon_3}{2}$	$\dfrac{\epsilon_1 + \epsilon_2 + \epsilon_3}{3}$	$\dfrac{\epsilon_1 + \epsilon_4}{2}$
B	$\dfrac{\epsilon_1 - \epsilon_3}{2}$	$\epsilon_1 - \dfrac{\epsilon_1 + \epsilon_2 + \epsilon_3}{3}$	$\dfrac{\epsilon_1 - \epsilon_4}{2}$
C	$\dfrac{2\epsilon_2 - (\epsilon_1 + \epsilon_3)}{2}$	$\dfrac{\epsilon_2 - \epsilon_3}{\sqrt{3}}$	$\dfrac{\epsilon_2 - \epsilon_3}{\sqrt{3}}$

Equations (7-11) can be further simplified by rewriting them as follows:

$$\begin{aligned} \sigma_{\max} &= K_1 A + K_2 \sqrt{B^2 + C^2} \\ \sigma_{\min} &= K_1 A - K_2 \sqrt{B^2 + C^2} \\ \varphi_p &= \frac{1}{2} \tan^{-1} \frac{C}{B} \\ \tau_{\max} &= K_2 \sqrt{B^2 + C^2} \end{aligned} \tag{7-12}$$

where $K_1 = E/(1 - \mu)$

$K_2 = E/(1 + \mu)$

Since the stresses will depend on the values of the modulus of elasticity and Poisson's ratio for the material on which the gages are mounted, some means must be provided for varying the magnitude of the parameters K_1 and K_2 in the nomographic solution of the fundamental equations.

This can be accomplished by setting up two other terms as follows:

$$K_1' = \frac{E'}{E}\frac{1-\mu}{1-\mu'}K_1$$
$$K_2' = \frac{E'}{E}\frac{1+\mu}{1+\mu'}K_2$$

Thus, if the nomograph is set up for fixed values of E and μ, the results for any other values E' and μ' can be obtained by the use of the multiplying factors defined in the expressions for K_1' and K_2' as indicated above.

These fundamental equations (7-12) indicate that the maximum normal stress is obtained by adding the maximum shearing stress to some quantity K_1A, and the minimum normal stress is obtained by subtracting the shearing stress from the same quantity. We see further that the maximum shearing stress will be equal to a constant K_2 times the hypotenuse of a right triangle whose other two sides are B and C. The angle to the plane of maximum normal stress is determined by the quotient of C and B.

Hewson has designed and described nomographs for obtaining principal stresses from strain rosette data. The nomographs are constructed in such a manner that results can be obtained for any material for which the modulus of elasticity and Poisson's ratio are known. The description of the use of these nomographs, as shown in Figs. 7-7 to 7-9, follows.

NOMOGRAPH SOLUTION OF THE RECTANGULAR ROSETTE

As an example to indicate the procedure for obtaining a solution for stresses using the nomograph, assume the following strains are measured with the rectangular rosette:

$$\epsilon_1 = 0.0040 \text{ in. per in.}$$
$$\epsilon_2 = 0.0035 \text{ in. per in.}$$
$$\epsilon_3 = 0.0015 \text{ in. per in.}$$

For the material on which the gage is mounted

$$E = 30.6 \times 10^6 \text{ psi}$$

and

$$\mu = 0.34$$

The steps in the solution as shown in Fig. 7-7A are as follows:

(1) Connect 30.6×10^6 and 0.34 on the E and μ scales in two places.

(2) Connect strains $\epsilon_1 = 0.0040$ and $\epsilon_3 = 0.0015$ on their respective scales, and extend the line to intersect the y' line at point M.

(3) With the origin O as center and the displacement OM as radius, swing an arc clockwise 90° to intersect reference line at M'.

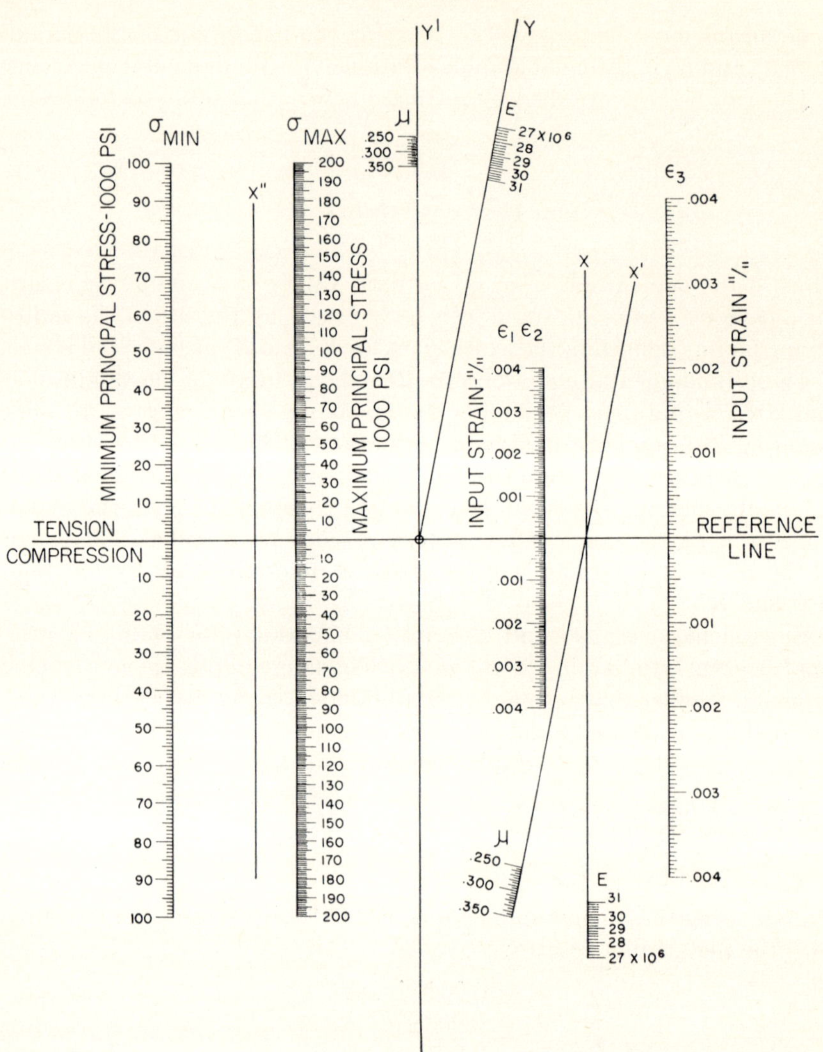

Fig. 7-7. Rectangular rosette nomograph. (*Hewson.*)

(4) Connect strain $\epsilon_2 = 0.0035$ with the intersection of line (2) and line X, extending the line to intersect y' at point N.

(5) Connect M' and N, and measure angle $OM'N = 2\varphi_p$ positive clockwise from the reference.

(6) Transfer displacement $M'N$ to line OY (from O to S'). Draw a line through S' parallel to (1) to intersect OY' at S.

(7) From T' on X, draw a line parallel to the second (1) to intersect X' at T. Transfer twice $O'T$ to X'' (from reference line to T'').

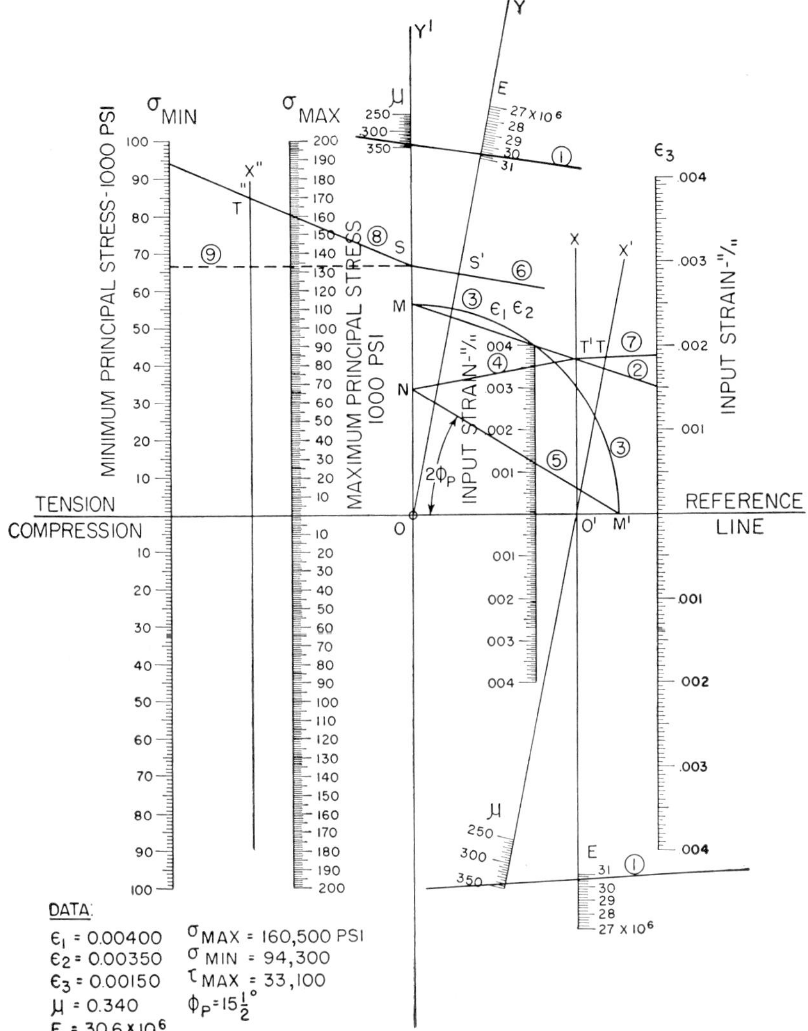

FIG. 7-7A. Nomograph solution of rectangular rosette data.

(8) Connect points S and T'', extending the line to intersect scales σ_{max} and σ_{min}.

(9) For τ_{max}, transfer OS to the σ_{min} scale, and divide the result by 2. The results give

$$\sigma_{max} = 160{,}500 \text{ psi}$$
$$\sigma_{min} = 94{,}300 \text{ psi}$$
$$\tau_{max} = 33{,}100 \text{ psi}$$
$$\varphi_p = 15°30'$$

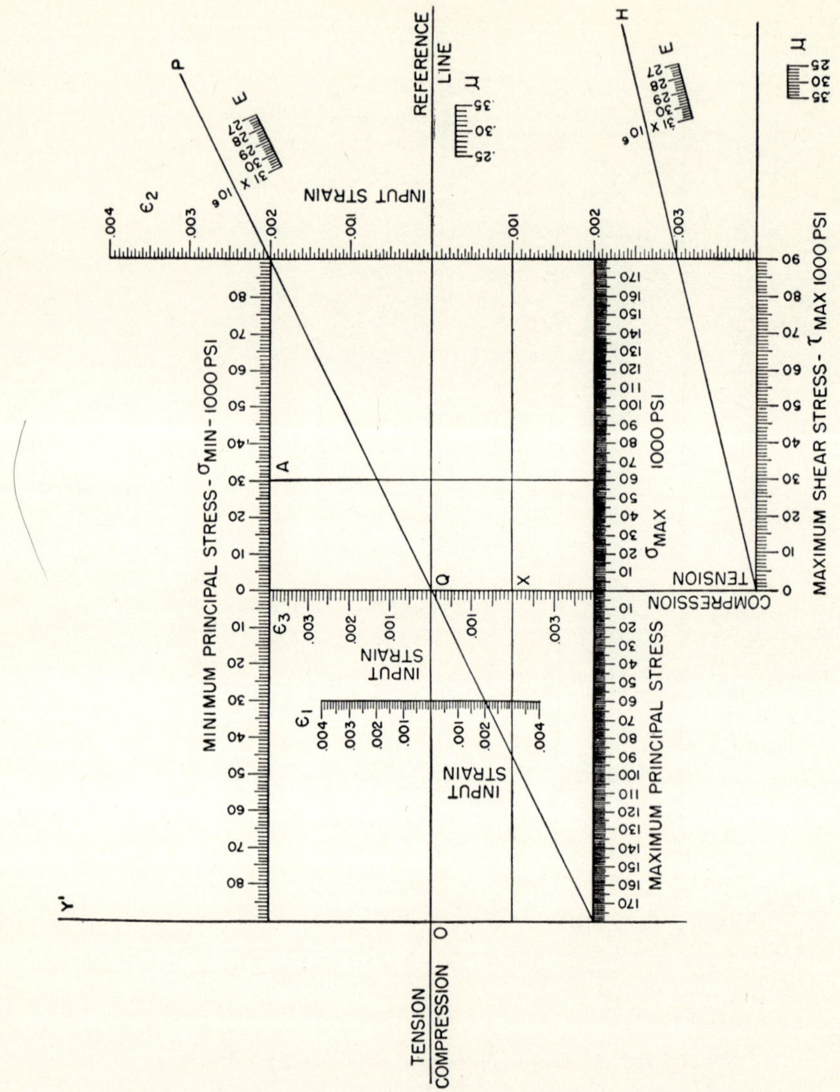

Fig. 7-8. Equiangular (delta) rosette nomograph. (*Hewson.*)

NOMOGRAPH SOLUTION OF THE DELTA ROSETTE

To illustrate the steps required to obtain a solution of the delta rosette by means of its nomograph, let us suppose we have measured

$$\epsilon_1 = 0.0035 \text{ in. per in.}$$
$$\epsilon_2 = -0.0005 \text{ in. per in.}$$
$$\epsilon_3 = 0.0030 \text{ in. per in.}$$

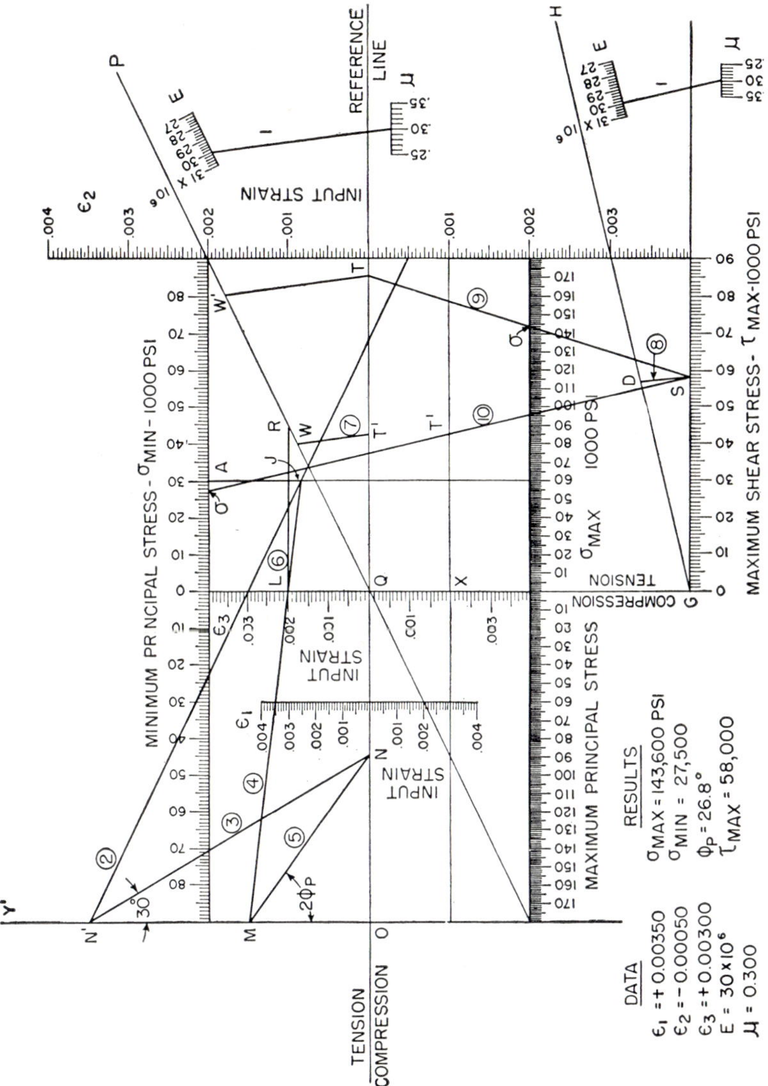

FIG. 7-8*A*. Nomograph solution of equiangular (delta) rosette data.

The material on which the gage is mounted has the properties

$$E = 30 \times 10^6 \text{ psi}$$

and

$$\mu = 0.30$$

The steps in the solution shown in Fig. 7-8*A* are as follows:

(1) Connect 30×10^6 and 0.30 on the E and μ scales in two places.

(2) Connect the strains $\epsilon_2 = -0.0005$ and $\epsilon_3 = 0.0030$, and extend the line to intersect OY at N'. The line crosses the vertical line A at point J.

(3) From point N', draw a line making an angle of 30° with the vertical locating its intersection N with the reference line.

(4) Connect strain $\epsilon_1 = 0.0035$ with point J on the vertical line A, and extend to intersect OY' at point M and the ϵ_3 scale at point L.

(5) Draw MN, and measure angle $OMN = 2\varphi_p$ counterclockwise from line $Y'O$.

(6) From L, draw a horizontal line to intersect line QP at point R.

(7) Lay off the distance LR along the line QP from Q to W and from W to W'. Draw lines from W and W' parallel to (1) intersecting the reference line at T' and T.

(8) Lay off the distance MN on line GH from G to D. Draw a line from D parallel to the second (1) to intersect the τ_{max} scale at S.

(9) Connect S and T. Intersection of this line with the maximum principal stress axis gives the value of σ_{max}.

(10) Lay off QT' along the horizontal line through X from X to T''. Connect S and T'', extending the line to intersect the minimum principal stress axis giving the value of σ_{min}.

The results give

$$\sigma_{max} = 143{,}600 \text{ psi}$$
$$\sigma_{min} = 27{,}500 \text{ psi}$$
$$\tau_{max} = 58{,}000 \text{ psi}$$
$$\varphi_p = 26°50'$$

NOMOGRAPH SOLUTION OF THE T-DELTA ROSETTE

As an example to demonstrate the solution of the T-delta rosette by means of the nomograph, assume the following strains were measured on a material having values of $E = 29.9 \times 10^6$ psi and $\mu = 0.30$:

$$\epsilon_1 = 0.00285 \text{ in. per in.}$$
$$\epsilon_2 = -0.00020 \text{ in. per in.}$$
$$\epsilon_3 = -0.00100 \text{ in. per in.}$$
$$\epsilon_4 = 0.00095 \text{ in. per in.}$$

The solution as shown in Fig. 7-9*A* is obtained by means of the following steps:

(1) Connect 29.9×10^6 and 0.30 on the E and μ scales in two places.

(2) Connect the strains $\epsilon_1 = 0.00285$ and $\epsilon_4 = 0.00095$, extending the line to intersect OY' at point M.

(3) Connect the strains $\epsilon_2 = -0.00020$ and $\epsilon_3 = -0.00100$, extending the line to intersect the reference line at point N.

(4) Connect points M and N, and measure the angle $OMN = 2\varphi_p$ positive counterclockwise from $Y'O$.

(5) Lay off the distance MN along the line OY from O to S'. Through S', draw a line parallel to (1) intersecting OY' at S.

(6) Through point T' on QX, draw a line parallel to the second (1) intersecting QX' at T.

(7) Lay off twice the length QT along the line $Q'X''$ from Q' to T''.

(8) Connect points S and T'', extending the line to intersect σ_{max} and σ_{min} scales.

(9) Draw a line through point S parallel to the reference line to intersect the σ_{min} scale. τ_{max} is half the intercept on the latter scale.

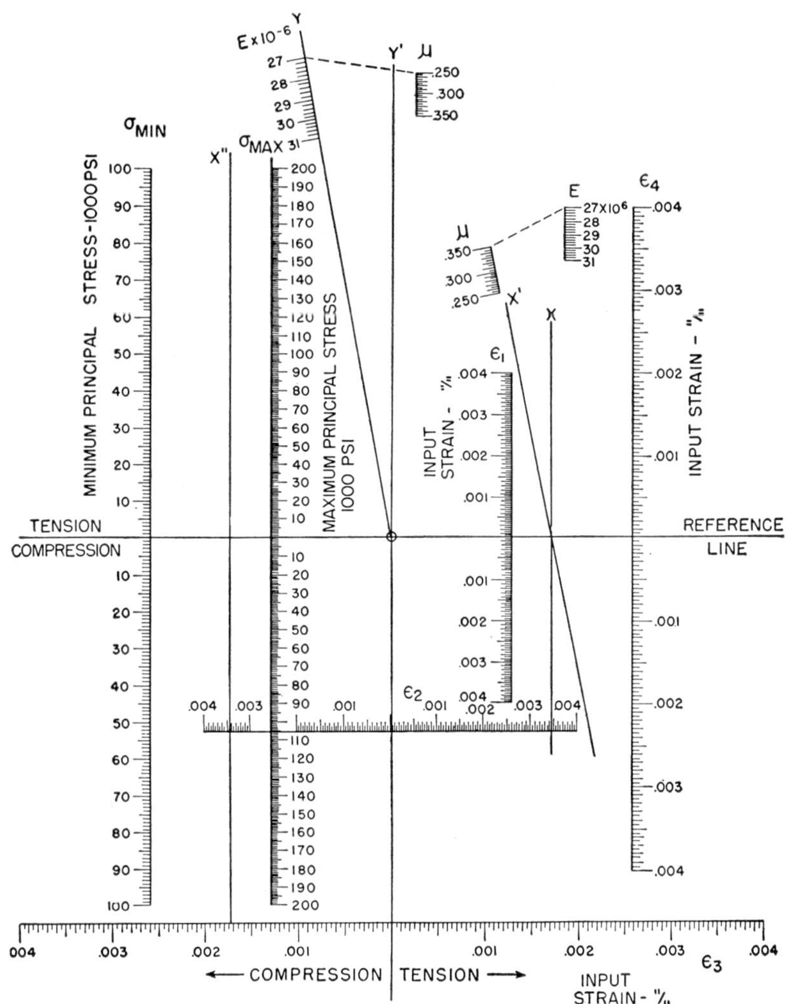

FIG. 7-9. T-delta rosette nomograph. (*Hewson.*)

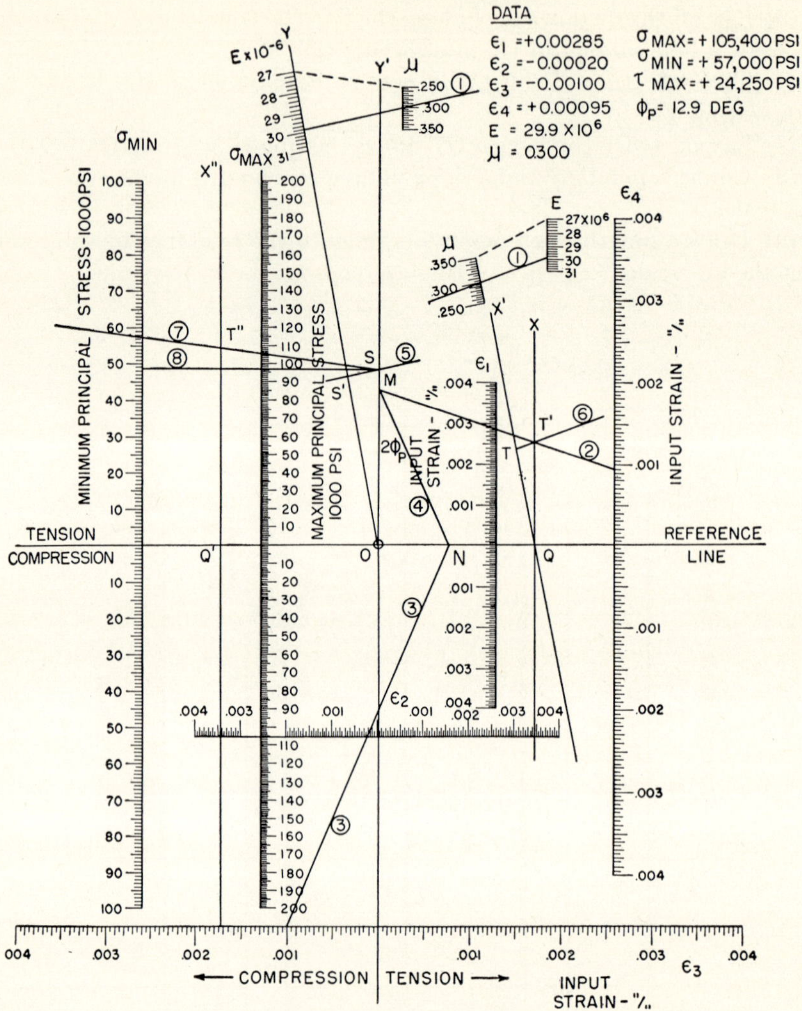

FIG. 7-9*A*. Nomograph solution of T-delta rosette data.

The results for this example are

$$\sigma_{\max} = 105{,}400 \text{ psi}$$
$$\sigma_{\min} = 57{,}000 \text{ psi}$$
$$\tau_{\max} = 24{,}250 \text{ psi}$$
$$\varphi_p = 12°55'$$

ERRORS DUE TO MISALIGNMENT OF GAGES AND ROSETTES

A single gage will indicate the strain existing along the axis on which it is mounted. If the gage is carelessly mounted so that its axis is 2 or

3° from the intended axis, the results obtained may in some circumstances be in considerable error. Consider a case in which the principal strains are 2,000 and 1,000 micro-inches per in. Suppose in this example that a gage is to be applied at a 45° angle with respect to the principal axis. In this direction the strain is 500 micro-inches per in., but at 43° it is 608 and at 47° it is 392 micro-inches per in. Thus, a 2° error in alignment of a gage which was supposedly at 45° to the principal axis would give an error of over 20 per cent in the strain reading. This is, of course, an extreme and unusual case. A 2° error in gage alignment when measuring the strain in the principal stress directions would result in an error of less than 1 per cent for the same example.

When a rosette is misaligned in applying it to the test piece, the magnitude of the principal stresses obtained will be correct but the direction of the principal stresses will be in error by the same angle as the misalignment of the rosette. The degree of error to be expected because of the misalignment of individual gages in a rosette has been investigated by the National Advisory Committee for Aeronautics. This problem is apt to occur only when the user makes up his own rosettes, as those supplied by the manufacturer can be relied upon to be accurate in this regard. The NACA investigation determined that if the individual gages were applied with angles in error by not more than $\pm 2°$, the error in the results obtained by means of the conventional equations for the solution of the rosette would not be greater than ± 2 per cent. This indicates that in making up a rosette from individual gages enough care should be exercised to ensure that the gages are applied within 2° of the direction they are supposed to have. Of course, if one or more of the gages is applied at an incorrect angle and the exact angles of application can be measured, the correct solution for the principal stresses can be obtained with the use of the general equations given in Chap. 6.

TRANSVERSE SENSITIVITY OF STRAIN GAGES

All wire strain gages, with the exception of the long-gage-length single-strand type and the Huggenberger (TEPIC) gages, have a small percentage of the strain-sensitive wire oriented in a direction transverse to the axis of the gage. The percentage of the wire in the transverse direction depends on the length and width of the gage and the length of the gage wire, but an average value is in the neighborhood of 4 per cent. Not only is this percentage of the wire inactive with respect to the axial strain, but it will respond to the strain existing in a direction at right angles to the gage axis. Even in a uniaxial stress field with the gage oriented in the principal stress direction, the transverse strain due to Poisson's ratio will affect the gage. The gage factor as given by the manufacturer corrects for the effect of this transverse strain, assuming Poisson's ratio to be 0.285. But, of course, it is impossible to correct for other transverse strains which may be present in a general biaxial stress field or for a material having a value of Poisson's ratio different from 0.285. The usual practice of stress analysts is to ignore this slight error introduced into the gage reading, but if the utmost accuracy is desired, it must be taken into account when ordinary wire gages are used. In the case of the foil gage, the amount and distribution of the foil connecting the long filaments serve to reduce the sensitivity of the gage to transverse strain. This is accomplished by increasing the width of the foil at the filament ends, decreasing its resistance, and thus its ability to respond to transverse strain. The same effect is achieved in the Huggenberger gage, in which parallel wire filaments are connected at the ends by relatively large wires having much lower resistance than the gage wire.

The gage factor F of wire gages supplied by the manufacturer is the ratio of the unit change in resistance to the strain in the direction of the gage axis. This is true only when a uniaxial strain field exists and the gage axis coincides with the maximum principal stress direction, and when Poisson's ratio μ_0 is 0.285 for the material to which the gage is cemented. The gage factor can be expressed as

$$F = \frac{\Delta R/R}{\epsilon}$$

or rewritten in the form

$$\frac{\Delta R}{R} = F\epsilon \tag{7-13}$$

If we were to write the expression in terms of the axial and transverse sensitivities F_a and F_t, we should have

$$\frac{\Delta R}{R} = F_a\epsilon + F_t\epsilon_t$$

where ϵ_t is the strain in a direction transverse to the gage axis. It should be kept in mind that throughout the following derivations ϵ always refers to the strain along the gage axis, and ϵ_t to the strain in a direction normal to the gage axis. By introducing a factor K equal to F_t/F_a, called the transverse sensitivity factor, this last equation can be rewritten

$$\frac{\Delta R}{R} = F_a(\epsilon + K\epsilon_t) \tag{7-14}$$

By eliminating $\Delta R/R$ from Eqs. (7-13) and (7-14) and substituting

$$\epsilon_t = -\mu_0\epsilon$$

(for the uniaxial stress condition with the gage aligned along the principal axis), we have

$$F = F_a(1 - \mu_0 K) \tag{7-15}$$

The apparent strain ϵ_c obtained in any strain field by the use of the gage factor supplied by the manufacturer will be

$$\epsilon_c = \frac{\Delta R/R}{F} = \frac{F_a(\epsilon + K\epsilon_t)}{F_a(1 - \mu_0 K)} = \frac{\epsilon + K\epsilon_t}{1 - \mu_0 K} \tag{7-16}$$

ERROR IN STRAIN INDICATION DUE TO TRANSVERSE SENSITIVITY

Expressing the error e as the difference between the apparent strain ϵ_c and the true strain ϵ, divided by ϵ, we obtain

$$e = \frac{\epsilon_c - \epsilon}{\epsilon} = \left(\frac{\epsilon + K\epsilon_t}{1 - \mu_0 K} - \epsilon\right)\frac{1}{\epsilon}$$

or

$$e = \frac{\epsilon + K\epsilon_t}{(1 - \mu_0 K)} - 1 \tag{7-17}$$

It is evident that when the transverse strain ϵ_t equals $-\mu_0\epsilon$, which is the condition for uniaxial stress with the gage along the maximum principal stress axis, the error is zero.

If the Poisson's ratio for the material is some value μ, other than μ_0, an error exists. When measuring the strain in the maximum principal stress direction in a uniaxial stress field, the error due to μ having a value other than 0.285 is obtained by substituting $-\mu\epsilon$ for ϵ_t in Eq. (7-17). The result is

$$e = \frac{1 - K\mu}{1 - K\mu_0} - 1$$

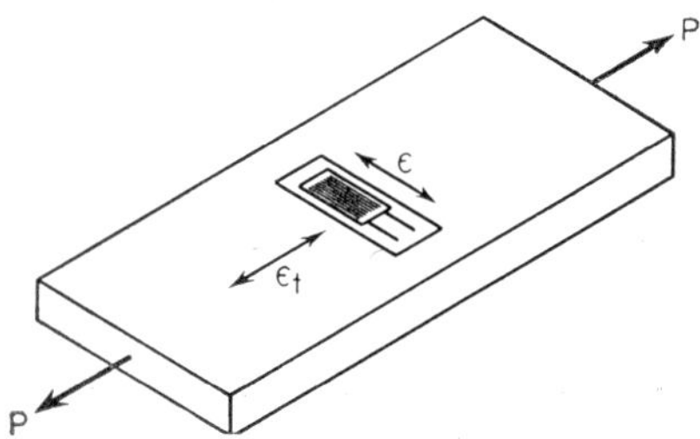

FIG. 7-10. Strain gage applied in the zero-stress direction. Notice ϵ is the strain along the gage axis, and ϵ_t is the strain transverse to the gage axis.

As an example of the use of Eq. (7-17), suppose we are to find the error in the indicated strain when the gage is applied in the zero-stress direction (Fig. 7-10). If we define the strain in the direction of the maximum principal stress as ϵ', the strain at right angles will be $-\mu\epsilon'$. Now applying the gage at right angles to the maximum principal stress direction, the strain along the gage axis is $-\mu\epsilon'$, and the transverse strain sensed by the gage is ϵ'. Then, in the basic equation for error [(Eq. (7-17)],

$$e = \frac{\epsilon + K\epsilon_t}{1 - \mu_0 K} - 1$$

$$\epsilon = -\mu\epsilon' \qquad \text{and} \qquad \epsilon_t = \epsilon'$$

Substituting these values we obtain

$$e = \frac{-\mu\epsilon' + K\epsilon'}{-\mu\epsilon'(1 - \mu_0 K)} - 1$$

$$e = \frac{1 - K/\mu}{1 - \mu_0 K} - 1$$

Let us determine the error with a type A-1 strain gage, mounted as shown in Fig. 7-10 on steel, having $\mu = 0.300$. From Table 7-4, giving the

TABLE 7-4. EXPERIMENTAL TRANSVERSE SENSITIVITY FACTORS FOR SOME SR-4 STRAIN GAGES*,†

SR-4 *Gage*	$K = \dfrac{\textit{transverse sensitivity}}{\textit{axial sensitivity}}$	*SR*-4 *Gage*	$K = \dfrac{\textit{transverse sensitivity}}{\textit{axial sensitivity}}$
A-1	0.02	C-10	0.0075
A-3	0.02	C-11	0.02
A-5	0.035	C-14	0.0075
A-6	0.0175	FA-600-75	−0.002
A-7	−0.01	FA-100-12	0.009
A-9	Negligible	FA-50-12	0.006
A-11	0.005	FA-25-12	0.01
A-12	0.01	FAP-50-12	0.002
A-13	−0.0075	FAP-25-12	0.002
A-14	−0.0075	FAP-12-12	0.004
A-15	−0.0075	FAP-06-12	0.012
A-18	−0.02	FAP-03-12	0.036
C-1	0.0175	FAB-50-12	−0.011
C-5	0.04	FAB-25-12	0.001
C-7	0.01	FAB-12-12	−0.006
C-8	0.02	FAB-06-12	0.007
		FAB-03-12	0.03

* Courtesy of Baldwin-Lima-Hamilton Corporation.

† Gages with the prefix F have foil filaments; those without the prefix have wire filaments.

experimental values of transverse sensitivity factors for various gages, we have $K = 0.02$. Substituting these values in the above equation results in

$$e = \frac{1 - 0.02/0.300}{1 - 0.285 \times 0.02} - 1 = -0.062, \text{ or } -6.2\%$$

ERROR IN A GENERAL STRESS FIELD AS A FRACTION OF THE MAXIMUM PRINCIPAL STRAIN

In order to find the gage position and the ratio of the minimum to maximum strain for which the greatest error will occur, let us express the error e' as a fraction of the maximum principal strain ϵ_{max} by multiplying Eq. (7-17) by ϵ/ϵ_{max}.

$$e' = \frac{1}{\epsilon_{max}} \frac{K(\mu_0\epsilon + \epsilon_t)}{1 - \mu_0 K}$$

Equation (6-7) can be rewritten for principal strains, noting that γ is zero.

$$\epsilon = \frac{\epsilon_{max} + \epsilon_{min}}{2} + \frac{\epsilon_{max} - \epsilon_{min}}{2} \cos 2\varphi$$

$$\epsilon_t = \frac{\epsilon_{max} + \epsilon_{min}}{2} - \frac{\epsilon_{max} - \epsilon_{min}}{2} \cos 2\varphi$$

Substituting, we obtain

$$e' = \frac{1}{\epsilon_{max}} \frac{K}{1 - \mu_0 K} \left(\mu_0 \frac{\epsilon_{max} + \epsilon_{min}}{2} + \mu_0 \frac{\epsilon_{max} - \epsilon_{min}}{2} \cos 2\varphi + \frac{\epsilon_{max} + \epsilon_{min}}{2} - \frac{\epsilon_{max} - \epsilon_{min}}{2} \cos 2\varphi \right)$$

$$e' = \frac{1}{\epsilon_{max}} \frac{K}{1 - \mu_0 K} \left[(1 + \mu_0) \frac{\epsilon_{max} + \epsilon_{min}}{2} - (1 - \mu_0) \frac{\epsilon_{max} - \epsilon_{min}}{2} \cos 2\varphi \right] \tag{7-18}$$

For $\cos 2\varphi = -1$, the gage would be applied in the minimum principal stress direction, and

$$e' = \frac{1}{\epsilon_{max}} \frac{K}{1 - \mu_0 K} (\epsilon_{max} + \mu_0 \epsilon_{min})$$

or

$$e' = \frac{K}{1 - \mu_0 K} \left(1 + \mu_0 \frac{\epsilon_{min}}{\epsilon_{max}} \right) \tag{7-18a}$$

When $\cos 2\varphi = +1$, the gage is aligned in the maximum principal stress direction and we obtain

$$e' = \frac{K}{1 - \mu_0 K} \left(\frac{\epsilon_{min}}{\epsilon_{max}} + \mu_0 \right) \tag{7-18b}$$

In evaluating the error for these two conditions it must be realized that both ϵ_{max} and ϵ_{min} may be negative; and also when ϵ_{min} is negative, it may be numerically greater than ϵ_{max}. Figure 7-11 shows the manner in which the error e' (in per cent of ϵ_{max}) varies with the ratio $\epsilon_{min}/\epsilon_{max}$ with the gage aligned in both the maximum and minimum principal stress directions.

As an example consider the percentage error obtained in using a type A-1 SR-4 strain gage having a transverse sensitivity factor $K = 0.02$ to measure the strain in the maximum principal stress direction when the minimum principal strain is equal to it in magnitude and sign. Such a case would exist on the surface of a spherical vessel subjected to internal pressure. Take Poisson's ratio, $\mu_0 = 0.285$.

$$e' = \frac{K}{1 - \mu_0 K}\left(\frac{\epsilon_{min}}{\epsilon_{max}} + \mu_0\right) \times 100$$

$$e' = \frac{0.02}{1 - 0.285 \times 0.02}(1 + 0.285) \times 100$$

$$e' = 2.73 \text{ per cent of the maximum strain reading}$$

For the case where ϵ_{max} is close to zero and ϵ_{min} has a large negative value, e' may become very large and approach infinity. But it should be remembered that e' is expressed as a function of ϵ_{max}, so the absolute value of the error in strain indication will not be very great.

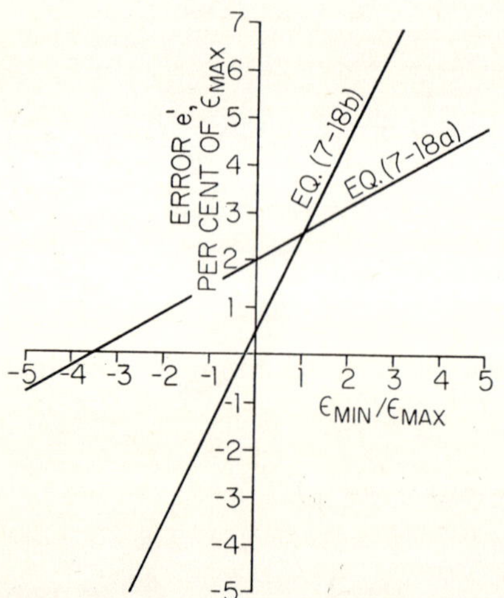

FIG. 7-11. Variation of error e' with ratio $\epsilon_{min}/\epsilon_{max}$ for a strain gage aligned in the minimum [Eq. (7-18*a*)] and maximum [Eq. (7-18*b*)] principal stress directions. Assumed: $K = 0.02$, $\mu_0 = 0.285$.

TRUE-STRAIN DETERMINATION

If two gages are used at right angles to each other, the true strains can always be obtained from the equations

$$\text{True } \epsilon_x = \frac{(1-\mu_0 K)(\epsilon_x - K\epsilon_y)}{1-K^2}$$
$$\text{True } \epsilon_y = \frac{(1-\mu_0 K)(\epsilon_y - K\epsilon_x)}{1-K^2} \qquad (7\text{-}19)$$

which are obtained by substitution into the relationship between true and apparent strain given in Eq. (7-16). ϵ_x and ϵ_y are the apparent values obtained from the strain gages. The value $1 - K^2$ can be assumed equal to 1 for all commercial gages without introducing an appreciable error into the results.

The transverse sensitivity factor K to be used in the above equations is obtained from Table 7-4 or from the manufacturer. The experimental values of K are given in this table, and they differ markedly from the theoretical values in some cases. For example, a negative K is theoretically impossible, but a number of gages exhibit this characteristic experimentally. In explanation of this fact, it should be pointed out that in the manufacturing process these gages are wound on a cylinder and then flattened. Because of this procedure, all the wire is not in the same plane, and this fact is not taken into account in the theoretical determination of K.

EXPERIMENTAL DETERMINATION OF POISSON'S RATIO

By definition, Poisson's ratio is the ratio of the transverse and longitudinal strains. Thus, if the true value of ϵ_y is divided by the true value of ϵ_x (Eq. 7-19), an expression for Poisson's ratio will be obtained.

$$\mu = -\frac{\text{true } \epsilon_y}{\text{true } \epsilon_x} = -\frac{(1 - \mu_0 K)(\epsilon_x - K\epsilon_y)/(1 - K^2)}{(1 - \mu_0 K)(\epsilon_y - K\epsilon_x)/(1 - K^2)}$$

$$\mu = \frac{-\epsilon_x + K\epsilon_y}{\epsilon_y - K\epsilon_x}$$

where ϵ_x and ϵ_y are the measured maximum and minimum principal strains, respectively, in a uniaxial stress field.

THE STRESS GAGE

Since the stress in any direction is dependent not only on the strain in the same direction but also on the transverse strain as indicated in Eq. (6-2),

$$\sigma_x = \frac{E}{1 - \mu^2} (\epsilon_x + \mu\epsilon_y)$$

it appears that the output of a gage would be proportional to the stress along its axis if a proper proportion of the grid were arranged in the transverse direction. This can be accomplished by embodying two orthogonal grids in the gage and proportioning the total filament lengths of the grids by the ratio μ. Figure 7-12 illustrates a combination stress-strain gage based upon this principle. When connections are made to the center and uppermost leads, the grids are placed in series and thus perform the mathematical operations within the parentheses of Eq. (6-2).

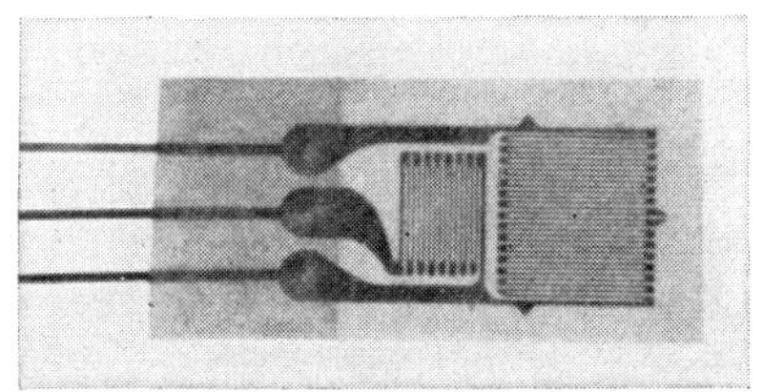

FIG. 7-12. Stress-strain gage. Gage elements can be used independently for conventional strain measurement or in series to produce readings that are proportional to stress along the gage axis. (*Courtesy of Baldwin-Lima-Hamilton Corporation.*)

The same gage can be used as a strain gage by making connections to only the two outside leads so that the larger grid is used alone.

A different approach (and the original one) to stress gage configuration is the V-shaped grid. A portion of the filament can be placed in the transverse direction by simply orienting the grid at an angle with respect to the gage axis. When this is done, however, one additional factor which must not be overlooked is that the presence of a shearing strain will also cause a change in length of the gage wire. This is apparent from Eq. (6-6), which reads

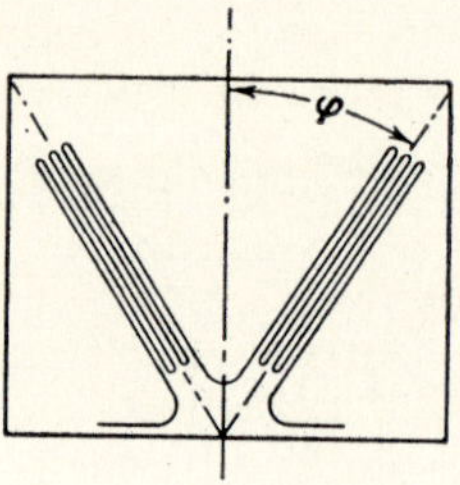

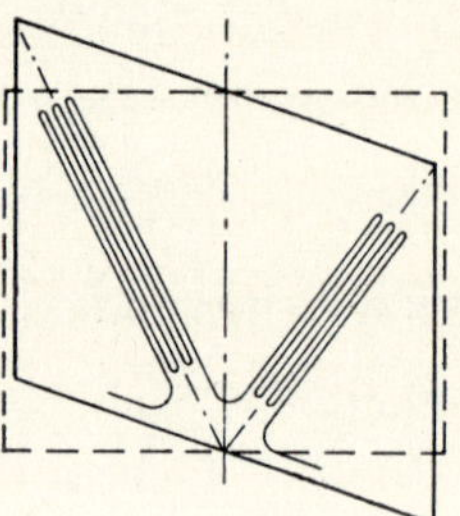

FIG. 7-13. Effect of shearing strain on gage filament.

$$\epsilon_\varphi = \epsilon_x \cos^2 \varphi + \epsilon_y \sin^2 \varphi + \gamma_{xy} \sin \varphi \cos \varphi$$

Or we can think of the shearing strain as changing a rectangle into a parallelogram, with one diagonal lengthened and the other shortened as shown in Fig. 7-13. Therefore, if the strain-sensitive wire is placed along one diagonal, an equal amount in series with it must be placed along the other diagonal to cancel the effect of the shearing strain on the deformation of the wire. This is accomplished in the commercial stress gage by winding the wire in the form shown in Fig. 7-14.

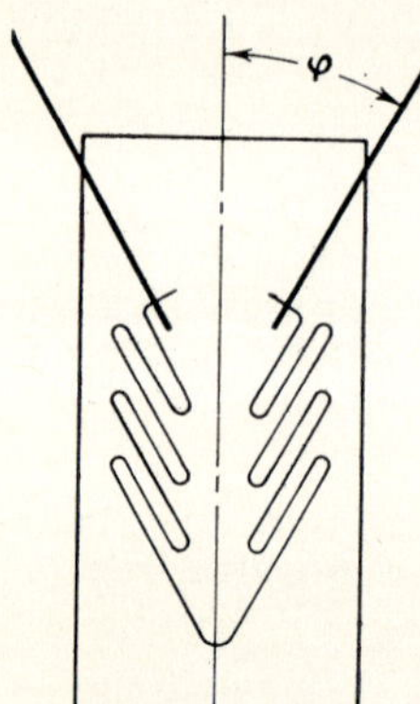

FIG. 7-14. A commercial form of stress gage.

To obtain the angle φ at which to orient the wire with respect to the gage axis, reference is again made to Eq. (6-6). Since the effect of shearing strain has been eliminated, we can omit the term involving shearing strain and write

$$\epsilon_\varphi = \epsilon_x \cos^2 \varphi + \epsilon_y \sin^2 \varphi$$

This can be written

$$\epsilon_\varphi = \cos^2 \varphi(\epsilon_x + \epsilon_y \tan^2 \varphi)$$

By making $\tan^2 \varphi$ equal to μ, we find that the equations for σ_x and ϵ_φ are of the same form; so the required angle $\varphi = \tan^{-1} \sqrt{\mu}$.

CONVENTIONAL STRAIN GAGE USED AS A PRINCIPAL STRESS GAGE

In the practical analysis of a biaxial stress field the maximum principal stress is ordinarily of primary interest. The principal stress directions can frequently be determined before applying strain gages. The directions of the principal axes can be obtained, for example, from a Stresscoat study, from the shape of the piece and mode of loading, or sometimes from the nature of a fracture. To measure the maximum principal stress, the commercial stress gage must be mounted with its central axis parallel to the corresponding principal axis. In this instance the element of matter upon which the gage is mounted is not subjected to shear strain, and therefore the second grid in the gage is superfluous.

The major limitation of the commercial stress gages stems from their special character. They are produced in a very limited range of gage types and sizes and are consequently too restricted in use to merit being stocked by most industrial laboratories. The minimum available gage length for the V-shaped stress gage is approximately ¾ in., and that for the dual-grid stress gage, about 5/16 in. Neither is applicable for use in a region of steep strain gradient. Furthermore, a particular type of stress gage is suitable for use only on a material with a Poisson's ratio corresponding to the included angle of the V-shaped grid, or the ratio of filament lengths in the dual-element grid. Both the V-shaped grid and the auxiliary grid in the dual-element stress gage are entirely unnecessary for the one most significant application—the measurement of principal stresses. In this important case any ordinary strain gage, irrespective of type or size, can be mounted so as to perform the duties of a stress gage.

The maximum (or minimum) principal stress in a general biaxial field can be indicated directly with a single conventional strain gage. This can be accomplished, once the principal stress directions are known, by mounting the strain gage at a particular angle from a principal axis as shown in Fig. 7-15. Since each principal stress in a biaxial field is a function of both principal strains, the gage must be mounted at such an angle to one of the principal axes that it is affected by the principal strains in the correct proportion. This angle is independent of the ratio between the principal strains and is determined only by the Poisson's ratio of the material. Thus, if the principal axes and Poisson's ratio are known, a strain gage mounted as described here will produce an electrical output which is always proportional to a principal stress.

The mechanism by which a strain gage indicates the principal stress when oriented at a particular angle from a principal axis can be readily understood from the following derivation: expressing first the principal stress in terms of the principal strains,

$$\sigma_p = \frac{E}{1 - \mu^2} (\epsilon_p + \mu\epsilon_q) \tag{7-20}$$

which indicates that a strain gage must be so oriented in a biaxial field that it will be properly affected by both principal strains in order to produce an output proportional to a principal stress.

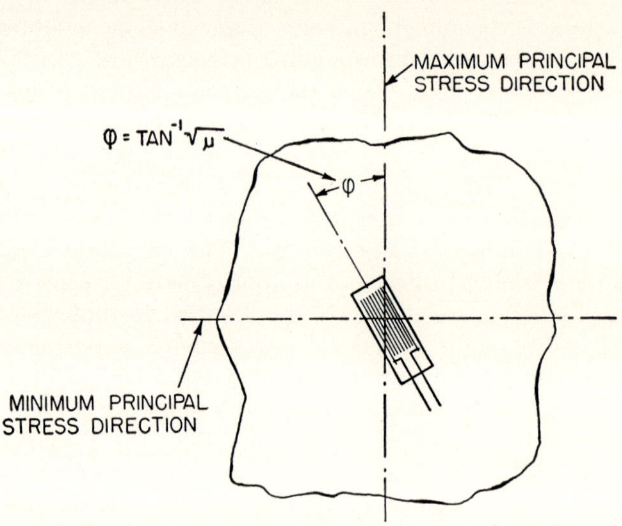

Fig. 7-15. Strain gage mounted for direct indication of maximum principal stress. The gage output would similarly be proportional to the minimum principal stress if oriented φ degrees from the corresponding principal axis.

The strain at any angle φ from a principal axis can be written

$$\epsilon_\varphi = \epsilon_p \cos^2 \varphi + \epsilon_q \sin^2 \varphi$$

or

$$\epsilon_\varphi = \cos^2 \varphi(\epsilon_p + \epsilon_q \tan^2 \varphi) \tag{7-21}$$

Equations (7-20) and (7-21) are roughly similar and can be made much more so by letting $\tan^2 \varphi$ equal μ and thus $\cos^2 \varphi$ equal $1/(1 + \mu)$. This substitution fixes the angle at which the strain gage must be mounted and results in

$$\epsilon_\varphi = \frac{1}{1 + \mu} (\epsilon_p + \mu\epsilon_q) \tag{7-22}$$

Dividing Eq. (7-20) by Eq. (7-22),

$$\frac{\sigma_p}{\epsilon_\varphi} = \frac{\dfrac{E}{1-\mu^2}(\epsilon_p + \mu\epsilon_q)}{\dfrac{1}{1+\mu}(\epsilon_p + \mu\epsilon_q)} = \frac{E}{1-\mu} \tag{7-23}$$

from which

$$\sigma_p = \frac{E}{1-\mu}\epsilon_\varphi$$

or

$$\sigma_p = \lambda E \epsilon_\varphi \qquad \text{where } \lambda = \frac{1}{1-\mu}$$

As a result, it is evident that if the strain gage is mounted at

$$\varphi = \tan^{-1}\sqrt{\mu}$$

the strain output can be converted to the associated principal stress through multiplication by λE, where λ can be considered a biaxial coefficient for the modulus of elasticity. It will be noticed that both φ and λ are determined only by the Poisson's ratio of the material. Figure 7 16 shows the manner in which these quantities vary. The principal

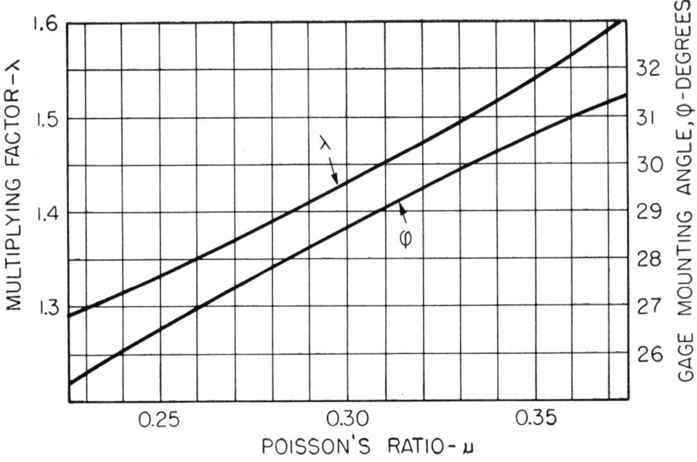

Fig. 7-16. Variation of multiplying factor and gage mounting angle with Poisson's ratio.

stress gage technique can be demonstrated graphically with Mohr's circles for stress and strain. It can be shown that in order to draw the two circles concentrically, and based upon the same origin (Fig. 7-17), it is necessary to rationalize their scales. It develops that the scale ratio between stress and strain to accomplish this is $E/(1 - \mu)$—the same factor derived algebraically to translate from a particular strain to the principal stress. On the Mohr's circle diagram this means that a vertical projection from the maximum principal stress point should intersect the strain circle at the angle 2φ. This can be checked, noting that the ratio of the radius of the stress circle to that of the strain circle is $(1 - \mu)/(1 + \mu)$,

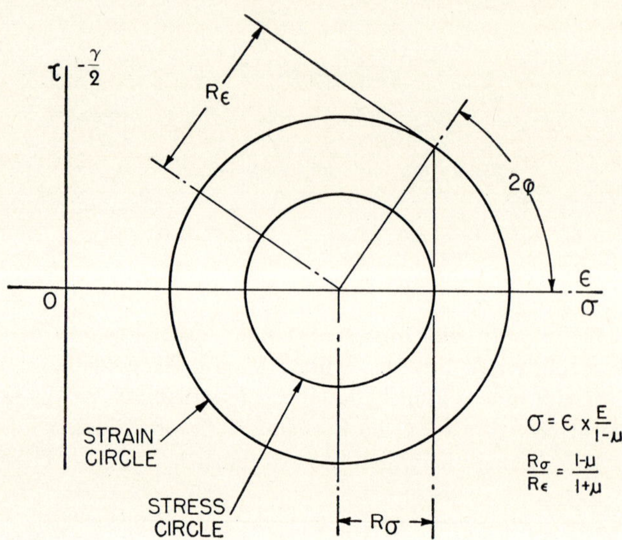

FIG. 7-17. Concentric Mohr's circles of stress and strain demonstrating the operation of the principal stress gage.

which is also $\cos 2\varphi$. Since $\cos^{-1} (1 - \mu)/(1 + \mu)$ is trigonometrically identical to $2 \tan^{-1} \sqrt{\mu}$, it becomes apparent that with a strain gage mounted at the angle φ, ϵ_φ is graphically equivalent to the principal stress and can be converted numerically through the scale factor $E/(1 - \mu)$.

BIBLIOGRAPHY

Baumberger, R., and F. Hines: Practical Reduction Formulas for Use on Bonded Wire Strain Gages, *Proc. SESA*, vol. 2, no. 1, pp. 113–127, 1944.

Duke, M. E., and E. Wenk, Jr.: The Graphical Solution of 45 Degree Strain Rosette Data and Determination of Error in the Calculated Stresses Due to Errors in Measured Strain, *David Taylor Model Basin, Rept.* 600, 1949.

Flynn, P. D.: Discussion of Paper Entitled "Conventional Wire Strain Gage Used as a Principal Stress Gage," *Proc. SESA*, vol. 13, no. 1, p. 33, 1955.

Grossman, N.: A Nomographic Rosette Computer, *Proc. SESA*, vol. 4, no. 1, pp. 27–35, 1946.

Hewson, T. A.: A Nomographic Solution to the Strain Rosette Equation, *Proc. SESA*, vol. 4, no. 1, pp. 9–26, 1946.

Hoskins, E. E., and R. C. Oleson: An Electrical Computer for the Evaluation of Strain Rosette Data, *Proc. SESA*, vol. 2, no. 1, pp. 67–77, 1944.

Kern, R. E.: The Stress Gage, *Proc. SESA*, vol. 4, no. 1, pp. 124–129, 1946.

Lissner, H. R., and C. C. Perry: Conventional Wire Strain Gage Used as a Principal Stress Gage, *Proc. SESA*, vol. 13, no. 1, p. 25, 1955.

Manson, S. S., and W. C. Morgan: Effect of Misalignment of Strain Gage Components of Strain Rosettes, *NACA*, *Tech. Note* 1133, 1946.

McClintock, F. A.: A Letter to the Editor—On Determining Principal Strains from Strain Rosettes with Arbitrary Angles, *Proc. SESA*, vol. 9, no. 1, pp. 209–210, 1952.

Meier, J. H.: On the Transverse Sensitivity of Foil Gages, *Experimental Mechanics*, vol. 1, no. 7, pp. 39–40, July, 1961.

Meier, J. H.: Strain Rosettes, "Handbook of Experimental Stress Analysis," pp. 390–437, John Wiley & Sons, Inc., New York, 1950.

Meier, J. H., and W. R. Mehaffey: Electronic Computing Apparatus for Rectangular and Equiangular Strain Rosettes, *Proc. SESA*, vol. 2, no. 1, pp. 78–101, 1944.

Williams, S. B.: The Dyadic Gage, *Proc. SESA*, vol. 1, no. 2, pp. 43–55, 1944.

EXERCISES

7-1. For the case in which principal stress directions are known, can the principal stresses be determined by two gages applied in arbitrary but known directions? Explain.

7-2. Derive Eq. (7-9).

7-3. Develop the rosette equations for the case in which $\varphi_1 = 0°$, $\varphi_2 = 30°$, and $\varphi_3 = 60°$ [the equivalent of Eqs. (7-3) and (7-4)].

7-4. A delta rosette yields the following strain indications: $\epsilon_1 = 815$ micro-inches per in.; $\epsilon_2 = 1{,}220$ micro-inches per in.; $\epsilon_3 = 710$ micro-inches per in. Calculate the angle from the axis of gage 1 to the principal axis, the maximum principal stress and the maximum shear stress. $E = 30 \times 10^6$ psi, $\mu = 0.285$.

7-5. Gages 1, 2, and 3 of a T-delta rosette read 357×10^{-6} in. per in., -254×10^{-6} in. per in., and 312×10^{-6} in. per in., respectively. Determine the expected reading for gage 4.

7-6. Solve Exercise 4 using the nomograph in Fig. 7-8.

7-7. A T-delta rosette is used to obtain the stress conditions in a problem in which the stresses are due to a single impact load. The maximum gage readings obtained are as follows: gage 1, -435×10^{-6} in. per in.; gage 3, 212×10^{-6} in. per in.; and gage 4, 824×10^{-6} in. per in. Unfortunately, gage 2 failed to record. Since the load could be applied only once, the stresses must be determined from these readings. What are the maximum principal stresses, maximum shearing stress, and the angle from gage 1 to the maximum principal stress direction?

7-8. A rectangular rosette, when mounted on a structural member, produces the following strain indications with the application of load: $\epsilon_1 = 1{,}680$ micro-inches per in.; $\epsilon_2 = -1{,}110$ micro-inches per in.; $\epsilon_3 = 620$ micro-inches per in. Calculate the maximum normal stress, maximum shear stress, and the angle between gage 1 and the principal axis using the nomograph in Fig. 7-7.

7-9. A strain gage is mounted at 30° from the longitudinal axis of a tensile specimen. Including the effects of transverse sensitivity, calculate the strain indicated by the gage as a fraction of the maximum principal strain (in terms of μ and K).

7-10. Two gages are applied to a tensile test piece, one in the direction of the stress field, the other at right angles to this direction. The gage in the direction of the stress field indicates a strain of 550 micro-inches per in. If Poisson's ratio is 0.32 and the gage transverse sensitivity factor is 0.035, what reading should the transverse gage exhibit? What is the maximum stress in the piece if $E = 30 \times 10^6$?

7-11. Derive the scale ratios in Fig. 7-17.

7-12. For a delta rosette with gage readings $\epsilon_1 = 315$ micro-inches per in., $\epsilon_2 = -20$ micro-inches per in., and $\epsilon_3 = 955$ micro-inches per in., calculate the true maximum and minimum principal strains if Poisson's ratio for the material is 0.33 and the transverse sensitivity factor K of each gage is 0.025. NOTE: This problem can be solved by the method of successive approximations.

7-13. A cylindrical steel tank 4 ft in diameter has a wall thickness of 0.25 in., and is subjected to an internal pressure of 350 psi. Calculate the expected strain reading from a gage used as a maximum principal stress gage.

7-14. Mount a commercial stress gage on a tensile specimen and compare the results obtained from the gage with the stresses computed from the actual applied loads.

7-15. Mount a rosette in a general stress field (on a highly stressed portion of the testing machine, a press, or other structure in the laboratory). Determine the principal stresses and maximum shear stress.

7-16. Derive Eqs. (7-19).

8 MOISTUREPROOFING OF STRAIN GAGES

It often occurs in problems of stress and strain determination that the surface to which a strain gage is to be attached must be exposed to conditions of very high humidity during the testing procedure. An extreme case of this type is the installation of strain gages on the inner surfaces of pressurized liquid containers. Another instance of rather severe operating conditions is that of a strain gage mounted on a ship's propeller or other hydrodynamic device. Since the basic phenomena exhibited by electrical strain gages are small changes in resistance, any electrical shunting of the strain gages by the effects of moisture will result in erratic and false strain indications. Such shunting can occur in several manners. One possibility is that the cement employed in the bonding and manufacture of the strain gage can absorb enough moisture to become slightly conductive. On the other hand, moisture may collect on the gage installation in a manner so as to produce a leakage path between the leads or between the leads and ground. For accurate indication of static strains and for extended-time strain gage applications, these conditions are unacceptable. This situation has resulted in the development of numerous techniques for moistureproofing strain gages.

Fundamentally, moistureproofing involves nothing more than the provision of a physical barrier between the source of moisture and the gage. The selection of a particular technique for any one strain gage application will depend principally upon two criteria. The primary consideration is the comparative severity of moisture conditions to be encountered. The other factor is the degree of accuracy required from the strain gages. For long-time strain measurements on concrete reinforcing rods, for example, the ultimate in stability and accuracy is necessary since the maximum stress to be measured is comparatively low. Concrete stresses seldom exceed 300 psi in tension; and with 3 per cent reinforcement this would result in a stress of only about 10,000 psi in the reinforcing steel. The corresponding strain in the steel would be approximately 300 micro-inches per in. Conditions are still more critical when strain measurements are to be made directly on concrete surfaces. In the latter case the maximum strain for tension surfaces will ordinarily be less than 100 micro-inches per in. At the other extreme there are strain gage installations being employed to measure the strains resulting from underwater explosions. In this particular application the strain will exist for a very short period of time, and static stability of the strain gages becomes relatively insignificant. Strain gages have been employed successfully in measuring impact stresses at impedances to ground on the order of 1 megohm and less.

Conditions of strain gage moisture exposure have been arbitrarily subdivided into four classes of generally increasing severity. They are:

1. Long-time indoor installations.
2. Out-of-door installations in which the gages may be subjected to near saturation humidity or actual water splash.
3. Operation while submerged in water.
4. Operation while exposed to or submerged in mediums other than water.

These subdivisions will be discussed individually, particular instances of each being noted and one or more of the applicable moistureproofing techniques being listed. In general, bakelite-type strain gages, because of their lower rate of moisture absorption and greater dimensional stability, should be employed for all gage applications which are expected to operate with stability over long periods of time or which are to be exposed to the effects of moisture. Paper or epoxy gages, however, if adequately protected, can be and have been employed quite satisfactorily under such conditions.

LONG-TIME INDOOR INSTALLATIONS

There is ordinarily little need for moistureproofing strain gages when they are to be used in short-term strain investigations conducted in the laboratory. Demands for greater stability over longer periods of time may, however, necessitate protection of the gages from humidity variations. As an example, laboratory technicians often build up reference strain gage installations for the single purpose of testing for zero drift of strain-indicating instruments. The reference installation can be accomplished by bonding two strain gages to a small piece of metal. The metal will never be strained except by temperature variations, and these will not affect the output of a Wheatstone bridge if the two strain gages are connected in adjacent legs. This reference circuit can at any time be connected to the strain indicator so that instability of the indicator will be manifested as zero drift. The ratio of resistances of the two reference strain gages should remain precisely constant indefinitely. To ensure the constancy of this ratio, it is considered advisable to moistureproof the strain gages. This will not require particularly refined moistureproofing technique since the reference gages will ordinarily not be used outside the laboratory.

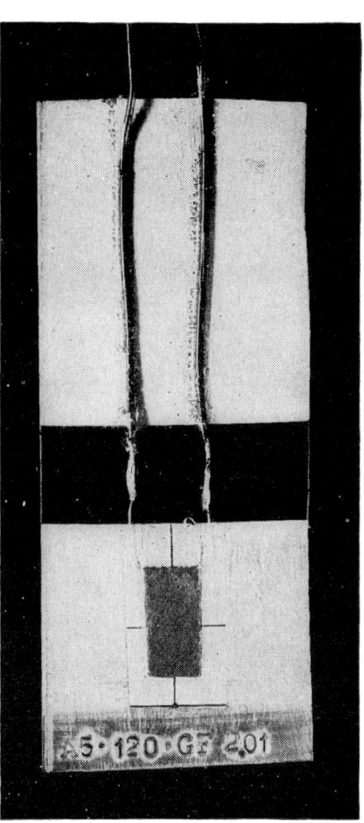

Fig. 8-1. Single gage reference, or dummy block with gage and leads attached and gage specifications recorded.

A satisfactory waterproofing technique for the above instance might consist in applying a coating of Petrosene-A wax approximately $\frac{3}{32}$ in. thick over the strain gages and the entire piece of metal while the metal is at about 150°F. This can be accomplished before the metal cools from the final gage curing cycle when bakelite bonded gages are used. In all cases it is of the utmost importance that the metal surface be heated prior to wax application. When the metal and coating have cooled, the entire installation can be wrapped with a layer of tape to prevent the wax from chipping off during the use of the strain gages. This procedure presumes that the gages were adequately cured or dried to achieve an impedance of at least 100 megohms above ground. Before the wax is applied, the lead wires must naturally have been soldered to the strain gages. These lead wires should be secured very tightly to the metal block and so looped that no direct tension can ever be applied to the strain gage filaments through the lead wires. It is well to etch or otherwise mark the block as to the type of strain gages employed, their resistance, gage factor, and possibly their lot number, as well as the date of installation. Figure 8-1 is a photograph of a single gage reference block with the gage and leads attached and the significant data stamped on the block. After waxing and taping the block, another measurement of the resistances between the gages and ground should be made. These resistances can be checked from time to time as a measure of the effectiveness of the moistureproofing. The protective technique described here is very commonly employed where conditions are comparatively mild. Actually, the foregoing installation, if carefully performed, can be used in areas of very high humidity and even exposed to direct splash of water for limited periods of time without detrimental effects.

The class of strain gage application under discussion might also encompass most of those cases in which strain gages are employed as transducers for variables other than strain. Examples include pressure pickups, force-measuring beams, drawbars, and similar devices. For many of these it may be known in advance that the installation will never be used outside of the laboratory. For others the humidity conditions may be somewhat indeterminate as in the case of the drawbar. The Petrosene wax will be satisfactory for all these applications if conditions do not become too severe or if the ambient temperature does not go too high or too low. Petrosene wax tends to become brittle and crack when strained at temperatures of 40°F or less and melts at 175°F. Cracking of the wax may allow moisture to reach the strain gage. Another moistureproofing material in common use is Ozite-B, a bitumastic compound. Ozite-B has the advantage of remaining plastic and free from cracks down to much lower temperatures. Still another easy-to-apply and effective agent is Glyptal. Glyptal is a liquid synthetic resin which can be painted over the strain gage and surrounding metal surface. It can be either air-dried or baked. Polymerization and the accompanying resistance to moisture are more rapidly and thoroughly obtained by baking to temperatures recommended by the manufacturer. Epoxy self-polymerizing cement is also a convenient moistureproofing compound.

If conditions become slightly more severe, thicker layers of the above compounds (sources for which are given at the end of this chapter) can be applied, at least within the limits of practicability. Other techniques that have been successfully employed include protective coatings of vaseline or DC-4 silicone grease. The selection of a moistureproofing method for indoor strain gage installations is, then, largely a matter of practicality and convenience. In general, covering the strain gages and sealing them from the atmosphere with any moisture-resistant dielectric compound will suffice.

OUTDOOR INSTALLATIONS FOR SATURATION HUMIDITY AND DIRECT SPLASH

In the class of outdoor strain gage installations for which additional measures must be taken are all those applications on buildings, bridges, automobiles, locomotives, railway tracks, and similar machines and structures. Although these strain gage installations may often be subjected to very high humidity, adequate protection can sometimes be effected by merely using greater thicknesses and covering larger areas around the strain gages with the compounds already mentioned. Care should be exercised that moisture cannot seep into the gages along the lead wires, and lead wires with non-moisture-absorbing insulation should be employed. Further protection can be obtained by carefully wrapping the complete installation with an adhesive dielectric tape such as "scotch" electrical tape. An alternative method is to enclose the entire strain gage installation in a rubber boot after having coated the gage and the surrounding areas with one of the insulating and sealing compounds.

A certain amount of judgment and experience will be required to decide how extensive a moistureproofing method to employ for any particular strain gage installation. As in the previously described cases, this will depend upon the conditions surrounding the gages, upon the accuracy and stability required, and upon the length of time over which the gages must function properly. For temporary installations from which but a few strain readings are to be taken, one of the quickest and easiest techniques will be merely to coat the gage and surrounding areas well with petroleum jelly or silicone grease and tie a rubber boot around the entire installation. Where this is impossible because of the shape of the structure, a thick coating built up of several layers of Glyptal or epoxy cement may perform adequately.

STRAIN GAGES SUBMERGED IN WATER

It is occasionally necessary to measure strains on the inner surfaces of water tanks or on the outer surfaces of vessels floating in water. In some instances the water may be under very high pressure. A number of methods have been developed in attempting to protect strain gages against damage from such conditions. One of the more successful and generally applicable is that employed at the David Taylor Model Basin. An area approximately 6 in. square is cleaned in preparation for applying the strain gage and moistureproofing. The strain gage is mounted and dried or cured in the recommended manner. A patch of $\frac{1}{32}$-in.-thick rubber is then cut to about the same size as the cleaned metal surface. This patch should be pierced by the proper number of holes for taking out lead wires, the holes being made somewhat smaller in diameter than the lead wires. This situation is illustrated in Fig. 8-2. The strain gage is then coated with a protective compound such as Petrosene-A, Ozite-B, or Glyptal. After this coating has set, the rubber patch can be cemented to the metal by a band of rubber-to-metal cement about $\frac{3}{4}$ in. wide around the outside. The cement found most suitable for this application is that manufactured by the General Cement Company of Rockford, Ill. These final steps in the process of waterproofing are indicated in Figs. 8-3 and 8-4. Additional rubber-to-metal cement is built up in the form of a small fillet all around the outside of the patch; and the point where the leads come through the rubber is further reinforced with cement. This type of installation has withstood water at 700 psi for as long as 3 months and maintained a resistance to ground in excess of 500 megohms. This constitutes excellent waterproofing under what are admittedly rather extreme conditions.

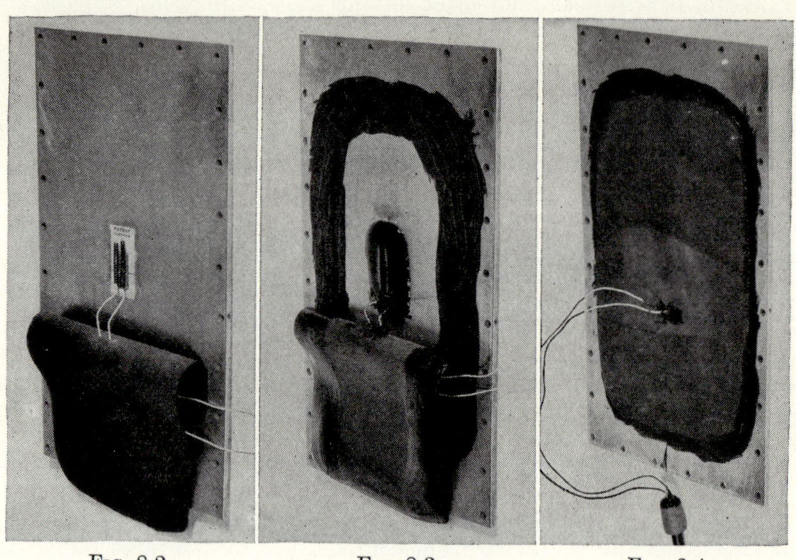

Fig. 8-2 Fig. 8-3 Fig. 8-4

Fig. 8-2. Strain gage applied and ready for installation of protective covering. (*Courtesy of David Taylor Model Basin, United States Navy.*)

Fig. 8-3. Waterproofed strain gage with protective covering partially in place. (*Courtesy of David Taylor Model Basin, United States Navy.*)

Fig. 8-4. Completed installation of a waterproof strain gage. (*Courtesy of David Taylor Model Basin, United States Navy.*)

For still more severe conditions, Dean, of the David Taylor Model Basin, has developed the method described below. This approach to protecting strain gages consists of a multilayer treatment, including wax, synthetic rubber, stainless-steel shim stock, and more rubber. It was developed for use on the propeller struts of ships and for similar applications involving abrasion and erosion in addition to submersion. The complete installation instructions are given here.

> For gages mounted on carbon steel, stainless steel, or S-T types of aluminum, carefully clean the gaging area to ensure that all the surfaces to be waterproofed are free from grease, oil, and fingerprints. Using absorbent cotton dampened with acetone, swab around the gage and up and down the lead

wires until a fresh piece of cotton shows no discoloration. For paper-base gages, apply a wax buffer precoat of Zophar C-276 or Di Jell 171[1] over each gage. This prevents direct contact of the 3-M[2] compounds with gages. Bakelite gages ordinarily do not require this precoat. If 3-M, EC-864 synthetic rubber is to be used as the principal coating, a single thin coating of a 3-M metal primer should be applied next. No primer is needed for the number EC-801 synthetic rubber as it contains added bonding resins. EC-853 primer thinned 50 per cent with methyl isobutyl keytone may be used for all steels, including stainless, and for S-T types of aluminum. Brush the primer over the area of freshly cleaned metal around the gage. The primer may not be applied over the wax buffer coating nor over bakelite gages, but should cover all adjacent bare metal surfaces thoroughly. Allow the primer to dry for at least 1 hour at room temperature or longer if humidity is high. Mild heat up to 130°F will speed the drying. No adverse effects have been noted if the primer is allowed to dry for an extended time period prior to the application of 3-M compound provided the installation has been kept free of oils, fingerprints, dust, etc. Clean the plastic insulation on connecting wires with acetone and coat thinly with EC-1217 thinned 50 per cent with methyl isobutyl keytone. Clean rubber insulation with acetone and naphtha solvent and then coat thinly with EC-853. Primer-application brushes should be washed out with acetone. A partial coating of either EC-864 or EC-801 mixed with EC-807 accelerator is applied next. Mix 10 parts by weight of the base to 1 part of the accelerator in absolutely clean mixing vessels and do all mixing thoroughly. If the accelerator has settled out in storage, stir or shake jar vigorously until any top fluid is completely blended. EC-864 may be mixed in clean cans or bowls. EC-801 requires more thorough mixing on a flat surface such as a slab of safety glass. Stir and fold in the accelerator with a stiff spatula. Do not permit the accelerator to dry out around the edges and flake into the fresh mix. Do not mix more material than can be used in the next 30 min. EC-864 and EC-801 are available in 1-pt cans, and the proper bonding accelerator is furnished in separate glass jars. Apply the mixed compound over the gage area with a putty knife or spatula to the desired thickness. A cap of stainless-steel shim stock 0.002 in. thick is rolled on and pressed down into the fresh 3-M waterproofing compound, and then the coating of synthetic rubber is applied over the entire placement. When using EC-864, the stainless-steel shim cap requires a primer such as EC-853.

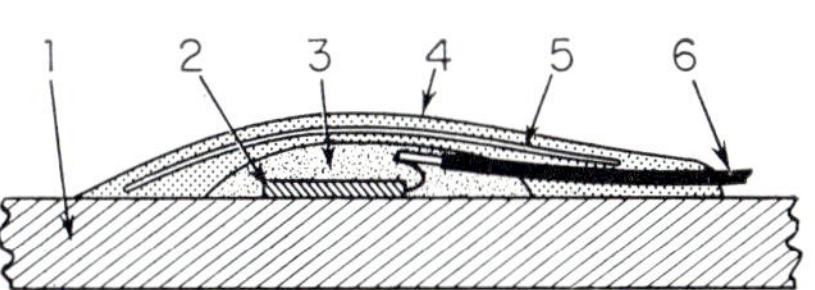

FIG. 8-5. The Dean shim-cap method of waterproofing strain gages: (1) metal specimen under test; (2) mounted strain gage; (3) soft wax, Di Jell 171 or Zophar Mills wax C-276; (4) self-vulcanized rubber cover; (5) stainless-steel shim cap 0.002 in. thick; (6) connecting cable.

[1] L. Sonneborn & Sons, Inc., Building Products Division, New York 16.

[2] Minnesota Mining & Manufacturing Company, Detroit, Mich.

With the use of EC-801, however, no primer coat is required for the stainless-steel shim stock. The total thickness of the build-up over the gage will be approximately ⅛ in. After the 3-M compound has cured, apply several coats of Herecrol RC-9 primer as a surface sealer. This is quick-drying, and may be applied with a brush. A cross section of a completed water-proofing installation is shown in Fig. 8-5. This type of protection has worked satisfactorily at the David Taylor Model Basin for gages subjected to extremely severe conditions of submersion, erosion, and long-time applications.

EFFECTS OF HYDROSTATIC PRESSURE

It will be noted that the strain gages in Figs. 8-2 to 8-4 were not protected from the effects of water pressure as transmitted through the rubber. The possible effects of hydrostatic pressure on the operation of the strain gage should be considered. For one thing, if the surface to which the strain gage is bonded is characterized by lack of flatness, having holes, pits, or depressions, the gage wire will by hydrostatically pressed down into these. As a result, strain gage operation at low pressures may be quite erratic and nonlinear. At a pressure high enough so that the gage wire assumes the contour of the supporting metal, the gage may perform normally again if it has not failed in reaching such a pressure. When the surface where the strain gage is to be mounted is not flat, it will be found advantageous to smooth-grind or scrape this area before applying the gage.

A second possibility is that the hydrostatic pressure will by itself cause a strain in the filament of the strain gage which might be superimposed upon the strain in the metal surface on which the gage is bonded. When the strain-sensitive wire is surrounded by cement, backing material, and moistureproofing compound, this effect is a little obscure. Tests were conducted at the University of Illinois to determine the effect of high hydrostatic pressures on ¼-in. bakelite strain gages. The tests were accomplished by bonding three bakelite gages to a metal coupon, which was then placed in a pressure chamber filled with oil. No protective coating was used over the gages. A dummy gage was mounted on a similar coupon and placed alongside the pressure chamber in the open. In testing to pressures as high as 25,000 psi, it was found that the effect of pressure on the strain gages themselves (independent of the strain on the pressurized coupon) was 2 to 5 micro-inches per in. of indicated compressive strain per 1,000 psi. The pressure effect can therefore be considered negligible for this type of strain gage.

One precaution to be observed is in the mounting and placement of a dummy gage in connection with such an installation. If the dummy gage is mounted on a block of material which is exposed to the same hydrostatic pressure as the active gage, an entirely different strain pattern will generally exist in the dummy-gage block than in the material to which the active gage is attached. An appreciable error will be introduced into the readings obtained unless a correction for this effect is made. The recommended practice is to employ a temperature-compensated active gage. The dummy gage, whether used for bridge completion or for temperature compensation as well, should not be subjected to hydrostatic pressure if this can be avoided.

STRAIN GAGE INSTALLATION SUBMERGED IN MEDIUMS OTHER THAN WATER

Strain gage applications in reinforced concrete structures have become relatively commonplace. The gages are ordinarily bonded to the reinforcing rods before the concrete is poured. Lead wires can be run to some remote point where it is convenient to read or record the strains. Such strain gage installations have been employed to study the stress in buildings and other concrete structures due to service loads. This same technique is also utilized to observe the dimensional changes which concrete undergoes as it ages after setting.

Since it is a little difficult to replace any malfunctioning strain gages once the concrete has set, the necessity for making sound gage installations is quite evident. The gages must be protected not only from the effects of moisture but also from mechanical damage due to pouring the concrete. The following is a description of the method which is used at the Wayne State University Engineering Mechanics Department, where a number of such installations have been made. The particular technique to be described here is not, of course, the only one that can be used. This example is meant to indicate the degree of protection that has been found necessary for satisfactory strain gage operation under these conditions.

The reinforcing rods to be instrumented are first brought into the laboratory for application of the strain gages. The surface areas where gages are to be located are prepared by grinding, filing, and sanding. These operations are used to remove the scale and rust and develop a surface of approximately the correct degree of smoothness for best bonding. The surfaces are then cleaned thoroughly with a volatile solvent and bakelite gages cemented in place. Next, lead wires are securely tied to the rods, after which they are soldered to the strain gages as indicated in Fig. 8-6*A*. Generous loops are placed in the lead wires before binding so that external forces can never be transmitted to the strain gage filaments. The lead wires, incidentally, should have rubber or other moistureproof insulation for satisfactory operation. The entire section of the reinforcing rod in the vicinity of the strain gages is then heated and coated with a layer of Petrosene-A wax approximately $\frac{3}{16}$ in. thick, as shown in Fig. 8-6*B*. Finally, the waxed area is wrapped well with rubber tape. The completed installation is shown in Fig. 8-6*C*. Throughout this procedure, occasional checks of the resistance to ground should be made. As indicated earlier, a minimum of 100 megohms is desirable, and 1,000 megohms can be obtained by thorough curing of the strain gages. Other investigators have built Plexiglas shields over the strain gages, protecting them from moisture and from the pressure of the shrinking concrete. The exact effect of pressure from the concrete on

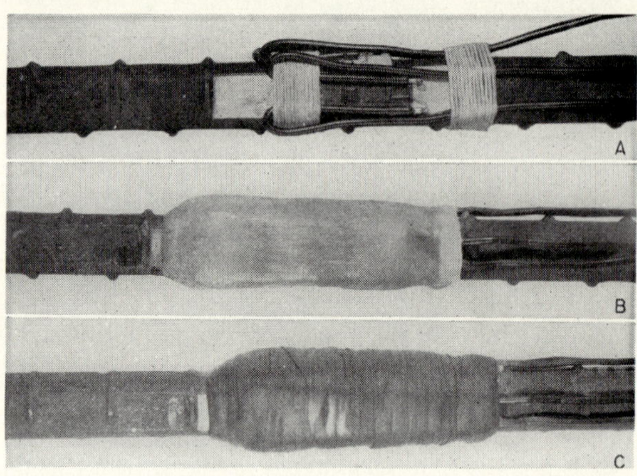

Fig. 8-6. Instrumentation of concrete reinforcing rod with strain gages: (*A*) gages and leads applied and leads securely bound in place; (*B*) successive layers of Petrosene-A wax applied to build up a protective coating; (*C*) completed installation after wrapping with tape. (*Courtesy of Wayne State University.*)

the operation of the gages is somewhat indeterminate but can apparently be minimized by mounting the temperature-compensating gages so that they are subjected to the same pressure. This can be accomplished by bonding the compensating gages to the same rods in the immediate vicinity of the active gages. The compensating gages must in this case be mounted with their axes transverse to the rod axes in the Poisson arrangement described in an earlier chapter.

A different technique which has been used to eliminate the effect of concrete pressure involves splitting the reinforcing rods. The rods are split longitudinally and enough metal removed locally from the mating surfaces to leave room for strain gages. After the gages have been properly bonded in place, the rods are reassembled and welded, completely covering the gages. This procedure has the advantage of retaining the full bonding area between the rod and the concrete.

OPERATION IN ENGINE OIL

Oils are generally nonconductors. Based on the dielectric properties of oils, some attempts have been made to waterproof strain gages by enclosing them in a bath of transformer oil. This technique has never been too successful because of the difficulties involved in containing the oil over long periods of time. It may occasionally be necessary, however, to make strain measurements on surfaces either submerged in lubricating oil or subject to the vapors and splash of the oil. Examples which come to mind include strain measurements on gears, shafting, crankcases, transmission cases, and crankshafts. Bakelite cement, when polymerized, is highly resistant to oils. The usual practice, therefore, is to employ bakelite gages for such applications. After the gages have been mounted and cured, it is customary to apply an additional layer of bakelite cement over the entire gage area and bake again. Gages applied by this procedure have been used with considerable success over long periods of time when subjected to hot oil.

SPECIALIZED TECHNIQUES

In addition to the methods already described, there are numerous other techniques for minimizing the environmental effects on strain gages. As an example, it will sometimes be necessary to make strain gage installations on concrete or other porous surfaces which might allow moisture to reach the underside of the gages. For such cases, a piece of thin aluminum foil or similar material should be cemented to the porous surface prior to applying the strain gage. The gage and additional moistureproofing can then be applied on top of this moisture barrier in the manner described in this chapter. Another approach is to completely encase the gage in metal foil as described in Chap. 12.

A novel technique which has been applied in outdoor strain gage installations is the use of a premolded rubber cover cemented over the gage area. The latter device allows for considerable elaboration if desired. As an example, the lead wires can also be premolded into the rubber, thus eliminating the possibility of leakage at the points where the lead wires pass through the sealing barrier. A further refinement is the inclusion of silica gel or other moisture-absorbing agent within the rubber-covered gage area to give an additional factor of safety and to remove the last vestiges of moisture once the gage is sealed.

In general, there is a wide enough choice of commercially available nonhygroscopic dielectric compounds so that strain gages can be amply protected from moisture under almost any conceivable conditions.

TABLE 8-1. AUXILIARY MATERIALS USEFUL IN MOUNTING AND MOISTUREPROOFING STRAIN GAGES

Name	Supplier*	Use
Bakelite varnish B-51	Union Carbide Plastics Company, Division of Union Carbon and Carbide Corporation, Bound Brook, N.J.	Simple protective coating for gages not exposed to severe moisture or erosion
DC-4 silicone grease	Dow Corning Company, Midland, Mich.	First coating of a multilayer built-up protection
Glyptal varnish	General Electric Company, Schenectady, N.Y.	Simple protective coating for gages not exposed to severe moisture or erosion
Petrosene-A wax	General Petroleum Company, San Francisco, Calif.	First coating of a multilayer built-up protection
Ozite-B bitumastic compound	G and W Electric Specialty Co., Chicago, Ill.	First coating of a multilayer built-up protection
Di Jell 171 wax	L. Sonneborn Sons, Inc., Building Products Division, New York	First coating of a multilayer built-up protection
Zophar C-276 wax	Zophar Mills, Inc., Brooklyn, N.Y.	First coating of a multilayer built-up protection
Rubber-to-metal cement	General Cement Company, Rockford, Ill.	Used to cement a protective rubber shield over gage installation
EC-864 synthetic rubber EC-801 synthetic rubber	Minnesota Mining and Mfg. Co., Detroit, Mich.	For coating over Di Jell, Petrosene-A wax, etc.
EC-807 accelerator	Minnesota Mining and Mfg. Co., Detroit, Mich.	To be mixed with synthetic rubber
EC-853 metal primer	Minnesota Mining and Mfg. Co., Detroit, Mich.	Used to prepare metal for adhesion of synthetic rubber
Herecrol RD-9 primer	Heresite and Chemical Co., Manitowoc, Wis.	For coating and sealing synthetic-rubber installation
Adhesive cellophane and electrical tape	Minnesota Mining and Mfg. Co., Detroit, Mich.	For insulation and mounting gage leads
Thiokol EC 755	Minnesota Mining and Mfg. Co., Detroit, Mich.	Used as a protective waterproof coating
Ten X sealing compound	Electro Cote Company, St. Paul, Minn.	Used as a protective waterproof coating
SR-4 cement precoat	Baldwin-Lima-Hamilton Corp., Waltham, Mass.	Applied as undercoat before cementing paper gage in place
Metal Prep No. 10	Nielson Chemical Co., Detroit, Mich.	Used as a metal-surface conditioner before cementing gage in place
NBS No. L-6AC ceramic precoat	O. Hommel Co., Pittsburgh, Pa. (designated No. 3E-2334)	Used to precoat surfaces for bakelite gage application to temperatures of 500°F. Must be fired at 1750°F

* A general source for a variety of adhesives and moistureproofing compounds will frequently be your local distributor of radio and electronic components. W. T. Bean (19556 Bretton Drive, Detroit, Mich.) supplies a complete kit of materials used in the application and moistureproofing of strain gages.

BIBLIOGRAPHY

Adams, L. H., R. W. Goranson, and R. E. Gibson: Construction and Properties of the Manganin Resistance Pressure Gauge, *Rev. Sci. Instr.*, vol. 8, pp. 230–235, July, 1937.

Anderson, A. R.: How to Use Strain Gages in Concrete, *Eng. News-Record*, vol. 146, no. 10, pp. 46–47, Mar. 8, 1951.

Barker, R. S., and J. B. Murtland: Protection of Underwater SR-4 Strain-gage Installations on Tunnel Liner of a Hydroelectric Development, *Proc. SESA*, vol. 14, no. 2, p. 131, 1957.

Beyer, F. R.: Stresses in Reinforced Concrete Due to Volume Change, *J. Am. Concrete Inst.*, vol. 20, no. 10, pp. 713–722, June, 1949.

Boodberg, A., E. D. Howe, and B. York: Stability of SR-4 Electric Strain Gages and Methods for Their Waterproofing and Protection in Field Service, *Trans. ASME*, vol. 70, no. 8, pp. 915–920, November, 1948.

Campbell, W. R.: Errors in Indicated Strain for a Typical Wire Strain Gage Caused by Prestraining, Temperature Changes, and Weathering, *NACA, Tech. Note* 1011, April, 1946.

Clough, W. R., M. E. Shank, and M. Zaid: The Behavior of SR-4 Wire Resistance Strain Gages on Certain Materials in the Presence of Hydrostatic Pressure, *Proc. SESA*, vol. 10, no. 2, p. 167, 1953.

Dean, M. III: Strain Gage Waterproofing Methods and Installation of Gages on Propeller Strut of USS Saratoga, *Proc. SESA*, vol. 16, no. 1, p. 137, 1958.

Dean, M. III: Techniques for Protecting and Waterproofing Resistance Wire Strain Gages, *David Taylor Model Basin, Rept.* 797, October, 1957.

Guerard, J. P., and G. F. Weissman: Effect of Hydrostatic Pressure on SR-4 Strain Gages, *Proc. SESA*, vol. 16, no. 1, p. 151, 1958.

Hognestad, E., and I. M. Viest: Some Applications of Electric SR-4 Gages in Reinforced Concrete Research, *J. Am. Concrete Inst.*, vol. 21, no. 6, pp. 445–454, February, 1950.

MacNair, C. S.: Use of Electronic Gages to Determine the Fatigue Point in Corrugated Containers, *Tappi*, vol. 36, suppl. 138A–142A, January, 1953.

Majors, H., Jr.: Influence of Fluid Pressure on SR-4 Strain Gages, *Proc. SESA*, vol. 13, no. 1, p. 13, 1955.

McHenry, D.: Rubber Housing for Waterproofing Bonded Wire Strain Gage, *ASTM Bull.* 133, pp. 18–19, March, 1945.

Moncher, F. L., H. R. Lissner, and C. H. Lipson: Long-time Electric Strain Gage Measurements on Concrete Reinforcing Rods at the Packard Proving Grounds Test Track, *Proc. SESA*, vol. 6, no. 1, pp. 29–34, 1948.

Morris, R. E., and R. R. James: Method for Waterproofing Bonded Electrical-resistance Strain Gages, *J. Am. Soc. Naval Engrs.*, vol. 69, no. 3, pp. 527–530, August, 1957.

Palermo, P. M.: Methods of Waterproofing SR-4 Strain Gages, *Proc. SESA*, vol. 13, no. 2, p. 79, 1955.

Sherlock, R. H., and A. Belgin: Protection of Electric Strain Gages in Concrete, *J. Am. Concrete Inst.*, vol. 19, no. 3, pp. 189–192, November, 1947.

Tannahill, A. L.: Application of Electrical Resistance Strain Gages, *Engineer*, vol. 187, pp. 630–633, June 10, 1949.

Thompson, J. N.: Techniques Used in the Experimental Stress Analysis of Reinforced Concrete Structures, *Proc. SESA*, vol. 8, no. 2, pp. 111–116, 1951.

Todd, J. D.: Waterproofing Electrical Resistance Strain Gages, *Engineering,* vol. 171, no. 4434, p. 67, Jan. 19, 1951.

Wells, F. E.: A Rapid Method of Waterproofing Bonded Wire Strain Gages, *Proc. SESA,* vol. 15, no. 2, p. 107, 1958.

Wenk, E., Jr., and T. D. Tuft: Letter to the Editor, *Proc. SESA,* vol. 8, no. 1, pp. 14–16, 1950.

Zick, L. P., and C. E. Carlson: Strain Gage Survey around the Supports of a Hortonsphere, *Proc. SESA,* vol. 6, no. 2, pp. 41–52, 1949.

Zick, L. P., and C. E. Carlson: Strain Gage Technique Employed in Studying Propane Tank Stresses under Service Conditions, *Steel,* vol. 122, no. 15, pp. 86–88, Apr. 12, 1948.

Installation of Strain Gages on Pressure Vessels, *Product Eng.,* vol. 20, no. 12, pp. 143–144, December, 1949.

EXERCISES

8-1. Apply a strain gage to a metal specimen with Duco or nitrocellulose cement. After curing the cement and connecting lead wires, suspend the specimen in a container of water in such a fashion that the lead wires are not immersed. Check periodically the resistance between gage and ground, and the gage resistance itself, to determine the effect that moisture has on the ability of the gage to perform satisfactorily.

8-2. Cement a strain gage to a steel specimen with Duco or nitrocellulose cement. After connecting lead wires and after the cement has cured properly, apply a uniform coating of Petrosene-A wax about ⅛ in. thick over the installation. Submerge the specimen in water as in Exercise 1. Test for resistance to ground and element resistance as a function of time to evaluate the waterproofing performance.

8-3. Mount single strain gages on each of three identical metal coupons. After proper curing, waterproof one of the gages thoroughly by covering it with Petrosene-A wax. Using one of the unwaterproofed gages as a dummy, successively connect the other two gages to a static strain indicator and record the balance reading. Immerse the waterproofed and unwaterproofed gage installations in a beaker of water. Reconnect to the static strain indicator and take new readings. Leave the gages in the water and record indicator readings at intervals. Add table salt to the water and repeat the measurements.

8-4. Describe in detail the technique you would use to waterproof a strain gage mounted on the frame of an automobile that was to be used in routine fashion for a period of 6 months. The gage is to be active at various times during this period.

8-5. Develop and test a coating or other protective covering intended to preserve the operating characteristics of a strain gage when submerged in mercury (or gasoline, strong acid, hot oil, paint, etc.).

8-6. Describe the protective procedure required for a strain gage mounted on the outside of a missile designed to reach the moon. State the elements against which protection is desired and your proposed method for meeting the problem in each case.

8-7. A strain gage is to be used inside a container, where it will be subjected to a pressure of 80,000 psi normal to the surface. The problem is to devise a system of compensation for the gage for temperature variations. Describe the temperature-compensation system you would use and estimate the error in gage reading which might result from the pressure applied to the gage wire.

9 LONG-TIME STRAIN GAGE INSTALLATIONS

It is not uncommon to require of strain gages that they produce an accurate, stable indication of strain over an extended period of time. In extreme cases, this may run into many months or even several years. Wherever a small, compact, shock-resistant, remote-indicating strain transducer is required, the bonded resistance strain gage is likely to be the best answer. Examples of long-time strain gage installations include their use on the reinforcing rods in concrete buildings and highways, on bridges and similar structures, and in various strain gage actuated instruments and control devices. All these cases require stable, accurate, and dependable performance of the strain gages and of their associated instruments. If a bonded strain gage is to be employed successfully under these circumstances, it will be necessary to take a number of precautionary measures in the selection, bonding, and protection of the gage. Likewise it is of equal importance that the instruments to be used with the strain gage have characteristics which are unaffected by time, temperature, and humidity. Any apparent instability in static strain measurement can be caused either by the strain gage itself or by almost any portion of the electrical measuring system, such as the Wheatstone bridge, amplifier, indicator, or lead wires.

ZERO DRIFT

The usual indication of instability of either the gage or the measuring system is a shift of the null-balance point. Zero drift is the term commonly used to describe this phenomenon and includes any bridge unbalance which occurs with time and which is due to factors other than strain. For instance, if two strain gages were cemented to a piece of unstrained metal and the bridge balanced under this condition, the galvanometer needle should remain pointing at zero indefinitely. Or if, upon balancing the bridge, the setting of the balancing control were noted, it should be possible to return some time later and have the galvanometer reading be zero when the balancing control was reset to the noted position. Failure to act in the above manner is described as zero drift.

The following factors can cause zero drift:

1. Incomplete temperature compensation of the active strain gage.
2. Instability of the Wheatstone bridge, power supply, or amplifier.
3. Improperly bonded strain gages.
4. Creep of one or more strain gages.
5. Insufficient protection from humidity, or reduction in the impedance between the gage filament or lead wires and ground.
6. Variations in the impedance of the lead wires.

There are two basic types of long-time strain gage installations. In one type it is necessary to obtain a continuous record based on an initial zero reference point. This category would include static strain measurements on buildings or other structures which, once loaded, cannot be unloaded to check the zero point. In the second class of long-time strain gage installations it is unnecessary to base all strain measurements on an initial zero. This is true for any application in which the load can be removed from time to time. When strain gages are used on drawbars or on other force-measuring instruments, the zero can be checked before every test. Even though the gages may be used occasionally over a great period of time, the stability requirements apply only for the periods of actual use.

TEMPERATURE COMPENSATION

Techniques for temperature compensation by employing a second strain gage in an adjacent leg of the Wheatstone-bridge circuit have already been described at some length in Chap. 4. Merely employing an extra, or dummy, gage and connecting it into the bridge in the prescribed manner, however, is not enough to ensure complete temperature compensation. Full temperature compensation requires that both strain gages, the active and dummy, be attached to the same structure, being located as nearly adjacent as possible. Even this precaution will not suffice if the two strain gages do not have nearly identical thermal coefficients of expansion and resistance change and the same gage factor. Whenever available, self-temperature-compensating strain gages should be employed for both the active and dummy gages. Absolutely perfect temperature compensation is probably never accomplished; but satisfactory results can be achieved if the above conditions are rigorously maintained.

The simplest way to obtain strain gages having very nearly the same thermal and electrical properties is to employ two gages taken from the same lot as received from the manufacturer. This process is not a positive guarantee of identical properties in two or more strain gages, because occasionally there will be variations. The strain gage manufacturer attempts to have all gages in a given lot as uniform as possible with respect to the above characteristics. This is accomplished by employing wire lengths taken from the same spool, foil from the same sheet, cement from the same batch, standardized gage construction methods, and similar techniques. In addition, the manufacturer has a statistical quality-control system by which gages are spot-checked after assembly. Every gage is not checked for gage factor, of course, since this involves cementing the gage to a calibrating surface and destroys its utility for further strain measurement. All gages are checked for resistance, and about every fiftieth gage (depending somewhat upon the type) is set aside for complete testing and examination.

In order to make certain that both active and dummy strain gages are subjected to the same temperatures, they should be mounted as closely as possible together on the structure or structural component being tested. It should also be made certain that there are no temperature gradients in the test piece which could affect the strain gages differently. A further stabilizing influence can be brought about by shielding the gages from stray drafts. As an example of the sensitivity of strain gages to such conditions, it is possible to throw the bridge out of balance by merely holding one's hand cupped over either the active or the dummy strain gage for a few moments. This apparent strain is due to the radiated heat from the hand.

The importance of proper temperature compensation is emphasized by the peculiar results obtained in a series of laboratory static strain tests. The strain readings were taken periodically for a number of days. Occasionally the bridge would indicate considerable zero drift, but at other times the zero would be correct again. This was quite different from the usual type of zero drift due to battery decay (see Fig. 9-1). The cause of the erratic drift in the above tests, it was found, was that at a certain time of the day a beam of sunlight came in through the laboratory window and impinged upon one of the two gages which formed adjacent legs in a Wheatstone bridge. Whenever the testing time coincided with this occurrence, there was an indicated zero drift. When tests were made at other times, with the sunlight excluded or on cloudy days, the bridge acted normally and was characterized by a reasonably stable zero strain reference point. Cool or warm drafts over unshielded strain gages can cause very similar results.

The order of magnitude of the temperature effect can be readily calculated. If the thermal coefficient of resistance of Advance wire is taken as 1×10^{-6} ohm per ohm per deg F, then a temperature change of 20°

would cause a false strain indication of approximately 10 micro-inches per in. The material to which the gage is bonded can alter this magnitude if its thermal expansion differs from that of the wire, as will usually be the case.

WHEATSTONE-BRIDGE INSTABILITY

It was shown earlier that the Wheatstone bridge is balanced when R_1/R_4 equals R_2/R_3. It was also shown that this condition is independent of the voltage supplying the bridge. Thus, one might be led to presume that a Wheatstone bridge once balanced would remain so indefinitely if the active and dummy strain gages were fully compensated for temperature changes, and if these gages were not mechanically strained. In a Wheatstone-bridge circuit supplied by direct current this is very nearly true. To maintain balance, however, all four resistors in the circuit must constantly respond to temperature changes so that R_1/R_4 equals R_2/R_3. From this it should be evident that the resistors comprising the internal portion of the bridge circuit can be responsible for undesired bridge unbalance (zero drift) just as the strain gages themselves. It may well happen that although extreme precautions are taken to ensure full temperature compensation of the active and dummy strain gages, the Wheatstone bridge will be unbalanced by changes in one of the internal legs. The resistors making up the internal legs of the bridge circuit should have the same thermal coefficients of resistance and should be subjected to the same temperatures. In other words, the ratio R_2/R_3 should remain constant for any given setting of the bridge balancing control. If all four resistances are such that with no applied strain R_1/R_4 always equals R_2/R_3, then the bridge will theoretically remain balanced regardless of any decay in battery voltage.

STRAIN-INDICATOR INSTABILITY

Most portable strain indicators employ batteries to supply the necessary power for operating the instrument. In several of these an audio-frequency oscillator is then used to change the direct current into alternating current for powering the bridge circuit proper. These instruments are sometimes characterized by instability as the batteries decay, resulting in a more or less continual drift of the zero. The curve in Fig. 9-1 is a plot of the zero drift of such an indicator as the batteries decayed. From noting the effect of replacing the batteries with fresh ones it is apparent that the batteries were not exactly new at the beginning of the test. These test results are quite interesting in the light of our previous calculations, by which we so rigorously showed that bridge balance should be independent of the supply voltage. This, however, is the fault of neither our calculations nor the Wheatstone-bridge circuit. The drift is caused by circuit frailties in the indicating instrument itself.

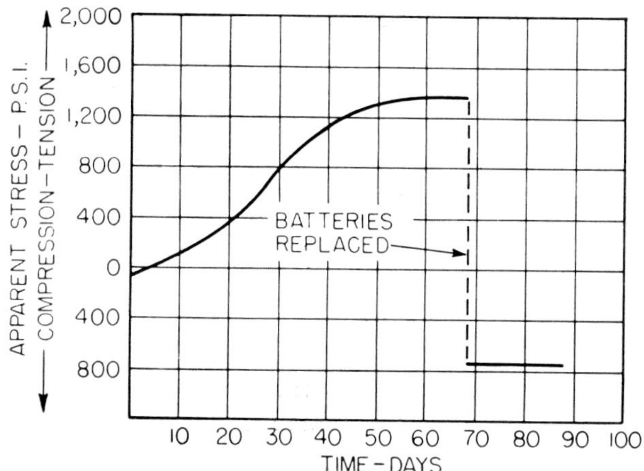

Fig. 9-1. Measured drift of a commercial portable strain indicator over a 2-month period. Note the effect of replacing the batteries. (*Beyer.*)

The block diagram of a typical static strain indicator is shown in Fig. 9-2. The oscillator, amplifier, and phase-sensitive detector can all contribute toward the tendency for zero drift. The over-all arrangement of the indicator is such that the null meter can actually indicate balance, even though the Wheatstone-bridge circuit is unbalanced. This can be

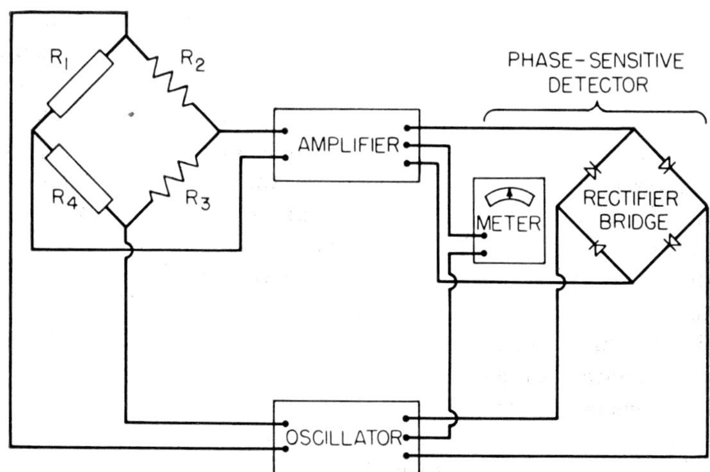

Fig. 9-2. Functional block diagram of a typical portable strain indicator.

easily demonstrated by balancing the null meter to a zero reading under any given strain conditions and observing the waveform at the amplifier output with an oscilloscope. If the carrier frequency appears on the oscilloscope screen, this must represent some unbalance signal fed to the amplifier from the Wheatstone-bridge circuit. Under these conditions, the equations for the balanced bridge are naturally not applicable. This initial unbalance, combined with the fact that the oscillator voltage and frequency, as well as the amplifier gain, are functions of battery voltage, gives the instrument a tendency toward zero drift with battery decay.

CEMENT INSTABILITY

Many different cements have been employed in bonding strain gages to test surfaces. These range from cellulose (Duco), through a variety of epoxy formulations, to the phenol resins and, more recently, to acrylate cements. All the adhesives demonstrate different stability characteristics, and the stability of any particular adhesive is strongly dependent upon the temperature at which it is used. Maximum recommended operating temperatures for static strain measurement with specific gage types and adhesives are supplied by the manufacturers. For optimum stability, the temperature should be kept well below the upper limit indicated by the manufacturer. Cement stability is also affected by the thickness of the adhesive layer and by the type and size of strain gage. In addition, the moisture-absorbing tendency, or hygroscopicity, of the cement is an important factor. Absorption of moisture by the cement not only produces volume changes and resultant strains, but may reduce the impedance to ground as well. Both effects are deleterious to stability.

The choice of cement for a specific task is often the result of a compromise between the ease, convenience, and speed of room-temperature-curing adhesives and the generally greater stability of the heat-cured adhesives such as bakelite cement. For indoor room-temperature operating conditions, Duco, cyanoacrylate, or one of the room-temperature-curing epoxy cements would ordinarily be adequate—even for long-time installations—if the selected cement is properly mixed and cured, and if the strain gages are protected from the atmosphere by a coating of wax or some other moistureproofing agent. Even the latter step may be superfluous for many installations. Unprotected strain gages, some bonded with Duco cement and others with cyanoacrylate, have been used for several months in the laboratory without significant zero drift or other manifestations of instability.

As either operating conditions or stability requirements become more severe, it may be necessary to employ a glass-fiber-filled epoxy cement or bakelite cement. For the ultimate in stability, bakelite gages bonded with bakelite cement can be highly recommended. These too should be moistureproofed for best performance.

It is vital to the performance of any strain gage installation that the adhesive be thoroughly cured before the gage is used. Following the manufacturer's curing procedure is the best start toward achieving a properly cured installation, but this still does not give positive assurance that the cement is fully cured. McWhirter and Duggin, for example, found that paper-base gages, bonded with cellulose cement and cured at 140°F until the impedance to ground was in excess of 10,000 megohms (a considerably longer cure than recommended by the manufacturer), exhibited very little drift after 60 days at a strain of 2,900 micro-inches per in. Under optimum conditions drifts of 1 per cent or less can be achieved with paper gages and cellulose cement.

Most adhesives demonstrate increasing dielectric qualities as the cure progresses. Occasional measurements of impedance to ground can thus be used to monitor the curing process. For maximum stability the impedance to ground should exceed at least 1,000 megohms, and preferably 10,000 megohms.

It has been observed that a thin "glue line," or adhesive layer, is conducive to improved stability. The type and size of strain gage are also known to influence stability. Generally, the long gages are more stable, and flat-grid gages are noticeably better than those having wrap-around construction. Other things being equal, foil gages are potentially superior to the best of the wire gages in terms of stability.

CREEP DUE TO CEMENT INSTABILITY

Gage creep is the term used to describe slip of the strain gage relative to the surface on which it is bonded. As an example, at the time of initial load application, a bar of steel and the strain gage cemented to its surface will ordinarily undergo equal strains. If the bar is loaded for a considerable length of time, however, the strain gage may relax somewhat and indicate a correspondingly reduced strain (Fig. 9-3). This is gage creep and, of course, is hardly conducive to accuracy in the strain data obtained. The creep may be due to slip, softening, or yielding of the cement employed in either the manufacture or the bonding of the strain gage. Cellulose materials are

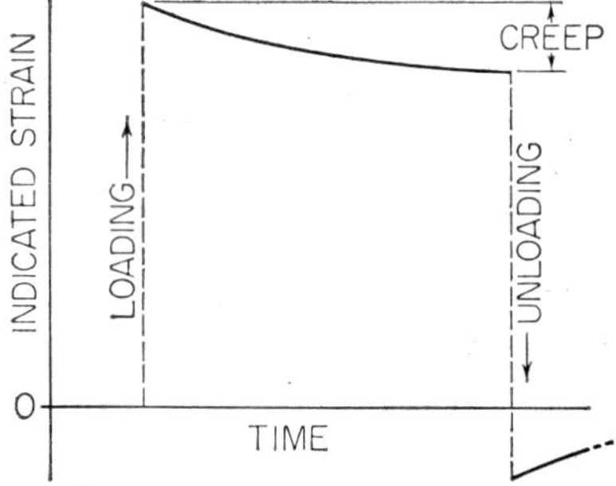

FIG. 9-3. Characteristic manifestation of creep in strain gages.

generally incapable of withstanding a sustained load without exhibiting a considerable amount of creep, as is the case with most thermoplastic compounds. Bakelite strain gages, because of their thermosetting nature, are generally much less susceptible to creep than paper- or epoxy-backed gages.

The exact mechanism of strain gage creep has yet to be determined, but enough information has been accumulated so that creep can be minimized. For least creep it is advisable to use bakelite strain gages of no smaller gage length than absolutely necessary. There is also the possibility of gaining temporary stability by thermal or elastic cyclic prestraining. Goodman, Campbell, and other investigators have detected creep in both paper and bakelite strain gages. In these tests the bakelite gages generally demonstrated slightly less creep than paper gages. Goodman found that cycling the strain gages to their maximum operating temperatures from six to eight times improves their thermal stability. This improvement is lost, however, if the gages are left at a lower temperature for any length of time. Campbell discovered a similar phenomenon in cyclic loading of strain gages. Gage stability is improved by cycling the gage to its maximum load several times. This stability is likewise lost if the gage is left without load for a few days or if the sign of the load is reversed.

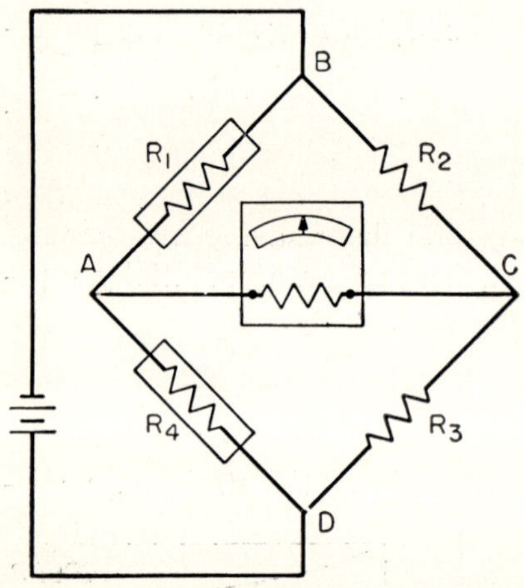

Fig. 9-4. Wheatstone-bridge circuit. By reversing the electrical positions of strain gages R_1 and R_4, the apparent sign of strain can be reversed.

DETECTION OF ZERO DRIFT

Perfect stability of the strain gage system would imply that if a strain analyst were to mount active and dummy strain gages on some structure for a long-time test, he could balance the bridge under conditions of zero strain (or stress), take a reading on the reference dial of the bridge, and turn off the bridge to return some time later when the structure is loaded, rebalance the bridge and accept any difference between the initial and final reference dial readings as significant strain. This statement is based upon the premise that the zero-strain reference point has not shifted or drifted. The principal difficulty in this technique is that the structure being tested may well be such that once loaded there is no means of unloading it so that the zero-strain reference point can be rechecked.

Thus, the strain analyst has no positive means of determining whether changes in the Wheatstone-bridge balance point are due to strain or to zero drift. Regardless of how certain he may be that there was no zero drift and that what he was measuring was really strain, he should make some check on the validity and accuracy of his data.

There is one technique by which zero drift of the instrument section of a strain-measurement system (that is, everything except the gages and leads) can be determined with reasonable certainty. Reexamining the Wheatstone-bridge circuit (Fig. 9-4), if strain gage R_1 is being strained in tension, its resistance will increase and the voltage at point A will drop slightly with respect to that at point C. Therefore, when the voltage at C is greater, one can interpret the sign of the strain as tensile and, when that at A is greater, as compressive. The sign of the strain can be correlated with the direction of displacement of the galvanometer needle or with the direction in which it is necessary to move the balanc-

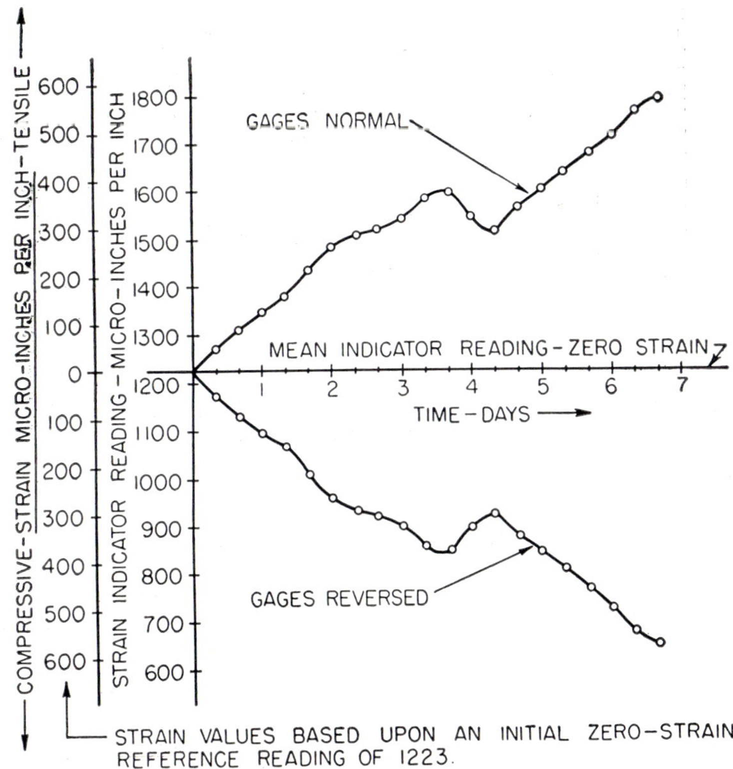

FIG. 9-5. Plot of hypothetical strain readings illustrating the technique of determining zero drift by electrically reversing active and dummy gages. For the case shown there was no zero drift.

ing control to rebalance the bridge. It is evident that if the positions of the active and dummy strain gages (R_1 and R_4) were reversed, it would be possible to reverse the relative voltages at points A and C. Such a procedure would also reverse the apparent sign of the strain when read from the indicator dial. If, every time strain readings were taken on a long-time strain gage installation, the strain analyst were actually to take two readings, one with the active and dummy gages in their normal

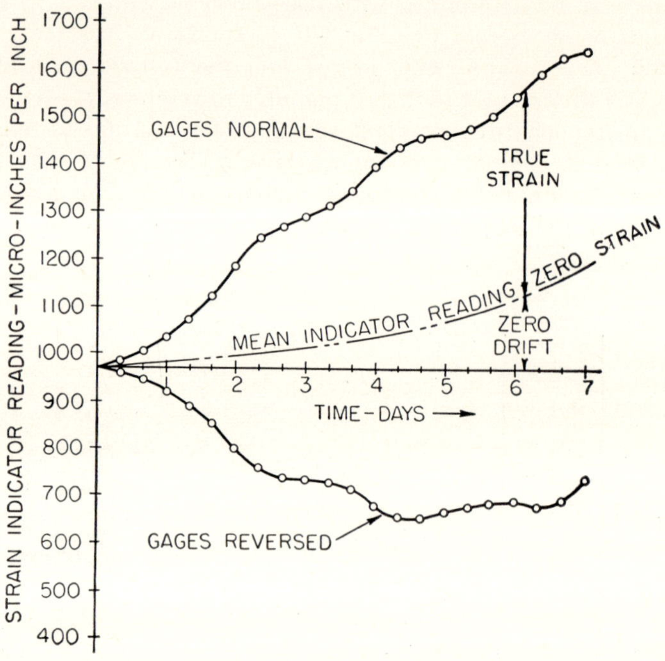

FIG. 9-6. Plot of hypothetical strain readings illustrating the determination of zero drift by electrically reversing active and dummy gages.

positions and one with their positions reversed, he could secure rather definite information as to the magnitude of zero drift in the instrument.

In Fig. 9-5 are shown the results of a series of hypothetical strain gage readings by the above technique. Since the two curves (gages normal and reversed) are symmetrical about the initial zero-strain reference point, one can infer that there has been no zero drift in the instrument. The true strain, therefore, assuming that all gages and leads function properly, is that indicated by the normal curve. If the zero point had drifted because of changing instrument characteristics during the time interval shown, the recorded data might look like those graphed in Fig. 9-6. When the data have been recorded and plotted as in this figure, a median curve representing the zero-strain reference level can be drawn.

The true strain at any designated time is then indicated by the distance between the zero-strain reference line and the line resulting from the data taken with the gages connected in their normal positions in the bridge circuit.

In general, the resistances of the active and dummy gages will not be precisely equal. When the gage positions in the bridge circuit are

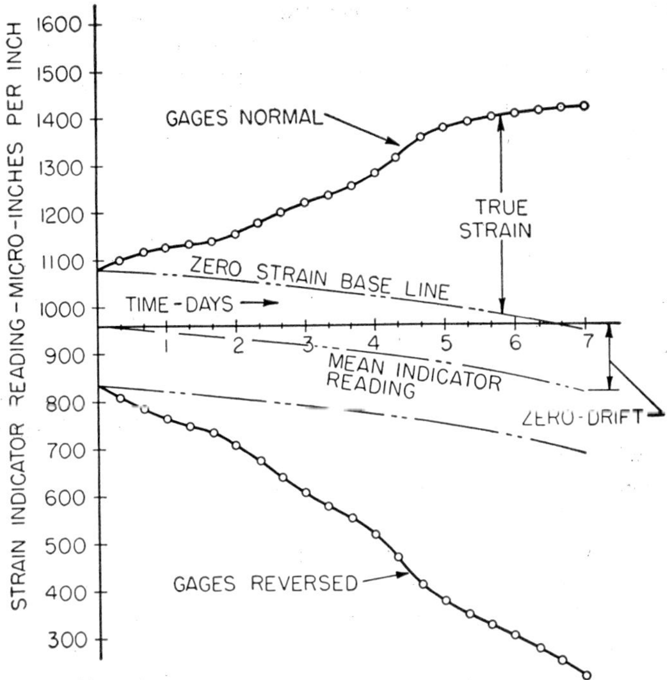

FIG. 9-7. Graph of hypothetical strain readings illustrating zero drift and method of obtaining true strain. This is the general (and common) case in which R_1 and R_4 are not precisely the same resistance.

reversed, the bridge zero will not occur at the same position of the balancing control. This will cause the normal and reversed data curves to be separated at the time of taking the initial readings. By again plotting a median curve, as shown in Fig. 9-7, the zero drift can still be followed. The true strain at any specified time will be represented by the distance from the median curve to the normal curve less the initial distance between these curves.

If the structure to which these gages are bonded is capable of being returned to a condition of no load and no strain at will, then the problem of detecting zero drift essentially disappears. In this case, merely rebalancing the bridge after the structure is unloaded and noting the zero-strain reference point will indicate any zero drift.

MINIMIZING ZERO DRIFT AND ITS EFFECTS

In cases of Wheatstone-bridge drift, such as indicated above, there appear to be several measures which can be taken. One of these is to let the bridge drift as it will and keep track of the drift by the technique of taking double strain readings as already described. Another is to use, in place of the batteries, a regulated power supply. Such power supplies take power from the a-c line and convert it into a stabilized current (alternating or direct) of very nearly constant voltage. This voltage is then supplied to the strain-indicating instrument. The use of a regulated power supply will have a very beneficial and stabilizing influence upon the operation of a strain indicator and will reduce zero drift originating in the indicator to a minimum. It also limits the use of the indicator to locations where the power is available to operate the regulated power supply, which, of course, eliminates many field applications. It should be kept in mind that all commercial strain-indicator power supplies operated from the a-c line are not especially regulated power supplies. If the characteristics of a regulated power supply are desired, it will be necessary to check this feature before making a purchase. The incorporation of an automatic-frequency control circuit in the strain indicator for stabilizing oscillator frequency over fairly broad supply-voltage limits would appear to be another means of reducing zero drift.

Regardless of any special measures taken to stabilize the bridge circuit of the strain indicator, some positive tests of zero drift should be made if long-time strain readings are to be trusted. Failure to consider the possibility of zero drift until 6 months later when some anomaly in the data becomes evident is poor practice. At best, it means an expensive retesting, and in cases where the loading cycle cannot be repeated it may mean the complete loss of data and the time and money spent in acquiring them. The procedure outlined above of reversing the strain gages is one of the most effective tests for establishing the amount of instrument zero drift. Another test that is often used is to set up a reference installation of strain gages on an unstrained piece of metal. If the reference, or secondary, gages are so connected in the Wheatstone bridge that they are fully temperature-compensating, this bridge, once balanced, should remain so for an arbitrarily long period of time. On each occasion that strain readings are taken on the gages cemented to the structure under test, parallel readings should be taken on the reference circuit. If the reference circuit ever indicates any strain, this is accepted as zero drift in the strain indicator and the active circuit readings are adjusted by this amount. It should not be forgotten, however, that both these procedures are capable of detecting only the zero drift which originates in the instrument. The zero drift caused by creep or other malfunctioning of the active strain gages on the test structure is not subject to measurement.

The commonly accepted procedure for long-time strain gage installations is to select the appropriate bakelite strain gage and cement it in place according to the methods described in Chap. 3. These and the manufacturer's recommendations should be followed quite closely since they represent the accumulated experience of many strain gage installations. For best results it will often be necessary to construct a moistureproof cover over the bakelite gages. This is an absolute necessity for gage installations such as those in locations of extremely high humidity, on concrete reinforcing steel, or under water. For less severe conditions waterproofing may be nothing more than a coating of wax or dielectric grease.

Aside from the importance of protecting strain gages from humidity because of the effect of moisture on the dimensional stability of the cement it is imperative that the impedance from the gage wires to ground be very high for electrical reasons. If the impedance is not extremely high compared with the resistance of the strain gage, erratic strain readings will result. For example, if a 350-ohm strain gage were shunted by a resistance of 10 megohms, the resultant resistance, by the law of parallel resistors, would be 349.98775 ohms. This is a resistance change of 0.01225 ohm. Equation (2-1) can be rewritten in the form

$$\epsilon = \frac{\Delta L}{L} = \frac{\Delta R}{R}\frac{1}{F}$$

If the above strain gage has a gage factor of 2.0, it is possible to solve directly for the equivalent unit strain which would be indicated falsely by the shunting effect. In this case ϵ equals 17 micro-inches per in., or approximately 500 psi stress in steel. It is usually maintained that for extended-time gage installations the resistance from strain gage to ground ought to be on the order of 1,000 megohms. One hundred megohms is considered to be near the low limit of acceptance for such applications.

BIBLIOGRAPHY

Beyer, F. R., and M. J. Lebow: Long-time Strain Measurements in Reinforced Concrete, *Proc. SESA*, vol. 11, no. 2, p. 141, 1954.

Boodberg, A., E. D. Howe, and B. York: Stability of SR-4 Electric Strain Gages and Methods for Their Waterproofing and Protection in Field Service, *Trans. ASME*, vol. 70, no. 8, pp. 915–920, November, 1948.

Campbell, W. R.: Errors in Indicated Strain for a Typical Wire Strain Gage Caused by Prestraining, Temperature Changes, and Weathering, *NACA, Tech. Note* 1011, April, 1946.

Campbell, W. R.: Performance Tests of Wire Strain Gages, Part I, Calibration Factors in Tension, *NACA, Tech. Note* 954, 1944.

Campbell, W. R.: Performance Tests of Wire Strain Gages, Part II, Calibration Factors in Compression, *NACA, Tech. Note* 978, 1945.

Campbell, W. R.: Performance Tests of Wire Strain Gages, Part III, Calibrations at High Tensile Strains, *NACA, Tech. Note* 997, 1945.

Campbell, W. R.: Performance Tests of Wire Strain Gages, Part VI, Effect of Temperature on Calibration Factor and Gage Resistance, *NACA, Tech. Note* 1456, January, 1948.

Campbell, W. R.: Tests of Six Types of Bakelite Bonded Wire Strain Gages, *NACA, Tech. Note* 1656, 1948.

Findley, W. N.: Creep Characteristics of Plastics, *Modern Plastics,* vol. 22, no. 4, pp. 153–159+, December, 1944.

Goodman, M. R.: Characteristics and Behavior of Bonded Wire Resistance Strain Gages in Thermal Coefficient of Expansion Measurements, Part I, SR-4 Paper Bonded A-7 and Bakelite Bonded AB-19 Gages, *Oak Ridge Natl. Lab., Document* 706, May, 1950.

Goodman, M. R.: Characteristics and Behavior of Bonded Wire Resistance Strain Gages in Thermal Coefficient of Expansion Measurements, Part II, SR-4 Bakelite Bonded Dual Lead Gages, *Oak Ridge Natl. Lab., Document* 707, June, 1950.

Matlock, H., and S. A. Thompson: Creep in Bonded Electric Strain Gages, *Proc. SESA,* vol. 12, no. 2, p. 181, 1955.

McClure, G.: Here's What Was Learned from a Study of Strain Gages on Big-inch Gas Pipelines, *Oil & Gas J.*, vol. 58, pp. 92–96, Apr. 4, 1960.

McWhirter, M., and B. W. Duggin: Minimizing Creep of Paper-base SR-4 Strain Gages, *Proc. SESA,* vol. 14, no. 2, p. 149, 1957.

Miller, B. L., and L. D. Anderson: The Performance of Wire-resistance Strain Gages as Influenced by the Drying Time of Three Mounting Cements, *David Taylor Model Basin, Rept.* R-213, January, 1946.

Moncher, F. L., H. R. Lissner, and C. H. Lipson: Long-time Electric Strain Gage Measurements on Concrete Reinforcing Rods at the Packard Proving Grounds Test Track, *Proc. SESA,* vol. 6, no. 1, pp. 29–34, 1948.

Rohrbach, C., and N. Czaika: Das Kriechen von Dehnungsmesstreifen als rheologisches Problem, *Materialpruefung,* vol. 2, no. 3, pp. 98–105, Mar. 20, 1960.

Rohrbach, C., and N. Czaika: Uber das Kriechen von Dehnungsmesstreifen unter statischer Zugbelasting, *Arch. tech. Messen,* no. 287, 289, 290, pp. 255–258, December, 1959, pp. 35–38, February, 1960, pp. 55–56, March, 1960.

Urwin, C. R., and K. H. Swainger: Minimizing Zero-drift in Electrical Strain Gauge Bridges, *J. Roy. Aeronaut. Soc.,* vol. 51, no. 443, pp. 867–873, November, 1947.

Wiles, E. G.: Physical Research Branch Bureau of Public Roads, *Public Roads,* vol. 27, no. 1, pp. 18–20, April, 1952.

EXERCISES

9-1. Mount a strain gage on a specimen of metal which can be subjected to steady stress for a period of time. Mount a second strain gage as a dummy on an unstressed block of the same material. After the gages are cured and wired, connect them to a static strain indicator. Subject the specimen to a constant strain of 3,000 microinches per in., and record gage reading versus time in order to detect creep in the gage.

9-2. Prepare a curve similar to Fig. 9-1 for the portable strain indicator in your laboratory.

9-3. With the static strain indicator connected to a stable strain gage installation, balance the indicator and then apply a differential temperature gradient to the instrument by directing a heat lamp on one side. Observe any drift that occurs with time due to the treatment of the indicator in this fashion.

9-4. Apply two strain gages to the same test specimen with one type of cement using the approved technique for application in one case and applying the gage in a very careless manner (inadequate surface preparation, etc.) in the second case. Apply a strain to the specimen after proper curing of the cement and observe differences in creep in the two gages with time.

9-5. Conduct a test demonstrating the effect of the thickness of the cement layer for epoxy cement on strain gage creep and stability.

9-6. Apply strain gages to a member, structure, or assembly which can be loaded incrementally over, say, a 10-day period. Check for zero drift of the strain indicator and determine the true strain recorded by the gage by setting up an experiment similar to that described in Fig. 9-7.

10 THE USE OF STRAIN GAGES WITH SLIP RINGS AND SWITCH CONTACTS

Stress analysts in many fields are faced with the necessity of securing strain measurements from rotating bodies. Examples of such strain gage installations include gas-turbine blades and disks, flywheels, pump and fan rotors, wheels, and crankshafts. A comparatively common application is that of measuring the shaft torque of propulsive machinery. Wherever it is difficult to measure torque with a conventional cradled dynamometer, a strain gage torque meter represents a very satisfactory method of instrumentation. Figure 10-1 is a photograph of a commercial strain gage torque meter.

In measuring strains on a rotating body the strain gages will be mounted and oriented in the conventional manner so as to indicate the strains which are significant to the investigator. Since the gages will be rotating, while the stress analyst and his instruments are presumably stationary, it is evident that some form of collector rings or slip rings will be necessary to maintain electrical contact between the instruments and the strain gages.[1] The usual practice is to run the leads from the strain gages toward the center of rotation and then out to some convenient point where slip rings can be installed on the rotating assembly. In some cases it may be necessary to add an extension shaft to carry the slip rings. The gage leads will be soldered at their extremities to individual slip rings. Conducting brushes attached to an adjacent stationary support can then be employed to complete the electrical connections between the gages and the recording or indicating instruments. Figure 10-2 illustrates a typical slip-ring and brush assembly for use with strain gages. This particular assembly was used by the NACA as a portion of a strain gage torque meter.

[1] The approach used by Campbell (see Chap. 5, under Telemetering), is an exception to this.

Fig. 10-1. Commercial strain gage torque meter. (*Courtesy of Baldwin-Lima-Hamilton Corporation.*)

Fig. 10-2. Slip-ring assembly for NACA torque meter. (*Courtesy of the National Advisory Committee for Aeronautics.*)

At one time, the process of measuring strains on rotating bodies with electric strain gages was considered quite a serious problem because of the difficulties which appeared to be inherent with slip rings. It will be recalled that the resistance change of a strain gage for a strain equivalent to 1,000 psi stress in steel is on the order of 0.01 ohm. If the resistance variations in the sliding connection between the brushes and slip

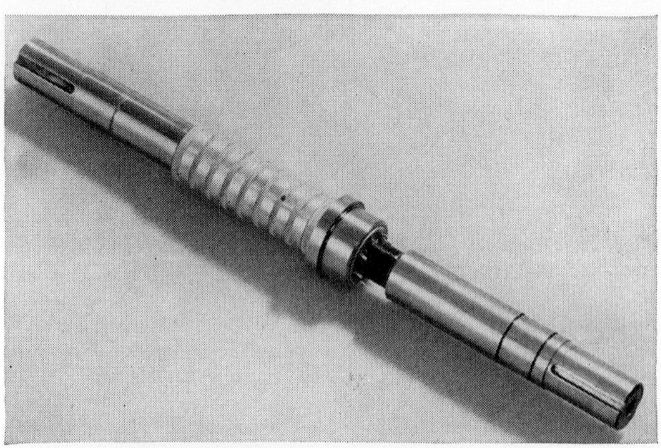

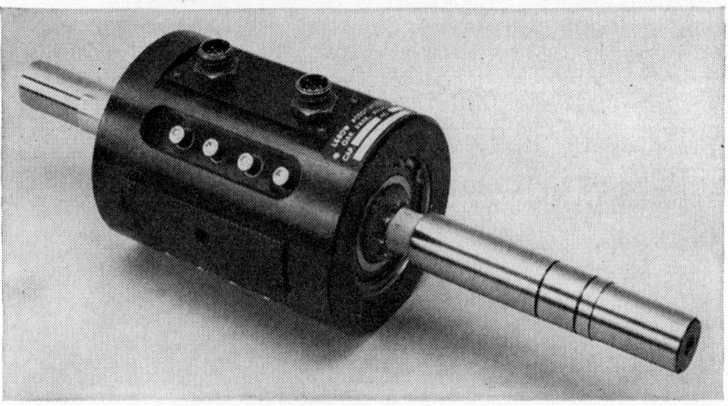

FIG. 10-3. Slip rings (*upper photo*) and slip-ring–brush assembly (*lower photo*) for operation at 24,000 rpm. Eight slip rings are molded integrally in epoxy plastic. (*Courtesy of Lebow Associates.*)

rings are of the same order of magnitude (as they very easily can be), it may become quite difficult to distinguish between the two sources of resistance change. Circuits and techniques have now been developed to the extent that slip rings need not be a source of significant inaccuracy. With sufficient attention to details, successful installations can be made for almost any application, whether it is to measure the strain in a gas-turbine blade rotating at 20,000 rpm or in a ship's propeller shaft at 100 rpm. Figure 10-3 shows a modern commercial slip-ring assembly rated for operation at 24,000 rpm.

Three general methods have been employed to combat slip-ring contact resistance variations and their effects on strain gage indications. One of these involves construction of an electrical circuit so that the slip-ring contact resistance is not in series with the strain gage itself but is placed instead at some point in the circuit where its effect is minimized. A second and less effective method is to employ high-resistance strain gages so that the resistance changes which correspond to strain will be large compared with those occurring between the slip rings and brushes. The third technique embodies the judicious selection of slip-ring and brush materials and brush pressures for optimum performance. The latter heading would also include the use of several brushes connected in parallel, riding each slip ring. Of course all three methods can be combined for best results. Piezoresistive strain gages are also being employed, because of the large resistance change with strain, to greatly increase the signal-to-noise ratio in slip-ring circuits. These techniques are described in detail later in this chapter.

A somewhat similar problem to that encountered with slip rings and brushes may occur when a number of different strain gages are to be connected to the same instrument through switches. Switch contact resistance variations may become large enough to interfere with accurate strain measurement. The problems to be overcome with switches are generally not so serious as those associated with slip rings, but elimination of switch contact resistance variations is discussed briefly at the end of this chapter.

STRAIN GAGE INSTALLATION

When strain gages are to be used for determining the stresses in some rotating body other than a shaft, the location and orientation of these gages will naturally depend upon the shape of the body being analyzed and the manner of load application. Many rotating bodies such as impellers and crankshafts may be sufficiently complex in shape and mode of loading for a preliminary investigation with Stresscoat to be required in order to locate regions and directions of maximum principal stresses so that strain gages can be properly oriented.

The comparatively common case of measuring the strain or torque in a shaft will, since it is more determinate, be discussed here in detail. From elementary strength of materials it is known that the maximum tensile and compressive strains of a shaft in torsion lie along 45° helices on the shaft surface. Because of this it will be necessary to bond the strain gages to the shaft at a 45° angle with respect to the shaft axis. The simplest installation would be as shown in Fig. 10-4. With torsional moments as indicated, gage R_1 would be strained in tension and gage R_4 in compression. It was shown in Chap. 4 that if these oppositely strained gages are connected as adjacent legs in a Wheatstone-bridge circuit, there will be automatic compensation of all thermally caused resistance changes. A little additional thought will show that the effects of any axial strains will also be canceled out in the bridge circuit, since they will always be the same in algebraic sign and magnitude in both strain gages.

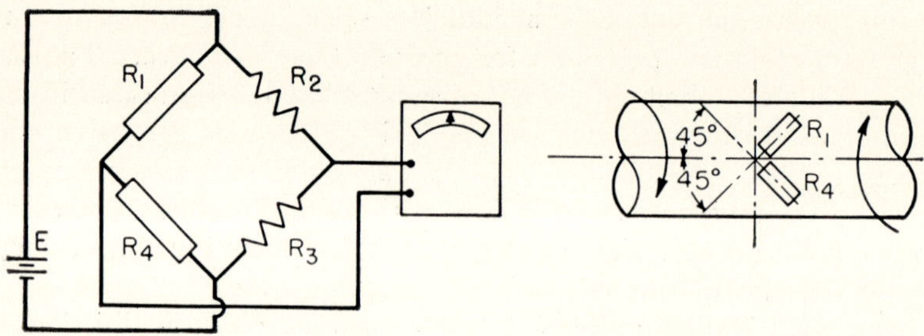

FIG. 10-4. Basic installation and connection of strain gages for measuring torsional strains.

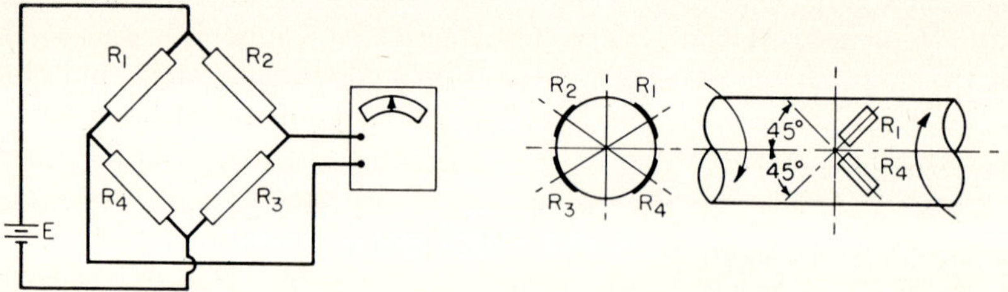

FIG. 10-5. Improved installation and connection of strain gages for measuring torsional strains while the effects of temperature and axial and bending strains are eliminated.

If the shaft were subjected to bending moments, however, the bending strains in gages R_1 and R_4 would not generally be equal in both sign and magnitude. As a result, the gages would indicate some indeterminate combination of bending and torsional strains. This situation can be remedied by placing two additional strain gages on the shaft in the manner shown in Fig. 10-5. This system results in automatic temperature compensation for all gages and elimination of the effects of all strains other than torsional strains. This assumes, of course, that the strain gages are accurately located and oriented. For full elimination of nontorsional strains, considerable care should be exercised in mounting the gages at precisely 45° with the shaft axis. Furthermore, gages, R_1 and R_3 in Fig. 10-5 must be diametrically opposite on the shaft surface, and the same restriction holds with gages R_2 and R_4. The relative circumferential locations of gages R_1 and R_2 or of R_3 and R_4 are incidental.

It should be noted here that a shaft in torsion is actually a special case of two-dimensional strain in which the strains are always numerically equal and of opposite sign. Because of this it is incorrect to calculate the shaft stress by multiplying the measured strain by the modulus of elasticity. As pointed out in Chap. 6, the true stress is

$$\sigma = \frac{\epsilon E}{1 + \mu}$$

where ϵ is the strain of one gage, or one-fourth of the bridge output when four active gages are used.

One of the techniques which have been employed for accurately locating and orienting strain gages on shafts involves first cementing the gages to a paper jig. The jig is later wrapped around and cemented to the shaft. Accurate location of the gages can be accomplished quite easily because the paper jig is plane when the strain gages are cemented to it. After the gages have been cemented to the paper, it may be found that the resulting assembly is so stiff as to hinder wrapping it around the shaft. This situation can be improved by employing a thin piece of paper and also a very thin layer of cement. Wrapping the jig and gages around the shaft before the cement has fully hardened will also help.

In some cases it may be advantageous to cement the paper jig to the shaft first, before applying the gages. Once the jig or template has dried in place, the strain gages can be cemented along the helices formed by the 45° lines which were drawn on the jig when it was flat. Care should be taken to make certain that the jig itself is properly oriented relative to the shaft centerline. This can be accomplished accurately by simply ruling a transverse line the full width of the jig and wrapping the jig around the shaft so that the ends of the line meet (Fig. 10-6). An improvement in this technique involves cutting windows in the jig to allow the gages to be cemented directly to the shaft surface. When strain gages are bonded to small-diameter shafts, some such technique as the above will generally be found necessary if accurate orientation is to be obtained.

Many strain gage installations on shafts are used to measure torque. Because of this, the gages may be required to give accurate and stable indications for long periods of time and to maintain their calibration. To satisfy these requirements, it will ordinarily be found expedient to use bakelite-type strain gages for this kind of application. It may also be necessary to moistureproof the gages by any of the techniques described in Chap. 8. For stress studies which are not to persist for any great length of time or when it is possible to obtain zero readings before each test, paper- or epoxy-backed gages will often be satisfactory.

Special precautions should be taken in wiring strain gages for rotational use so that lead wires are securely mounted to the rotating body. This situation becomes more critical at very high speeds and large diameters. For relatively low-speed operation, such as strain measurement on an automotive crankshaft, it is often sufficient to bake the leads in place with a thermosetting resin such as bakelite or epoxy cement. When higher speeds are encountered, it will usually be necessary to construct some positive mechanical mounting means for the lead wires. This may

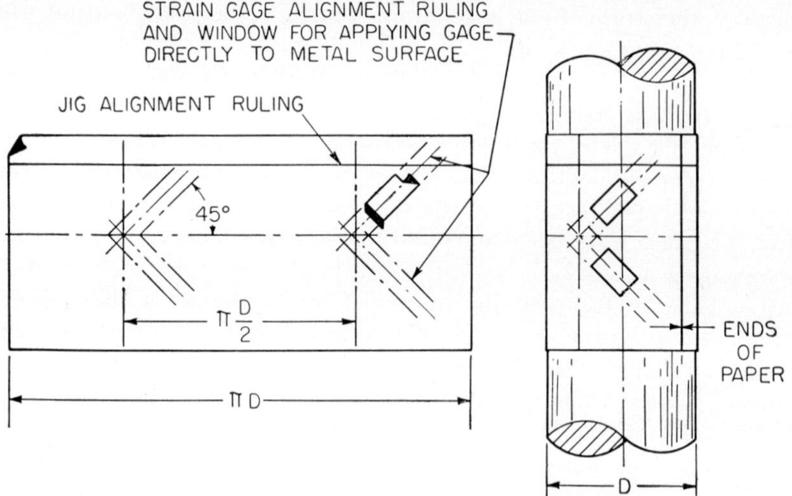

FIG. 10-6. Template or jig for accurately mounting strain gages on shafts.

consist, for instance, of sheet-metal clips tack-welded to the rotating structure.

ELECTRICAL CIRCUITS

As was mentioned earlier, slip-ring contact resistance variations can easily be of the same order of magnitude as the resistance changes in the strain gage itself due to applied strain. This difficulty can be alleviated by both electrical and mechanical techniques. The electrical methods will be discussed first. With the simple system shown in Fig. 10-7, if the brush-to-slip-ring contact resistance at point A changes with respect to that at point C, the bridge will apparently be unbalanced because the slip ring and brush are electrically in series with strain gage R_1 and the entire combination acts as one leg of the Wheatstone bridge. The meter will erroneously indicate this unbalance as a strain. The errors inherent in this type of system are apt to be intolerably large and cannot be adequately controlled by mechanical refinements.

One of the easiest and most practical methods for minimizing the effects of slip rings is to take them out of the bridge circuit proper and place

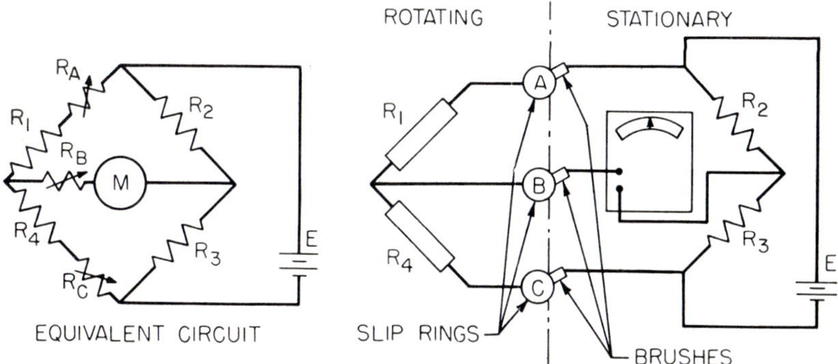

FIG. 10-7. Simple circuit for use with strain gages on rotating bodies. The presence of the slip-ring contact resistances in the bridge circuit proper constitutes a serious limitation on the utility of this circuit.

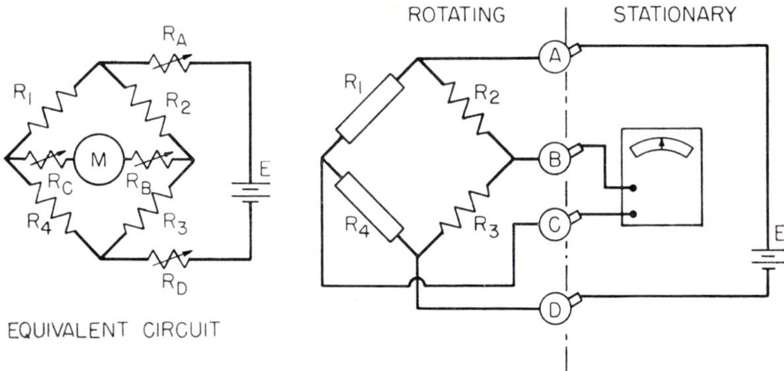

FIG. 10-8. Improved circuit for use with strain gages on rotating bodies. This arrangement isolates the bridge circuit proper from the effects of contact resistance variations. Note that there is no provision for null-balance operation.

them in series with the meter and power source as shown in Fig. 10-8. As is evident from the figure, this system requires one more slip ring than that of Fig. 10-7. With the circuit of Fig. 10-8, small variations in slip-ring contact resistance will have at most a very minor effect on the meter reading—especially under conditions of null-balance operation. It can be seen that the objectionable resistance variations are no longer able to affect the state of balance of the Wheatstone-bridge circuit. The particular arrangement indicated in Fig. 10-8, however, is incapable of operation as a null-balance system since the entire bridge circuit is rotating with the body being investigated, and no means of bridge balancing is shown. If null-balance operation is desired, as would usually be the case for steady-state strain measurements, it is necessary to place an additional resistor electrically in parallel with one of the bridge legs and on the instrument or stationary side of the slip rings. This is illustrated in Fig. 10-9. The balancing resistor will be a large variable resistor, say 10,000 ohms, in order to allow relatively accurate determination of the bridge balance point.

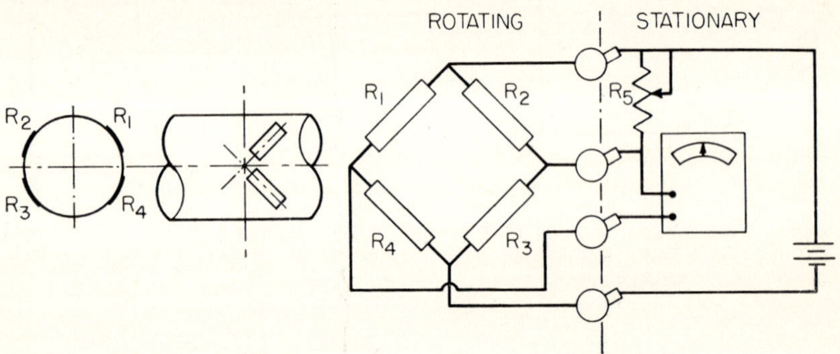

FIG. 10-9. Conventional arrangement of strain gages giving four active bridge legs on the rotating body. This system results in automatic temperature compensation and elimination of the effects of axial and bending strains, as well as minimizing inaccuracies due to contact resistance variations. R_5 is a balancing resistor for null-balance operation of the bridge.

Since resistors R_2 and R_3 are just "going along for the ride," they might as well be replaced by strain gages whenever possible. This situation is also shown in Fig. 10-9 and is the arrangement commonly employed for measuring torsional strains with electric strain gages. It has the combined advantages of temperature compensation, elimination of bending and axial strain effects, and comparative freedom from inaccuracies due to slip-ring contact resistance variations. The circuit as shown will perform satisfactorily for most applications, and the performance can be improved upon by judicious selection of slip-ring and brush materials and brush pressures.

The NACA developed a modified Wheatstone-bridge circuit which has certain advantages over that shown in Fig. 10-9. For cases in which extreme accuracy and freedom from error are desired, even though the slip rings may be required to operate at very high rotational speeds, the NACA circuit illustrated in Figs. 10-10 and 10-11 has been used with considerable success. This circuit is somewhat more elaborate than the one shown in Fig. 10-9, but it has been found to give excellent results at slip-ring surface velocities as high as 140 fps. The NACA circuit as shown includes four additional resistors which are known as *auxiliary bridge legs*. These resistors, R_6, R_7, R_8, and R_9, operate to reduce the effect of slip-ring resistance variations to an even greater extent than the circuit of Fig. 10-9. R_5 in Fig. 10-10 is a balancing resistor and acts in a manner similar to that in Fig. 10-9. In general, the actual resistance

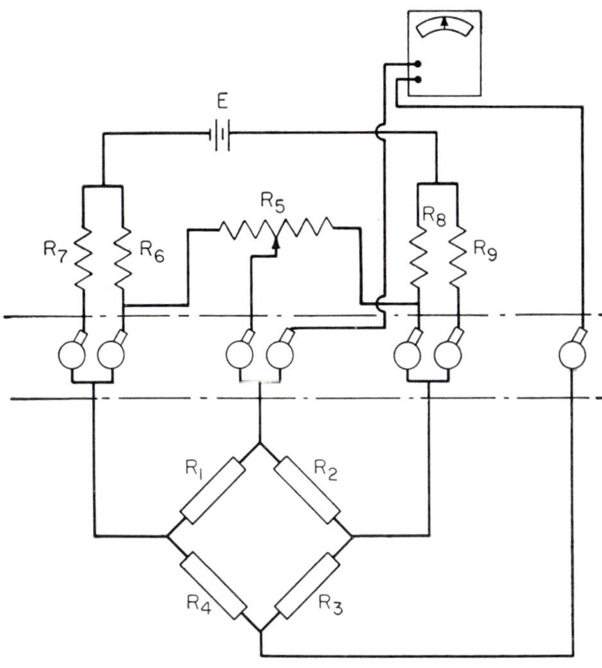

FIG. 10-10. Diagram of basic circuit employed by the NACA for control of slip-ring contact resistance variations.

values of the auxiliary bridge legs will depend upon the resistance of the strain gages and the magnitude of the supply voltage available. In the particular case shown, the strain gage resistors will all have the same nominal resistance, and the resistances of R_6, R_7, R_8, and R_9 will therefore be equal and determined largely by the available supply voltage. The theory behind the use of these auxiliary bridge legs is rather lengthy and will not be described here, but it is developed in detail in *NACA Technical Notes* 1031 and 2003. Because of the effects of the auxiliary resistors on circuit sensitivity and accuracy, the above publications should be consulted before selecting such resistors.

Figure 10-11 illustrates the actual circuit employed by the NACA in conjunction with its strain gage torque meter. If the bridge is initially balanced and then a torque is applied to the shaft carrying the strain gages, an unbalance voltage will reach the amplifier through slip rings *D* and *G*. This unbalance voltage is amplified and fed to a positioning motor (not shown) which drives the slide-wire contact to a new position

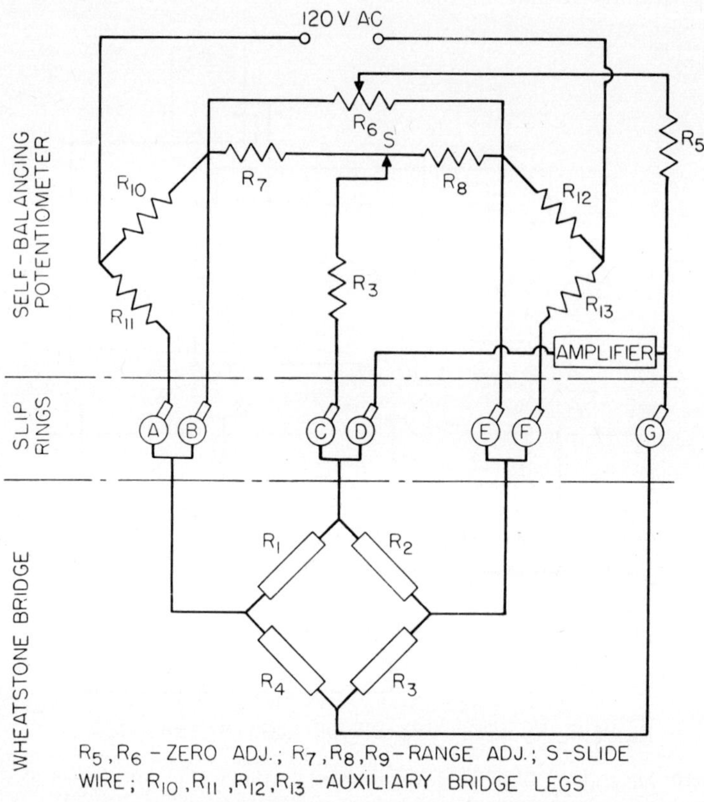

FIG. 10-11. NACA slip-ring circuit for minimizing the effects of contact resistance variations. (*NACA, Tech. Note* 2003.)

so that the bridge is again balanced. The position of the slide-wire contact is continuously indicated on a millivoltmeter. R_6 is used for adjusting the position of the slide-wire contact at zero torque so that the millivoltmeter will also read zero.

The NACA circuit just described is usable for steady-state strain measurement but cannot be used directly for dynamic strain instrumentation because of the frequency-response limitations of the automatic balancing system. Systems for measuring steady or near-steady torsional strains will ordinarily operate on the null-balance principle for greatest accuracy. In dynamic strain measurement it is usually impossible to balance the bridge because of the high-frequency strain variations. For this type of work it is necessary to accept the slight reduction in accuracy accompanying unbalanced bridge operation.

NONTORSIONAL STEADY-STATE STRAINS

A problem associated with strain measurements in a general rotating stress field is that of securing strain gage temperature compensation. This difficulty rears its ugly head whenever one wishes to determine steady-state or static strains on a rotating body, simply because there is no place to mount a compensating gage. One method of obtaining at least partial compensation is to bond a dummy gage to a small piece of metal and mount it on the rotating body so that the dummy gage will not be strained by centrifugal or other forces. The mechanical strains affecting the compensating strain gage should be either zero or some determinate function of those on the active strain gage. A second and easier method is the use of self-compensating strain gages (described in Chap. 4), which are particularly well-suited to this type of application.

DYNAMIC STRAINS

In measuring rapidly varying strains on a rotating body, the conventional potentiometer circuit illustrated in Fig. 10-12 is sometimes used.

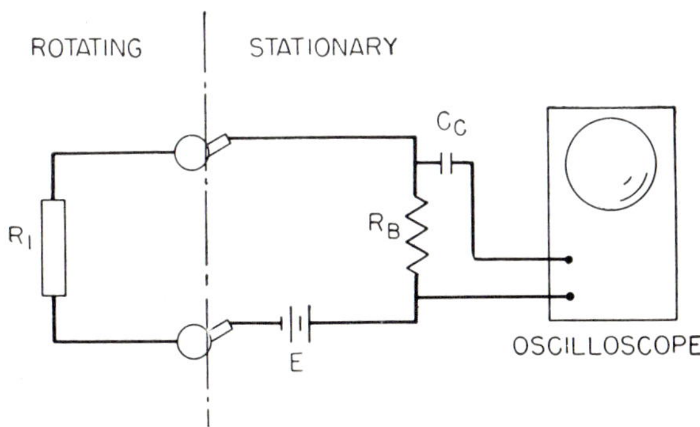

Fig. 10-12. Potentiometer-type slip-ring circuit for indicating dynamic strains on rotating bodies.

This circuit, however, is such that the slip-ring contact resistance variations are again electrically in series with the strain gage. Because of this, the strain indication may often be erratic. Such a condition would show on an oscilloscope or oscillograph as undesirable "noise" or superimposed disturbance. The preferable circuit, when it can be used, is the Wheatstone-bridge circuit of Fig. 10-9 with external slip rings. If the situation is such that only one strain gage can be placed on the rotat-

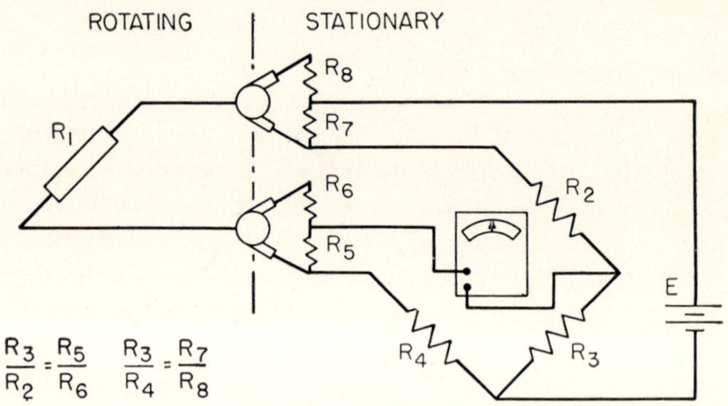

FIG. 10-13. NACA circuit for use where only one strain gage per Wheatstone bridge can be placed on the rotating body. Resistors R_5, R_6, R_7, and R_8 act as auxiliary bridge legs.

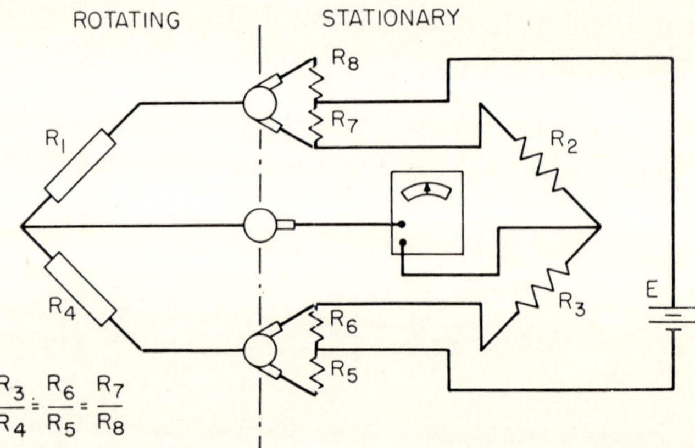

FIG. 10-14. NACA circuit for use where two strain gages per Wheatstone bridge are to be placed on the rotating body.

ing body for each Wheatstone bridge, as in measuring strain in a turbine blade, the circuit in Fig. 10-13 can be used. This circuit was also developed by the NACA and operates on the same principle as that of Fig. 10-10. Resistors R_5, R_6, R_7, and R_8 are auxiliary bridge legs which act to reduce the effect of slip-ring contact resistance variations. The sizes of these resistors are to be determined by the proportions $R_3/R_2 = R_5/R_6$ and $R_3/R_4 = R_7/R_8$. This system is very much superior to the conventional potentiometer circuit. If two gages per bridge circuit can be placed on the specimen, the circuit illustrated in Fig. 10-14 can be employed to advantage. In this circuit, $R_3/R_4 = R_6/R_5 = R_7/R_8$.

Attempting to reduce the effect of slip-ring contact resistance variations by employing strain gages of very high resistance is one of the least effective methods. One reason is that there is a distinct limit with present resistor materials to the amount of resistance which can be built into a strain gage. This is especially true when the gage length is limited to $\frac{1}{16}$ or $\frac{1}{32}$ in. Any gains in the desired direction are apt to be offset by added thermal and electrical instability in the strain gage itself. As noted previously, piezoresistive gages are very effective for use with slip-ring circuits.

SLIP RINGS AND BRUSHES

The mechanical design of the slip-ring system is an important factor in minimizing contact resistance variations. The slip-ring and brush materials and hardnesses, the brush pressure, the number and arrangement of brushes, and the eccentricity and surface finish of the slip rings all affect the contact resistance and therefore the performance of the assembly. The most widely used material combination consists of coin silver or silver-plated slip rings and silver-graphite brushes. Brush pressures are commonly held between 20 and 30 psi. With reasonable attention to surface finish and eccentricity (or axial runout if the ring surfaces lie in a transverse plane), the above combination has given satisfactory results for applications at speeds up to 4,000 or 5,000 rpm. Numerous other combinations of slip-ring and brush materials and brush pressures have been tested in the search for the most suitable arrangement. Tables 10-1 and 10-2 indicate the results of a series of such tests conducted by the NACA. Table 10-1, for dry operation of the slip rings, indicates that the silver-plated rings and silver-graphite brushes performed rather poorly in comparison with other materials. This is probably due to the high brush pressures employed by the NACA to satisfy their relatively strict requirements of allowable resistance variation. Monel metal (nickel-copper alloy) slip rings and silver-graphite brushes were found to give as good performance as any. This latter combination is in general use by the NASA for strain gage work on rotating bodies. Table 10-2 is of interest in that shim-brass slip rings and silver-graphite brushes were the only materials which were satisfactory when run in oil.

The brush pressures indicated in Tables 10-1 and 10-2 are considerably higher than those in common use. Ordinarily, brush pressures should be adjusted until there is the least noise or disturbance shown on an oscilloscope which is indicating the strain gage output. Figure 10-15

TABLE 10-1. COMPARISON OF SLIP-RING AND BRUSH MATERIALS TESTED DRY

Slip ring		Brush material	Results	
Material	Vickers hardness No.		Performance	Brush pressure, psi
Plate brass.......	116	Silver graphite*	Good	90 required
Plate brass.......	116	Copper graphite†	Good	125 required
Plate brass.......	116	Magnesium alloy	Poor	At 12, excessive wear of rings
Plate brass.......	116	Aluminum	Poor	At 12, excessive wear of rings
Plate brass.......	116	Soft carbon	Poor	At 175, unstable operation
Plate brass, shot-blasted.........	161	Silver graphite*	Good	80 required
Shim brass........	139	Copper graphite†	Good	150 required
Shim brass.......	139	Soft carbon	Good	175 required
Shim brass.......	139	Hard carbon	Good	150 required
Shim brass.......	150	Silver graphite*	Good	95 required
Silver-plated......	...	Silver graphite*	Poor	At 80, unstable and slight wear of rings
Silver-plated......	...	Copper graphite†	Poor	At 40, slight wear of rings
Silver-plated......	...	Soft carbon	Good	95 required
Silver-plated......	...	Hard carbon	Good	95 required
Monel metal......	124	Silver graphite*	Good	95 required
Monel metal......	124	Copper graphite†	Good	125 required
Monel metal......	124	Hard carbon	Good	225 required
Inconel...........	181	Silver graphite*	Good	100 required
Inconel...........	181	Copper graphite†	Good	125 required
Inconel...........	181	Soft carbon	Good	200 required
Stainless steel.....	185	Silver graphite*	Good	100 required
Stainless steel.....	185	Copper graphite†	Poor	At 100, unstable and slight wear of rings
Stainless steel.....	...	Soft carbon	Poor	Up to 250, unstable operation
Carbon steel, hardened	602	Magnesium alloy	Poor	At 12, unstable operation and excessive wear

* 60 per cent silver by volume.

† 50 per cent copper by volume.

TABLE 10-2. SLIP-RING AND BRUSH MATERIALS TESTED IN OIL

Slip rings		Brush material	Results	
Material	Vickers hardness No.		Performance	Brush pressure, psi
Plate brass......	116	Silver graphite*	Poor	At 185, slip rings worn excessively
Shim brass......	150	Silver graphite*	Good	175 required
Silver-plated.....	...	Silver graphite*	Poor	At 12, slip rings worn excessively
Silver-plated.....	...	Copper graphite†	Poor	At 60, slip rings worn excessively
Silver-plated.....	...	Hard carbon	Poor	At 60, slip rings worn excessively
Silver-plated.....	...	Soft carbon	Poor	At 60, slip rings worn excessively
Monel metal.....	124	Silver graphite*	Poor	Up to 400, unstable operation
Inconel.........	181	Silver graphite*	Poor	Up to 400, unstable operation

* 60 per cent silver by volume.

† 50 per cent copper by volume.

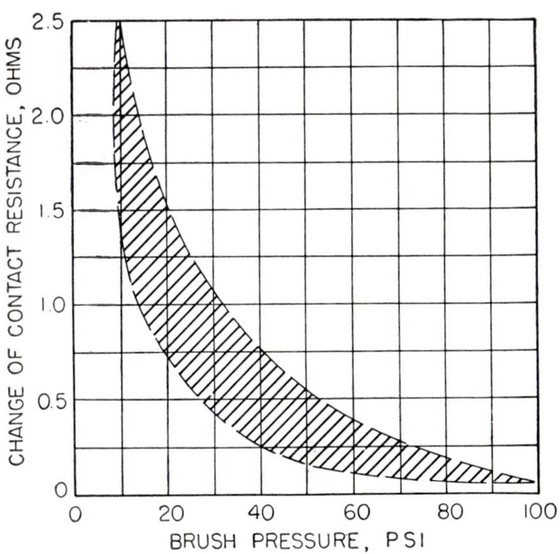

FIG. 10-15. Effect of brush pressure on contact resistance change—monel-metal slip rings and silver-graphite brushes. (*After Dutee, Phillips, and Kemp.*)

is typical of the NACA data showing the effect of brush pressure on contact resistance variations. The condition of minimum noise may not always be compatible with low rate of wear of brush and slip-ring materials. Too high brush pressures are likely to cause excessive wear of the brushes or slip rings. Too low brush pressure will result in undesirable variations in the contact resistance.

An additional technique that can be employed to minimize contact resistance variations is the use of several brushes riding on each slip ring. Some investigators have used as many as four brushes per slip ring. This can become rather clumsy mechanically. Usually, two or three brushes per ring will do a good job of controlling contact resistance variations. If the slip rings are rotating at extremely high velocities, it may be helpful to use brush springs with different spring rates for the brushes riding on any one ring. This will give different resonant frequencies and minimize the possibility of both brushes leaving the ring at the same time in case of operation at some critical shaft speed. For some installations it will be necessary for assembly purposes to split slip rings. Strips of silver-plated copper (or other material) cut accurately to length can be wrapped around the shaft and clamped in place by turnbuckled sheet-metal bands. In using split rings, multiple brushes will be an absolute necessity to assure continuous, uniform contact.

Another precaution for best performance is to limit the eccentricity of the slip rings on the shaft. For high-speed shafts (10,000 rpm and over) the eccentricity should not exceed 0.0003 in. On large-diameter shafts turning at several hundred rpm, slip-ring runouts as high as 0.015 have been found to give acceptable results. Still another consideration is the surface roughness of the slip rings. The effect of surface roughness, like that of eccentricity, appears to become more critical with high rubbing velocities. Experience indicates that for best results the surface roughness of the slip rings should be limited to 8 or 10 rms micro-inches.

PAINTED SLIP RINGS

A rather novel technique for fabricating slip rings was developed at the Case Institute of Technology. The slip rings are painted on the shaft with a du Pont silver paint (Silver Conducting Coating No. 4922) originally intended for making printed electronic circuits. The shaft is prepared by coating with an insulating material such as Glyptal, after which the rings are brush-painted at the desired locations. The paint is then baked and the rings polished prior to use. Connections from the strain gage leads to the rings are also made by painting. Bands of silver paint can be applied axially on the shaft over a first coat of Glyptal and each band insulated from all but the proper slip ring by a subsequent coat of Glyptal, over which the rings themselves will be painted. It is important in fabricating painted slip rings that the silver coating be built up thickly enough so that the resistance of the ring is negligible. Rings of this type have been tested at surface speeds up to 700 fpm using soft-carbon brushes at a pressure of 15 psi. The rings have operated over 100 hr under these conditions without ill effect. The painted-slip-ring technique is apt to be especially convenient for applications where conventional rings cannot be installed because of the geometry of the part or other limiting conditions.

MERCURY AS A ROTARY CONTACTOR

Several attempts have been made to secure continuous electrical connection between rotating and stationary bodies by running a conductive disk in a pool of mercury. One of the more successful of the mercury-type rotary contactors is that developed by the Goodyear Company. This contactor (U.S. patent No. 2,494,244) is built up of a number of electrically isolated sections for providing multiple circuit connections to strain gages or other transducers on rotating bodies. The Goodyear mercury-pool contactor is claimed to give trouble-free and low-noise-level operation over long periods of time. No data are available on its characteristics at extremely high shaft speeds.

STRAIN GAGE CONNECTIONS FOR NONROTATIONAL MOTION

There are occasionally instances in which it is desired to measure the strain in a body that has a linear or oscillatory motion. Examples might include dynamic strain measurements on connecting rods, pistons, rocker arms, chain links, bell cranks, and similar functional members. If sliding contacts are necessary, the foregoing circuit arrangements can be employed in the same manner as for slip rings. When the motion of the body under investigation is not too great, however, it may be possible to avoid the use of sliding contacts altogether. A technique which can sometimes be used successfully is to run leads directly from the instruments to the strain gages but so mount and support the leads that they will not be fatigued by the motion of the member being studied. There are several methods of accomplishing this, and two of these will be mentioned here. One method employs two or more articulating arms which follow the strain gage in its motion. The strain gage leads are fastened to the arms and coiled at all arm joints to prevent fatigue under the continuous flexing. The second method, employed in mak'ng strain measurements on reciprocating engine pistons, uses a small flexible coil spring with the strain gage conductors running through the center of the spring. In the latter instance, the strain gage leads must still undergo rather severe flexing, and it will be found necessary to use multiple-stranded leads.

SWITCH CONTACT RESISTANCE

Most of the same general principles affecting slip-ring operation are also applicable to the elimination of switch contact resistance variations. The switch problem is somewhat simpler than the case of the slip rings because there is no rubbing velocity with which to contend. The use of

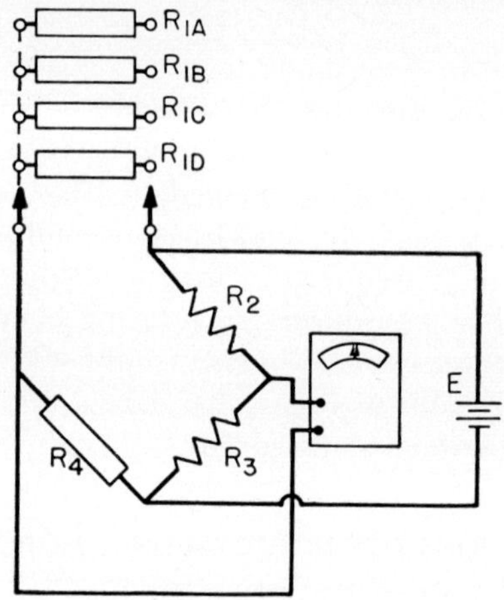

FIG. 10-16. Multiple strain gage switching circuit employing a common temperature-compensating gage for all active gages. When used for measuring static strains, this circuit can give quite large errors due to variations in contact resistance.

multiple switch contacts in parallel will be found beneficial, though mechanically complicated. It is common practice to use a single compensating gage for several active gages. This can be accomplished with the circuit shown in Fig. 10-16. By soldering one lead of each of the active gages to a common bus bar, as shown by the broken line, the switching problem is somewhat simplified. This latter circuit can also apparently tolerate twice the variations in switch contact resistance for a given error in strain indication. Both these systems, however, are such that bridge balance is affected by the contact resistance.

The general rule applicable to slip rings is equally true for switches. Whenever possible, the switch contacts should not be in series with the strain gages themselves. The circuit shown in Fig. 10-17 for multiple strain gage installations accomplishes this condition by using separate compensating strain gages for each active gage and connecting the gages to common busses wherever possible. If desired, the elaborate circuits of Figs. 10-11 and 10-13 can be used to eliminate switch contact resistance variations by the addition of auxiliary bridge legs. As far as these circuits are concerned, the slip-ring contacts can be replaced by switch

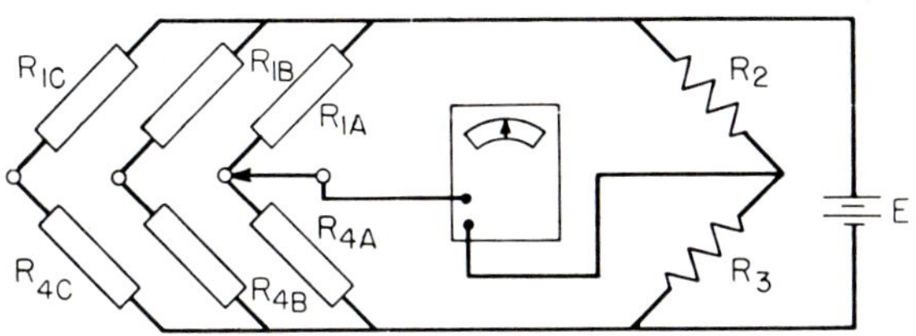

FIG. 10-17. Multiple strain gage switching circuit employing separate compensating gage for each active gage (sometimes referred to as a "chevron" circuit).

contacts with no difference in operation. It has been found that contact resistance variations can also be greatly reduced by employing high-quality radio-type switches in all strain gage circuits.

BIBLIOGRAPHY

Cottom, M.: Electrical Noise at the Sliding Contact, *Univ. Kansas, Eng. Bull.* 26, 1950.

Curtis, W. F.: Dynamic Strain Measurements in the Crankshaft of a Diesel Engine, *David Taylor Model Basin, Rept.* R-154, 1943.

Dutee, F. J., F. W. Phillips, and R. H. Kemp: Operating Stresses in Aircraft Engine Crankshafts and Connecting Rods, Part I, Slip Ring and Brush Combinations for Dynamic Strain Measurements, *NACA, Mem. Rept.* E5C30 (*Wartime Rept.* WR E-187), 1945.

Dutee, F. J., F. W. Phillips, and H. F. Calvert: Operating Stresses in Aircraft Engine Crankshafts and Connecting Rods, Part II, Instrumentation and Test Results, *NACA, Mem. Rept.* E5H18 (*Wartime Rept.* WR E-191), 1945.

Goloff, A.: Determination of Operating Loads and Stresses in Crankshafts, *Proc. SESA*, vol. 2, no. 2, pp. 139–149, 1945.

Gorton, R. E., and R. W. Pratt: Strain Measurements on Rotating Parts, *Trans. SAE*, vol. 3, no. 4, pp. 540–556, October, 1949.

Jonard, H. A., and M. H. Polzin: Commutator-Connector, U.S. patent No. 2,494,244, Jan. 10, 1950.

Maier, H. J.: Torque Tests on Ocean Vessel Propulsion System Using SR-4 Strain Gages and Torquemeters, *Testing Topics* (Baldwin-Lima-Hamilton Corporation), vol. 5, no. 1, January, February, March, 1950.

Manson, S. S., A. J. Meyer, Jr., H. F. Calvert, and M. P. Hanson: Factors Affecting Vibration of Axial Flow Compressor Blades, *Proc. SESA*, vol. 7, no. 2, pp. 1–16, 1950.

Nettles, J. C., and M. P. Hanson: Flight Tests of a P-63A-1 Airplane with an Electric Torquemeter, *NACA, Advance Restricted Rept.* E5B16 (*Wartime Rept.* WR E-64), 1945.

Rebeske, J. J., Jr.: Investigation of a NACA High Speed Strain Gage Torquemeter, *NACA, Tech. Note* 2003, 1950.

Wallace, W. A., and W. A. Casler: Device for Maintaining Continuous Electrical Connections with Reciprocating Engine Parts, *Proc. SESA*, vol. 4, no. 2, pp. 52–61, 1947.

Walstrom, D. P.: Measurement of Operating Stresses in an Aircraft Engine Crankshaft under Power, *NACA*, *Advance Restricted Rept.* E5B01 (*Wartime Rept.* WR E-41), 1945.

Warshawsky, I.: A Multiple Bridge for Elimination of Contact Resistance Errors in Strain Gage Measurements, *NACA*, *Tech. Note* 1031, 1946.

Wright, D. K., Jr., and J. R. Jeromson, Jr.: Letter to the Editor: Application of Silver-painted Slip Rings for Strain Gage Circuits, *Proc. SESA*, vol. 11, no. 2, p. 139, 1954.

Electronic Methods of Observation at the David Taylor Model Basin, Part 2, Measurements of Steady and Alternating Stresses in Rotating Shafts, *David Taylor Model Basin, Rept.* R-54, 1942.

EXERCISES

10-1. Mount a single gage on a rotating member, bringing the leads out through slip rings, and complete the bridge at the recorder. Load the member containing the strain gage and obtain a reading of the strain. Install an entire bridge of strain gages on the rotating member and bring the leads out through slip rings. Reload the member and again record the strain due to the load applied. Compare the results obtained in these two tests.

10-2. In an installation of a number of strain gages on a rotating shaft, the leads are to be brought out through slip rings to the measuring instrument. As the load is applied to the member and the strain recorded by the gages, vary the pressure on the brushes to determine the effect of pressure on the signal obtained. Determine and record the optimum brush pressure.

10-3. Design and build a simple mercury slip ring and investigate the noise level produced in its operation.

10-4. In an existing strain gage installation, open one of the leads to the active gage and insert (in series with the gage and in parallel with one another) a variety of switches and connectors (knife switch, toggle switch, binding post, alligator clip thermocouple switch, telephone relay, banana plug, Jones plug, etc.). Test the switches and connectors for comparative performance as indicated by stability and zero shift in static strain indicator reading.

10-5. Calculate the signal-to-noise ratio for the bridge circuit in Fig. 10-7 if resistance variations in individual slip-ring–brush contacts amount to 0.01 ohm. Gages R_1 and R_4 (119 ohms, gage factor 1.85) are subjected to strains of plus and minus 1,500 micro-inches per in., respectively.

10-6. Fabricate a set of painted slip rings and test for performance in terms of noise level and contact resistance.

11 TRANSDUCER APPLICATIONS OF STRAIN GAGES

The bonded resistance strain gage has many uses in addition to the direct determination of strain. Reference is being made to the variety of devices which employ strain gages as the sensing elements for measuring loads, forces, torques, pressures, displacements, and other physical variables. Such devices are commonly referred to as transducers, and a number of techniques for using the strain gage as a universal transducer will be described in this chapter.

Since strain is the fundamental quantity measured by strain gages, all transducers using them are constructed so that the physical variable being instrumented can deform one or more elastic members to which gages are attached. It can readily be seen that, in measuring the strain in an axially loaded straight bar of uniform cross section, the strain is proportional to the load. The constant of proportionality could be calculated if the modulus of elasticity and the cross-sectional area of the bar were known. Or, if desired, the bar could be calibrated by subjecting it to known loads and measuring the corresponding strains. To have the proportionality factor between load and strain remain constant, the load should never stress the bar to the proportional limit. Here, then, is a simple transducer for load measurement. This basic technique has been exploited in countless different ways to create instruments for studying physical and mechanical phenomena. While the elastic member in the preceding example was stressed axially, other transducers may employ bending, torsion, hydrostatic loading, or almost any combination of these. The unique properties of the Wheatstone-bridge circuit in conjunction with the laws of elastic stress distribution can be used to perform an amazing variety of measuring tasks.

It should be evident that any variable which can be instrumented by a strain gage transducer can also be controlled by the same device. Strain

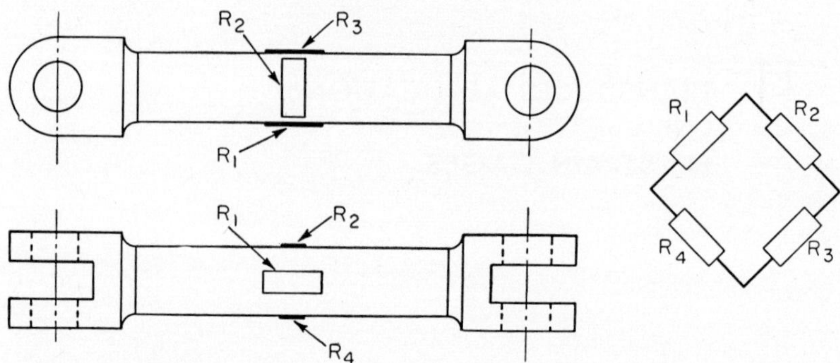

FIG. 11-1. Schematic drawing of tension link and strain gage arrangement.

gage pickups can be used to actuate switches, apply correcting signals, or sound alarms when the variable being sensed commences to deviate from a set of predetermined limits.

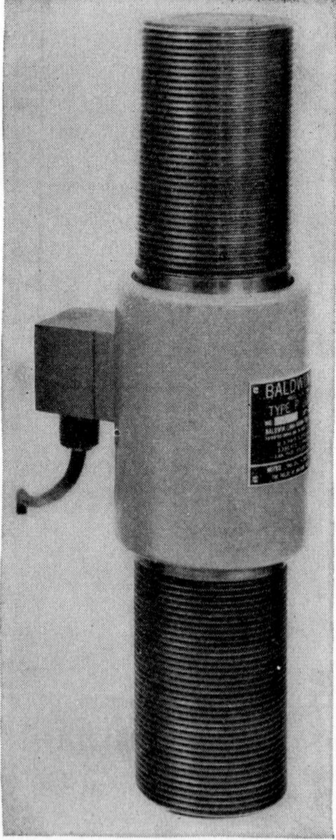

FIG. 11-2. Commercial strain gage tension link. (*Courtesy of Baldwin-Lima-Hamilton Corporation.*)

One of the most convenient features of strain gage transducers is their size. They are usually much smaller than corresponding mechanical instruments. A further advantage arises from the fact that their electrical output can be indicated or recorded at a remote point of greater safety and convenience than the immediate vicinity in which the phenomenon being measured is located. The primary disadvantage of these transducers lies in their comparatively low electrical output. This characteristic makes it necessary to employ considerable electronic amplification between the strain gage and the recorder stylus unless piezoresistive gages are used. Fortunately, instruments for this purpose have now been developed to a high degree of operational satisfaction and, unfortunately, at a correspondingly high cost.

DEVICES FOR MEASURING TENSILE AND COMPRESSIVE LOADS

The simplest device for measuring tensile loads is the strain gage tension link, which has already been mentioned and is shown in Fig. 11-1. This link is made up with shackles or other coupling devices on each end. It carries four strain gages arranged as indicated in the illustration. Two gages, R_1 and R_3, have their axes parallel to the axis of the link. These are the primary sensing elements and would produce a satisfactory electrical output with load if it were not for the necessity of temperature compensation. Gages R_2 and R_4 are placed on the tension link in the Poisson arrangement as discussed in Chap. 4 to obtain automatic temperature compensation. It will be noticed that gages R_1 and R_3 are placed diametrically opposite each other on the surface of the link, and because of their arrangement in the Wheatstone bridge they will not

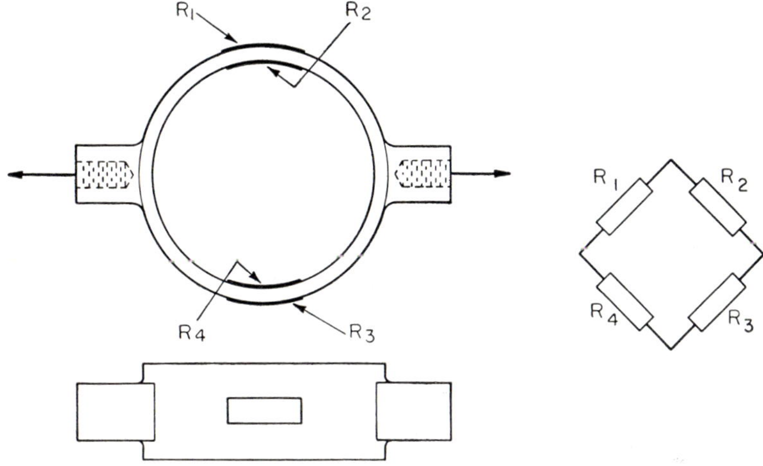

FIG. 11-3. Ring-type tension link.

unbalance the circuit as a result of loads other than pure tension. For instance, if the pivot friction at the end fastening of the link were to apply a slight bending stress to the gages, the arrangement shown would result in cancellation of any electrical output from this bending.

From a design standpoint the cross-sectional area of the tension link is selected to produce the greatest possible strain compatible with the necessity for remaining within the elastic limit of the link material under rated capacity loading. For precision transducers in which hysteresis is important the stresses should be kept well below the yield point. It is not uncommon, in fact, to limit the stresses to 30 per cent of the yield point. It will be necessary to strike a compromise between insufficient gage output and excessive hysteresis. This situation can be helped by selecting the material for the elastic element of the transducer on the basis of high strength and low hysteresis. A material whose modulus of elasticity is relatively unaffected by temperature will also improve transducer accuracy. The tension link shown in Fig. 11-1 should be covered so that the strain gages will be protected from the effects of moisture and other deleterious agents. The precautions described in the preceding chapters on long-time strain gage installations and on moistureproofing should be followed religiously in all transducer applications. Figure 11-2 is a photograph of a commercial strain gage tension link which is functionally similar to that of Fig. 11-1.

A somewhat different type of tension link is shown in Fig. 11-3. The ring construction illustrated is such as to bend the member in the vicinity

Fig. 11-4. Appearance of the DTMB ring dynamometer (tension link) assembly. (*Courtesy of David Taylor Model Basin, United States Navy.*)

of the strain gages. Thus, under a tensile load strain gages R_1 and R_3 are strained in compression, while gages R_2 and R_4 are strained in tension. It can be seen that the gage arrangement for the ring-type tension link gives complete temperature compensation, as does the Poisson arrangement in the bar-type link. The principal advantage of the ring-type tension link is its relatively high sensitivity to load without a corresponding sacrifice in transverse stiffness. Figure 11-4 illustrates a ring-dynamometer assembly developed at the David Taylor Model Basin. The design details and specifications for this link are shown in Fig. 11-5. A variation of the ring construction, as utilized in a commercial load cell, is shown in Fig. 11-6.

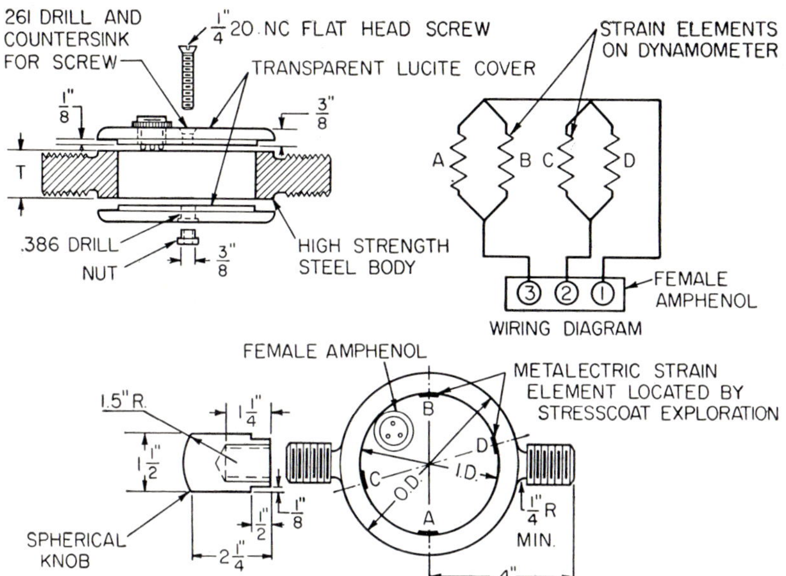

TMB DRAWING NO.	MAX LOAD	DIMENSION OF BODY			METALECTRIC STRAIN ELEMENT		SHANK THREAD SIZE
		I.D.	O.D.	T.	TYPE	RESISTANCE	
	KIPS	INCHES	INCHES	INCHES		OHMS	
S-3140	10	3.9	5	1.25	A-5	120	1-14 NF
S-5611	20	3.25	5	1.375	A-5	120	1-14 NF
S-3145	50	3.75	5.75	2.25	A-5	120	1½-18 NEF

FIG. 11-5. Construction, wiring, and specifications for the DTMB ring dynamometer. (*Courtesy of David Taylor Model Basin, United States Navy.*)

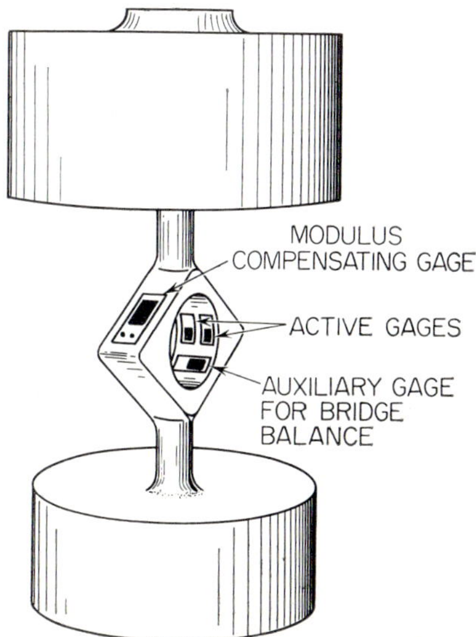

FIG. 11-6. Modified ring construction and strain gage placement for universal load cell. (*Courtesy of The Budd Company.*)

Testimony to the reliability and accuracy of strain gage load cells is their use in precision commercial instruments and testing equipment. Figure 11-7 shows the Instron testing machine and two types of strain gage load cells used in the machine for indicating the loads applied to test specimens.

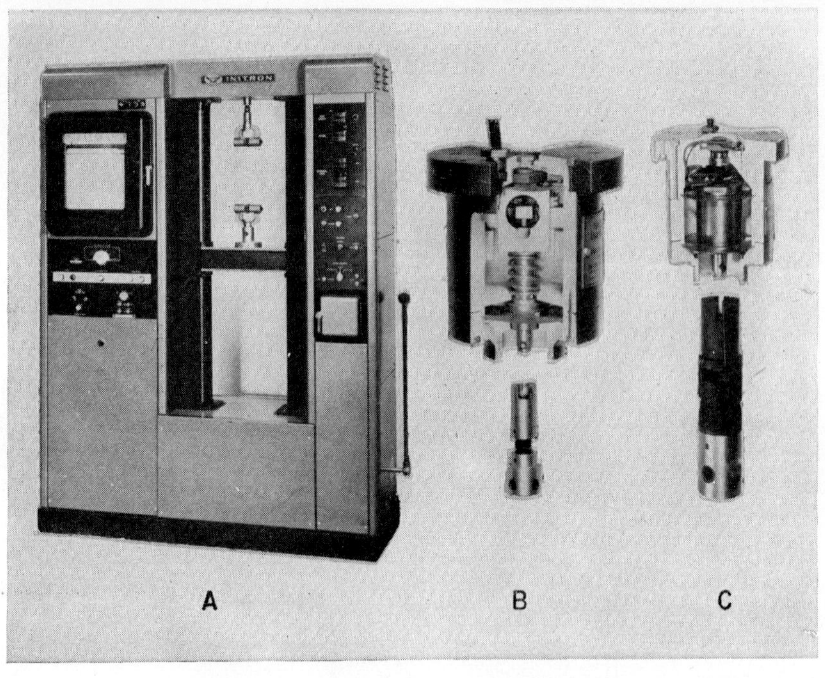

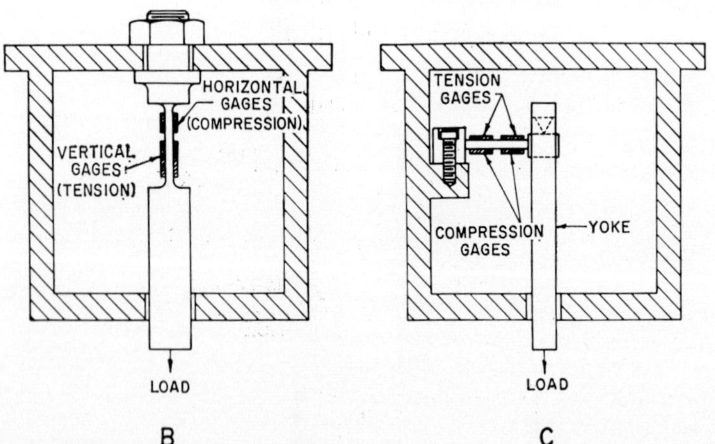

Fig. 11-7. Instron testing machine with strain gage load cells for load measurement: (*A*) testing machine; (*B*) cantilever-beam-type load cell; (*C*) tension-bar load cell.

COMPRESSIVE LOAD MEMBERS

The same general principle is employed for measuring compressive loads as tensile loads. The common practice is to select a column with a small l/r ratio to ensure freedom from buckling and to attach strain gages in such a manner that they are sensitive to axial loading, insensitive to bending, and insensitive to temperature variations. Figure 11-8 illustrates a simple compression-force-measuring unit or, as it is commonly known, a load cell. The particular load cell shown in the illustration is made by bonding four strain gages to the inner wall of a tube, after which the ends are capped and the lead wires taken out for remote indication or recording. While the assembly shown does not lend itself

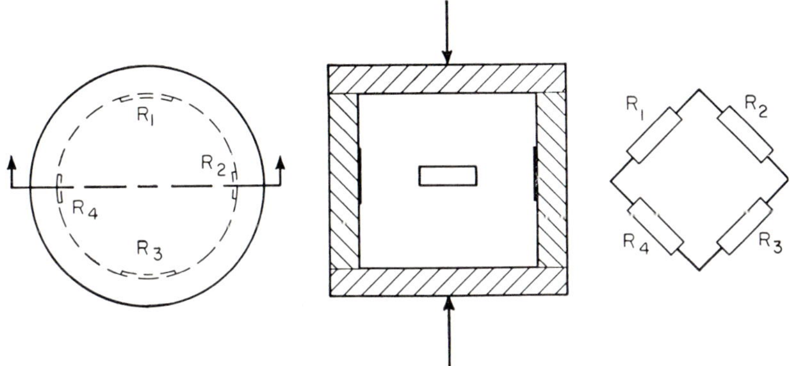

FIG. 11-8. Compression-force-measuring unit, or load cell.

to ease of strain gage application on the inner surface of the tube, it does provide automatic moistureproofing and general protection when the end caps are placed on the cylinder. Commercial strain gage load cells are not ordinarily made in this manner. The Baldwin-Lima-Hamilton strain gage load cell is fabricated in the form of a solid column with the strain gages on the surface but arranged in essentially the manner of Fig. 11-8. A commercial strain gage load cell is shown in Fig. 11-9. These and similar units are available in a wide range of capacities, from 500 to 200,000 lb.

The National Bureau of Standards has developed a series of heavy-duty compression load cells for the purpose of calibrating large materials-testing machines. These are of similar construction to the lower-capacity commercial load cells. It is general practice to calibrate testing machines by means of proving rings. These are rings of steel with a mechanical sensing device by which the deformation of the ring, and hence the load applied to the ring, can be obtained with a high degree of precision. Prov-

Fig. 11-9. Commercial strain gage load cell. (*Courtesy of Baldwin-Lima-Hamilton Corporation.*)

Fig. 11-10. NBS load cells (strain gage instrumented columns) of 1 million and 3 million lb capacity used for calibrating materials-testing machines. (*Courtesy of National Bureau of Standards.*)

ing rings are not particularly easy to use and require a certain dexterity in determining the exact amount of ring deformation. It has become evident that proving rings for calibrating testing machines of greater than ½ million lb capacity were getting beyond the portable stage. For such large machines it is the custom to use several lower-capacity rings acting in parallel, which generally multiplies the difficulties of calibration. The load cells developed by the NBS have been found to give sufficient accuracy to adequately replace proving rings in calibrating the large testing machines. Figure 11-10 shows two of the NBS load cells of 1 million and 3 million lb capacity. The 3-million-lb NBS load cell is shown in Fig. 11-11 prior to moistureproofing the gages and attaching the protective cover. Note the care with which the gage leads have been placed and secured to the member.

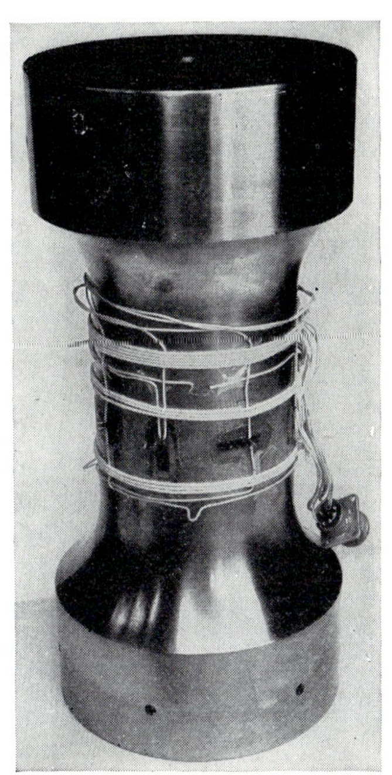

FIG. 11-11. Three-million-pound-capacity NBS load cell prior to coating the strain gages and attaching the cover. (*Courtesy of National Bureau of Standards.*)

TRANSDUCERS EMPLOYING BENDING STRESSES

The axially loaded tension link and load cell are not well-suited to measuring small forces or loads because the elastic member must be so small in cross-sectional area to produce the desired strain and electrical output. The more practical technique is to use a cantilever beam for small load measurement. An example of such a load beam is shown in Fig. 11-12. In this case strain gages R_1 and R_3 are mounted so that they are subjected to tensile strain, while gages R_2 and R_4 are strained in compression. These gages are arranged in the bridge circuit so that the strain signals in R_1 and R_3 are additive in one direction and those of R_2 and R_4 are additive in the other direction, thus producing four times the electrical output of a single strain gage. This arrangement also ensures complete temperature compensation. The capacity of the load beam can be changed over a range from 50 to 150 lb by merely setting the point of load application to the markings on the beam surface. Figure 11-13 is a photograph of an SR-4 strain gage load beam of 50-100-150 lb capacity. It should be kept in mind that these load beams can be used for direct weighing and for measurement of various forces and thrusts, or they can be used to measure torque when so arranged that the load beam resists the motion of the torque arm.

An interesting application of the load-beam principle is the electrical torque wrench illustrated in Fig. 11-14. At first glance one might presume that the torque on the wrench could be measured by four strain gages in an arrangement similar to that used on the load beam just described. The difficulty here lies in the fact that the point of load application is indeterminate. Thus, the bending stress, and therefore

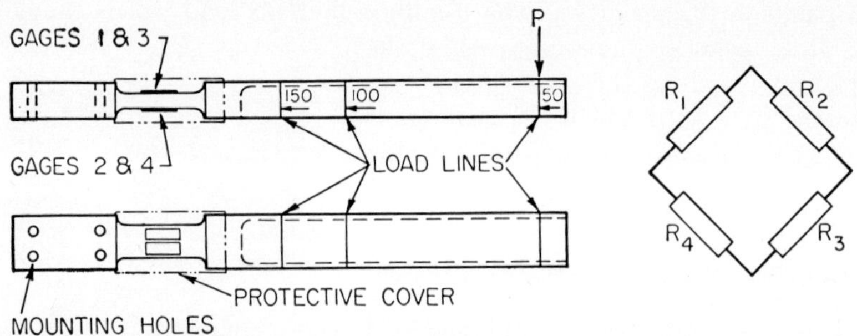

FIG. 11-12. Cantilever-type load beam illustrating construction employed by the Baldwin-Lima-Hamilton Corporation.

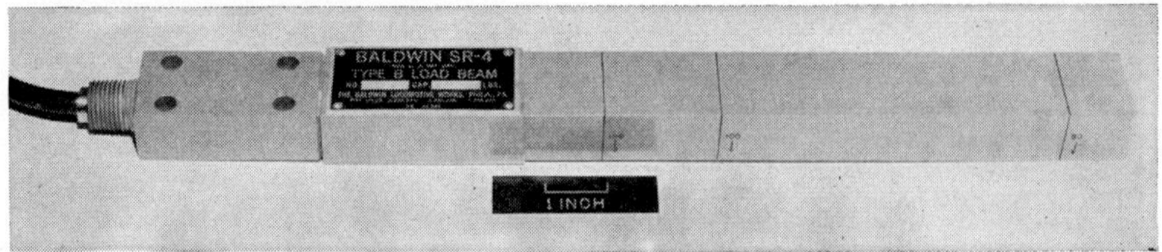

FIG. 11-13. SR-4 load beam of 50-100-150 lb capacity. (*Courtesy of Baldwin-Lima-Hamilton Corporation.*)

the bending moment, at the cross section containing the strain gages can be readily calculated, but this does not give the torque about the wrench-socket centerline. The actual torque on the bolt or nut can be obtained from the strain readings if the slope of the bending-moment diagram is known. This slope, however, depends upon the point of load application. The problem can be solved by attaching four more strain gages to any other section on the wrench handle, although if the distance from the centerline of the socket to section A is twice that to section B, the calculations will be simplified. The illustration shows that the even-numbered strain gages at each section are strained equally in magnitude and oppositely in direction to the odd-numbered gages. When these gages are arranged in the Wheatstone bridges as indicated in the figure, the usual temperature compensation and multiplication of electrical output will result.

The stresses and the bending moments at sections A and B can now be calculated directly. If the two moments at these points are known, it is possible to determine the torque on the wrench socket with a certain amount of additional calculation. This method requires two separate sets of strain readings for each torque measurement and will not be found very convenient. A better technique is that shown in Fig. 11-15. Here again, eight strain gages are used and are mounted on sections A and B. This time, however, the sections are located a little differently, and six

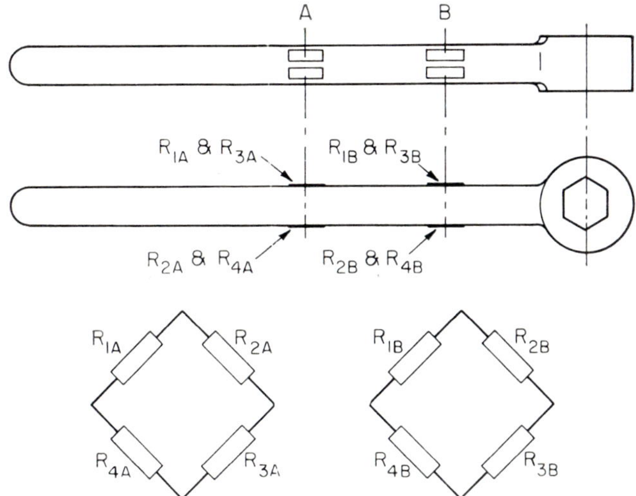

FIG. 11-14. Arrangement and connection of strain gages on a wrench handle. Wrench torque can be computed from the bridge outputs at sections A and B.

of the gages are mounted on section B, while two are mounted on section A.

With the strain gages connected in the Wheatstone bridge as shown in Fig. 11-15, the gages act so that the bridge unbalance is a linear function of the torque at the wrench-socket centerline regardless of the point of load application. This method, then, while not saving any strain gages, allows the torque measurement to be obtained with a single set of strain readings. The manner of functioning of the wrench can be looked upon as follows: from the bending-moment diagram in Fig. 11-15 it is apparent that $M_c = M_b + \frac{1}{2}(M_b - M_a)$. This can be rewritten as $M_c = M_b + (M_b/2) - (M_a/2)$. The indicated mathematical operations can all be performed in a single bridge circuit with eight gages properly located and connected. Gages R_{1b}, R_{2b}, R_{3b}, and R_{4b} produce a combined output representing M_b as in the previous example. The output of gages R_{1a} and R_{2a} can then be taken as equivalent to $M_b/2$; that of gages R_{3a} and R_{4a}, to $M_a/2$. The necessary algebraic summation is accomplished by connecting gages R_{1a} and R_{2a} so that they add to the

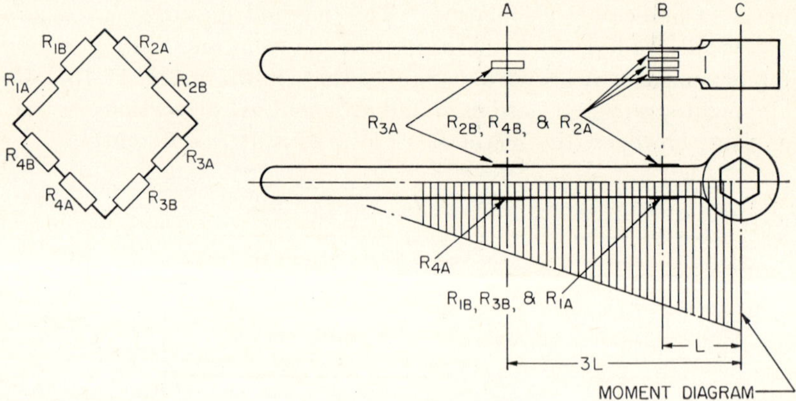

FIG. 11-15. Arrangement and connection of strain gages for measurement of wrench torque directly. (*Meier.*)

bridge output, and gages R_{3a} and R_{4a} so that they subtract. The result is a net signal whose magnitude is proportional to M_c. It can be seen that this action is independent of the point of load application on the wrench handle and is much simpler to use than the device shown in Fig. 11-14.

STRAIN GAGE TORQUE METERS

Strain gage torque meters can take a variety of forms. One form uses a load beam to measure the torque reaction. Measurement of the torque reaction has the advantage of eliminating slip rings and the associated problems of brush wear, noisy signals, etc. With a load beam, however, the device under test must be cradled in very low-friction bearings in order to produce accurate results.

Figure 11-16 illustrates a "torque table" developed by Lebow Associates to overcome both slip-ring and bearing problems. The torque table consists of a base plate which supports a mount for the test equipment on four inclined arms, the axes of which intersect the axis of rotation. Strain gages on the inclined arms are interconnected in such a manner that the output is proportional to the moment exerted by the test equipment, while effects of vertical forces, including the weight of the equipment, are canceled. This unit allows unlimited rotational speed of the test equipment and is free of friction and backlash. Another type of strain gage torque meter is that described in Chap. 10, in which four gages are mounted along 45° helices on a shaft. Still another form is the torque wrench just described. A novel strain gage torque meter with integral

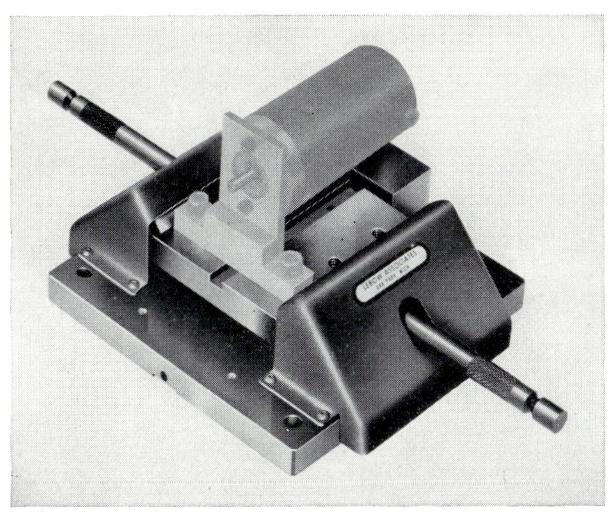

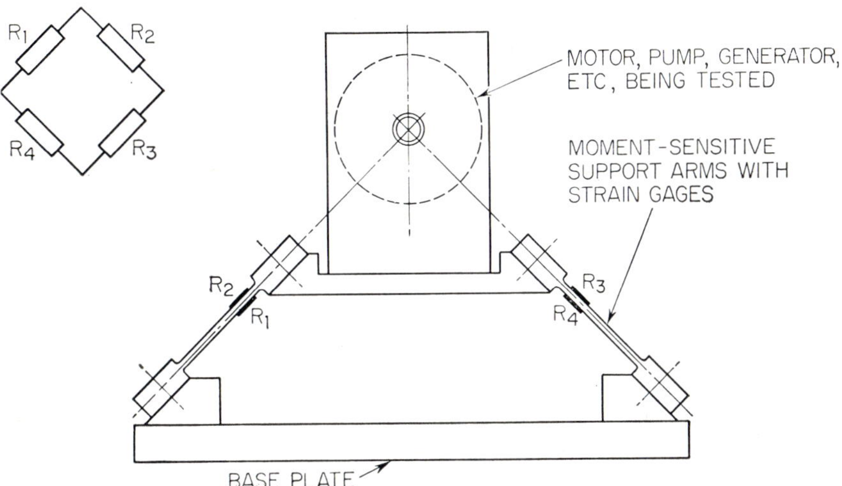

Fig. 11-16. Lebow "torque table." Transducer measures reaction torque, avoiding slip-ring difficulties, bearings, and friction. (*Courtesy of Lebow Associates.*)

slip-ring assembly and speed-sensing unit is shown in Fig. 11-17. The torque-sensitive element consists of a hollow structure with a cruciform section. Strain gages are mounted on the flat surfaces of the longitudinal members.

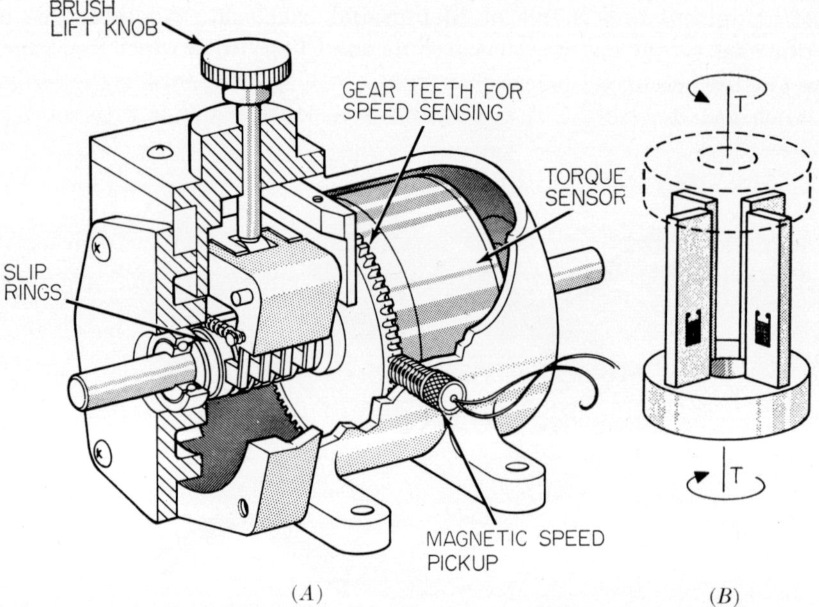

FIG. 11-17. (A) Lebow torque meter and slip-ring assembly with integral speed-sensing unit; (B) torque-sensitive element with strain gages.

SEPARATION OF FORCES AND MOMENTS WITH STRAIN GAGES

As an example of the versatility of strain gages, Fig. 11-18 shows a structural member which is subjected to both vertical and horizontal loads but in which the strain gages measure only the horizontal component. It will be noticed that strain gages R_1 and R_3 are mounted on the top and bottom of the member, respectively, and located at their usual points in the Wheatstone-bridge circuit. With this arrangement the electrical outputs of the gages are additive. If the member is subjected to a bending moment, the electrical outputs of the gages cancel

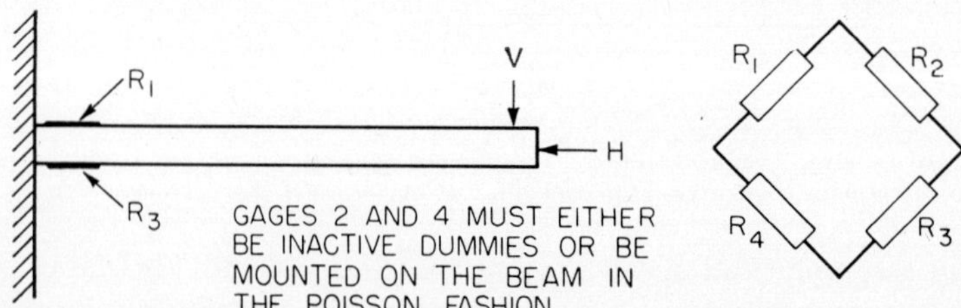

FIG. 11-18. Cantilever beam instrumented with strain gages for sensitivity to horizontal forces and insensitivity to vertical forces.

because of the difference in signs of their strains. A horizontal or axial load results in equal strains of like sign and a net electrical output from the bridge circuit. Gages R_2 and R_4 must either be used as inactive dummies on a separate unstrained piece of metal or be mounted on the member in the Poisson arrangement as previously described.

The opposite case could be represented by a structural member in which only the vertical component of load was desired. This can be accomplished as illustrated in Fig. 11-19 by mounting all four strain gages at the fixed end of the member. Gages R_1 and R_3 sense strains equal in magnitude and alike in sign, producing a bridge output proportional to the vertical component of load. The output of gages R_2 and R_4, which are also subjected to strains equal in magnitude and alike in sign (but opposite in sign to R_1 and R_3), will act to augment the bridge output of

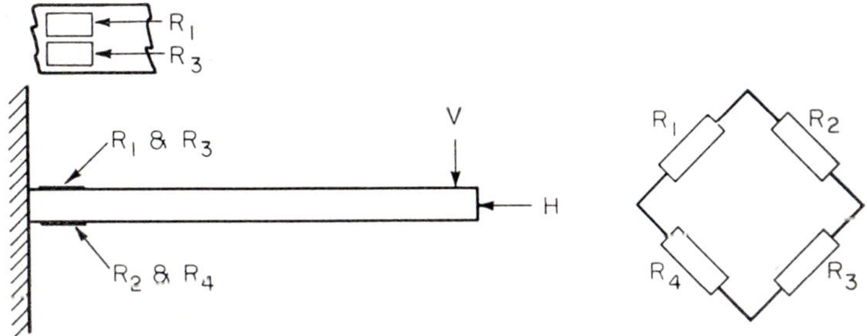

Fig. 11-19. Cantilever beam instrumented with strain gages for sensitivity to vertical forces and insensitivity to horizontal forces.

gages R_1 and R_3. If a horizontal load is applied to the member, gages R_1, R_2, R_3, and R_4 will all sense equal strains of the same sign and will cancel in the Wheatstone bridge to produce zero output. As a further elaboration, it might be desired to measure simultaneously and separately both the vertical and the horizontal load components on the member in question. This can be done by combining the arrangements of the two previous figures as illustrated in Fig. 11-20. Strain gages R_{1v}, R_{2v}, R_{3v}, and R_{4v} are arranged on the member and in the Wheatstone bridge in an identical manner to that shown in Fig. 11-19. Gages R_{2h} and R_{4h} are arranged as in Fig. 11-18. In this case, temperature compensation has been obtained by adding gages R_{1h} and R_{3h} in the Poisson arrangement, as can be seen from Fig. 11-20. With the two Wheatstone bridges shown, and with the outputs directed to separate amplifiers and indicators or recorders, the horizontal and vertical components of load can be obtained simultaneously and continuously.

Another technique for measuring two orthogonal components of a load is shown in Fig. 11-21. This device is a cylindrical cantilever beam, the end of which supports the unknown load. Four strain gages, R_{1y}, R_{2y}, R_{3y}, and R_{4y}, are arranged on the cylindrical surface so that they are sensitive to strains produced by load components in the y direction, but essentially insensitive to transverse loads. Likewise, gages R_{1x}, R_{2x}, R_{3x}, and R_{4x} produce an output proportional to the load component in the

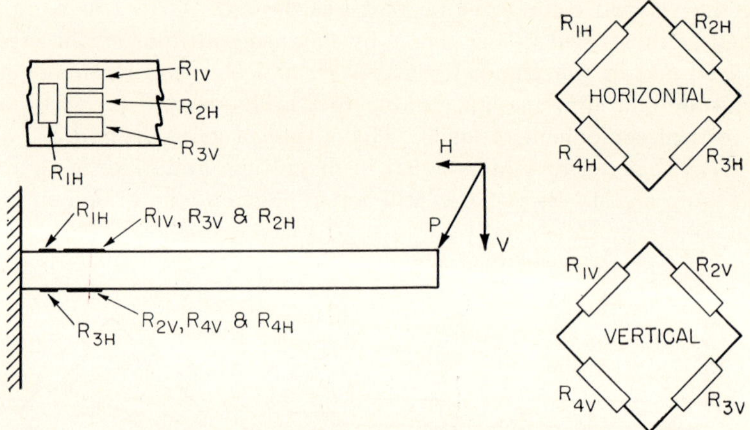

FIG. 11-20. Arrangement and connection of strain gages for measuring simultaneously the horizontal and vertical components of a load P in the plane of the beam.

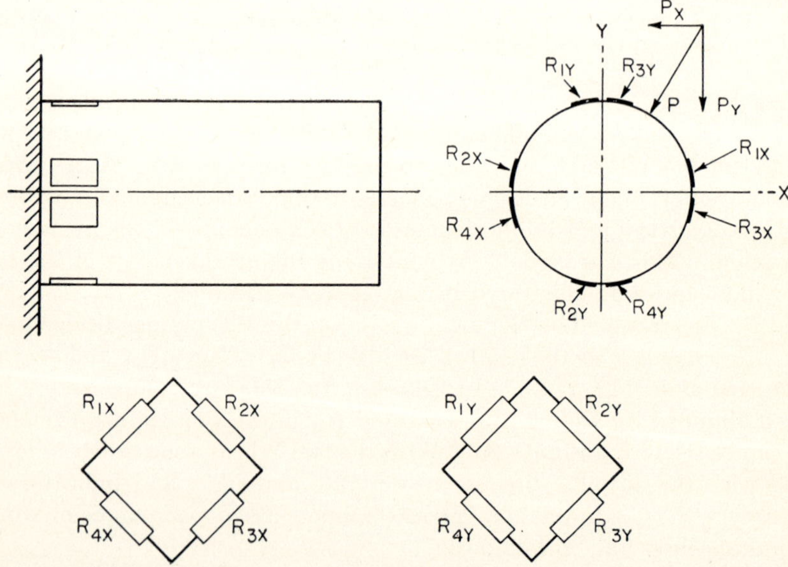

FIG. 11-21. Technique for determining x and y components of an unknown load P with a strain gage instrumented cantilever beam of circular cross section.

x direction and are insensitive to other loads. This system again uses two separate Wheatstone bridges and two channels of instrumentation for indicating or recording. The strain gage arrangements produce the usual augmented output and complete temperature compensation.

Figure 11-22 illustrates an extension of this principle employed by the Anderson-Fluke Engineering Company to measure simultaneously three

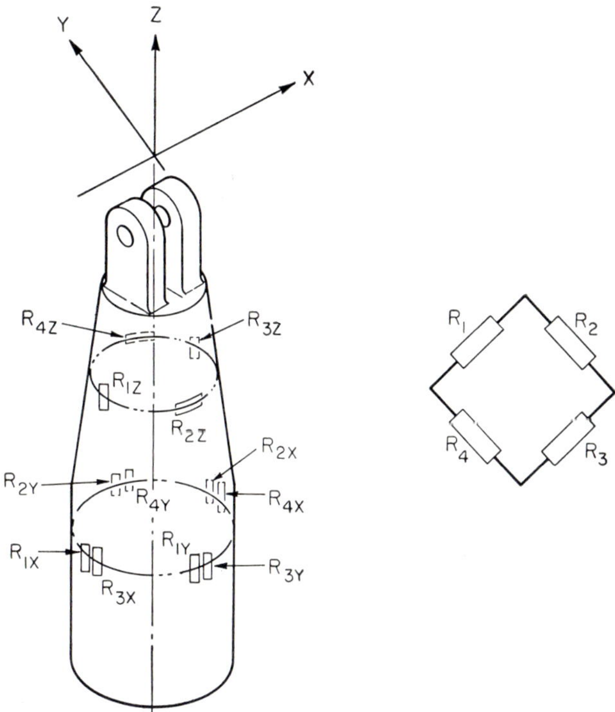

Fig. 11-22. Three-component force-sensing member employing twelve strain gages and three Wheatstone bridges and recording channels. (*Anderson.*)

orthogonal force components on an airship mooring mast. The three forces which are measured are those along the x and y axes which cause bending in the mooring mast and the axial force along the z axis representing vertical forces applied by the airship. It will be noticed that the arrangement of strain gages for the x and y forces is identical to that of Fig. 11-21. The strain gages used to measure the z component of force, R_{1z}, R_{2z}, R_{3z}, and R_{4z}, are mounted in the conventional Poisson arrangement for sensitivity to axial strain and insensitivity to bending. This force-sensing member uses three complete Wheatstone bridges and three channels of instrumentation for simultaneously recording the x, y, and z components of force.

Similar techniques were employed at Cornell University in developing a sting-type balance system for a supersonic wind tunnel. The Cornell balance is capable of simultaneous indication of lift, drag, yaw, and rolling moment. The theory and operation of this system are described by Mains in the *Proceedings* of the Society for Experimental Stress Analysis.

WAYNE STATE UNIVERSITY SIX-COMPONENT WIND-TUNNEL BALANCE

Professor M. J. Lebow of Wayne State University has developed a subsonic wind-tunnel balance which demonstrates the numerous possibilities of force and moment separation with strain gages. This balance continuously indicates the six components (three forces and three moments) which act upon an airplane in flight. Because of the universal applicability of the principles involved, the operation of the wind-tunnel balance will be described in detail.

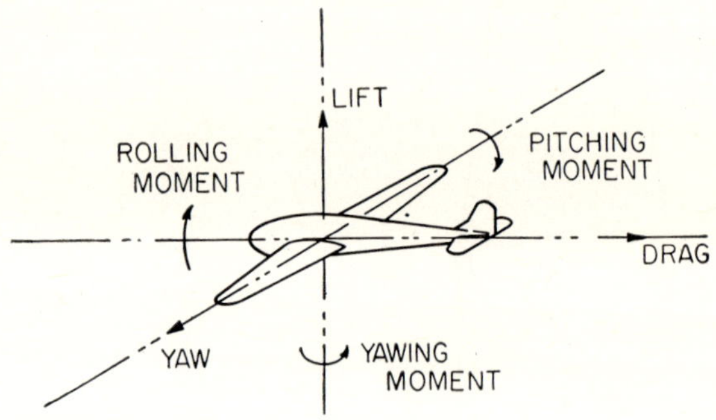

Fig. 11-23. General three-dimensional force system for an airplane model in a wind tunnel.

Figure 11-23 is a sketch of a model airplane and the general three-dimensional force system to which it responds. The forces acting on the model are (1) lift, acting upward; (2) drag, acting rearward; and (3) yaw, which tends to move the airplane laterally. The moments are the pitching moment about the transverse axis, the rolling moment about the longitudinal axis, and the yawing moment about the vertical axis. Aerodynamic engineers would like to measure all these components simultaneously and continuously to predict the performance of a prototype airplane.

Figure 11-24 is a simplified version of the system for instrumenting lift forces. The aerodynamic model (in this case a wing rather than a complete airship) is mounted on a vertical support strut which passes through the floor of the wind tunnel and rests on a platform below. The platform in turn is supported from a fixed base by slender beams fore and aft, as shown in the figure. Strain gages are placed on the upper and lower sides of the fixed ends of these beams. When the wind produces a positive lift force, the platform and the attached ends of the beams move upward, straining gages R_{1a} and R_{1b} in compression and R_{4a}

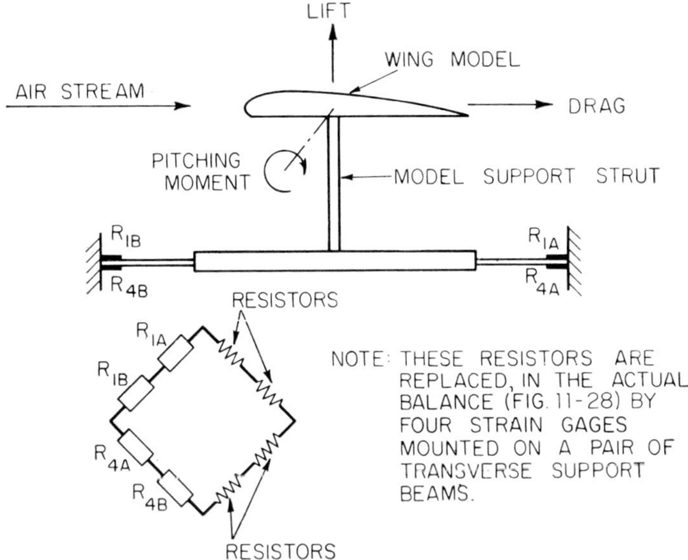

FIG. 11-24. Two-dimensional system for detecting lift forces on a wind-tunnel model. (*Lebow.*)

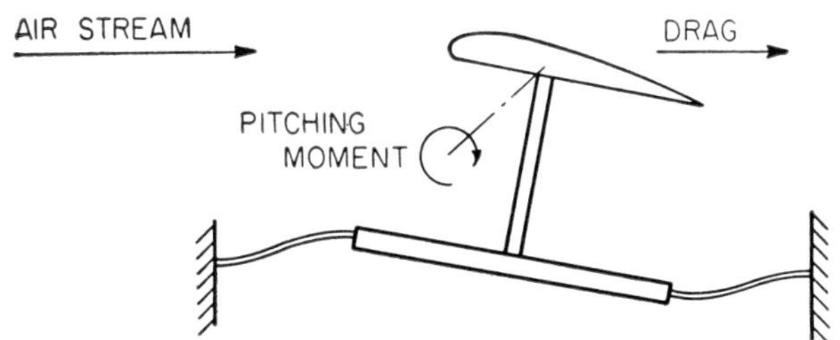

FIG. 11-25. Mode of deformation (greatly exaggerated) of longitudinal beams due to pitching moment and drag force. (*Lebow.*)

and R_{4b} in tension. With these gages located in the Wheatstone-bridge circuit as shown, the resulting resistance changes will all combine to produce a bridge unbalance proportional to the lift. If a pitching moment occurs, the two beams will deflect in opposite directions (Fig. 11-25) and their outputs will cancel in the bridge circuit. The drag force produces two actions on this system. Because of its moment arm, it causes a deflection similar to that produced by the pitching moment. The effect of this deflection is likewise canceled electrically. The drag force also tends to shorten the right-hand beam and extend the left-hand beam, and again the resistance changes due to this effect are canceled in the bridge circuit. Figure 11-24 shows only the fore and aft platform support beams. There are also two transverse support beams which function in

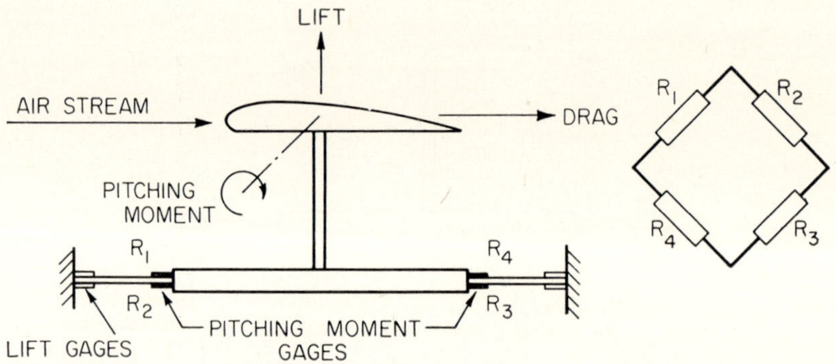

Fig. 11-26. Strain gage arrangement and connection for detecting pitching moment. The moment due to the aerodynamic drag of the model is deleted electrically by a technique described in the text. (*Lebow.*)

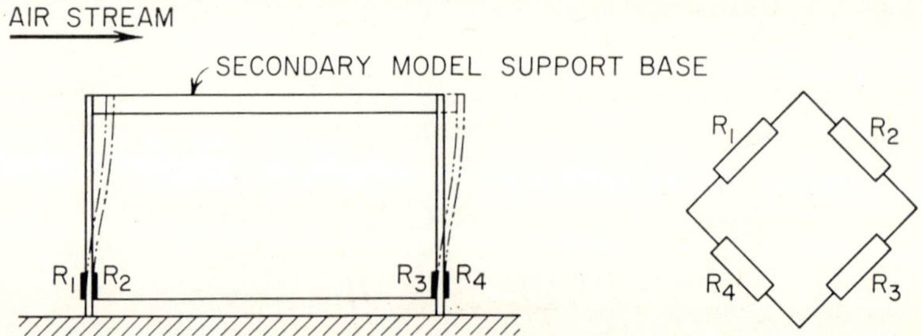

Fig. 11-27. Drag link and strain gage disposition for measuring drag on a wind-tunnel model. Refer to Fig. 11-28 for the functional position of the drag link in the balance assembly. (*Lebow.*)

the same manner. The four strain gages on the transverse beams make up the other half of the lift bridge circuit.

The sketch of Fig. 11-25 represents the mode of deformation of the fore and aft platform support beams when subjected to a pitching moment or drag force. In Fig. 11-26 is shown the method of using these beams to indicate the magnitude of the pitching moment. Figure 11-27 illustrates the configuration of beams used for isolating the drag force. The strain gages are mounted and connected so that this system is unaffected by other forces or moments. Two sets of strain gages can be attached to the drag links. The output of one set will be used for indicating the drag force itself; and the output of the second set will be used to cancel the effect of drag force in the pitching-moment bridge circuit.

The rolling moment of the aerodynamic model is sensed by the transverse support beams (see Fig. 11-28) in the same manner as the pitching moment by the longitudinal beams. The system used for measuring the yaw force parallels that for the drag force and acts in the transverse

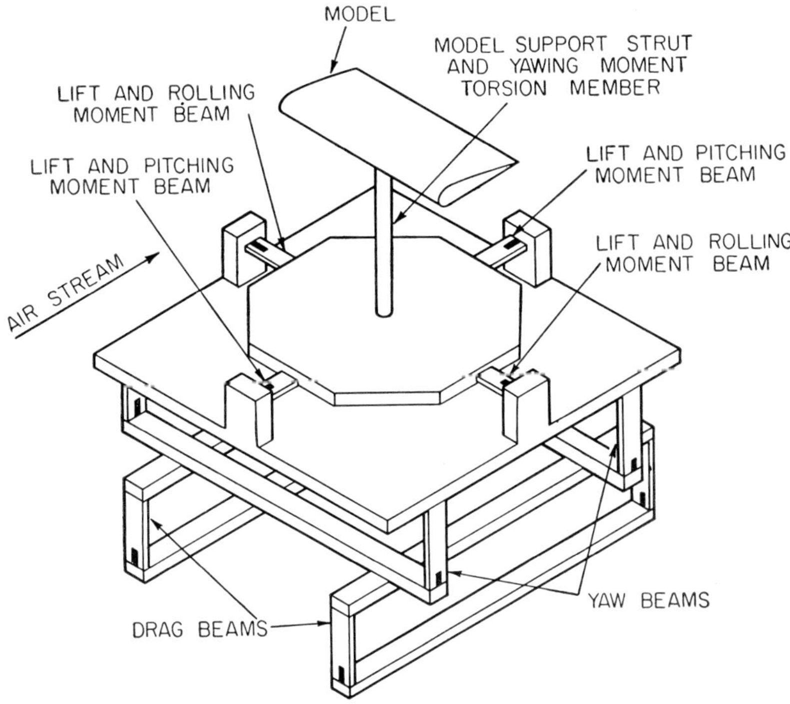

FIG. 11-28. Schematic arrangement of the Wayne State University six-component wind-tunnel balance. (*Lebow.*)

plane. The sixth component, the yawing moment, is measured by placing four strain gages on 45° helices on the model support strut so that they are strained by torsion about the strut axis. The complete assembly of beams is illustrated in Fig. 11-28.

The accuracy of this technique depends upon having very small deformations of the beam ends so that the geometry of the system does not change under the application of aerodynamic loads. Professor Lebow accomplished this by using aluminum beams for all load-measuring members. It can be shown that an aluminum beam will deflect less for a given load and strain than the corresponding steel beam. Assuming that two cantilever beams (one of steel and the other aluminum) of length L are to support a load P, let us calculate the comparative deflections for the same value of strain at the root of the beam. The deflection formula for a cantilever beam is

$$y = \frac{PL^3}{3EI}$$

Applying this equation to the above beams gives

$$y_a = \frac{PL^3}{3E_aI_a} \qquad \text{aluminum beam}$$

$$y_s = \frac{PL^3}{3E_sI_s} \qquad \text{steel beam}$$

The equation for the strain at the root of the cantilever beams is likewise

$$\epsilon_a = \frac{PLC_a}{E_aI_a}$$

$$\epsilon_s = \frac{PLC_s}{E_sI_s}$$

By definition, then, the strains of the two beams shall be equal when subjected to the same load P acting at the same moment arm L. Thus, equating the two expressions for strain

$$\frac{LPC_a}{E_aI_a} = \frac{LPC_s}{E_sI_s}$$

and since

$$I = \frac{bh^3}{12}$$

and

$$C = \frac{h}{2}$$

we have

$$\frac{h_a{}^2}{h_s{}^2} = \frac{E_s}{E_a}$$

for the case in which the two beams have the same width. If the modulus of elasticity of steel is taken as 3 times that of aluminum, then the aluminum beam should be 1.732 times the thickness of the steel beam to produce the same strain for a given load and moment arm. Substituting these thicknesses into the deflection formulas, we obtain

$$\frac{y_s}{y_a} = \frac{E_aI_a}{E_sI_s} = \frac{(1.732)^3}{3} = 1.732$$

In other words, an aluminum cantilever beam can be designed to carry the same load at the same length and with the same strain as a steel beam but with noticeably less ($\sqrt{E_a/E_s}$) deflection. This principle should be kept in mind in designing beam-type strain gage transducers where deflection is important. A similar (but much greater) reduction in deflection for a set value of strain and load can be obtained by using a shorter aluminum beam of the same thickness as the steel. In the latter case the reduction in deflection for equal strains is proportional to $(E_a/E_s)^2$. The practicality of this latter technique is limited by the length of the strain gages employed. The shorter the beam, the steeper will be the strain gradient. As the strain gradient becomes steep, the integrated strain along the length of the gage becomes considerably less than that existing at the root of the beam. If the strain gradient is linear, the gage output will correspond to the strain at the center of the gage.

OTHER FORCE MEASUREMENTS WITH STRAIN GAGES

As stated earlier in this chapter, measurement of forces merely requires placing an elastic member instrumented with strain gages at some point in the force system. The previous examples have indicated several of these applications. Still another field of use is that of measuring machining and forming forces. It is evident that the accumulation of such knowledge is extremely useful in studying and improving machine-tool performance.

Several different types of tool dynamometers have been built using strain gages as the load-sensing elements. One of the more interesting of these is a planer dynamometer developed at the Massachusetts Institute of Technology. The elastic members in this instance are four aluminum rings as pictured in Fig. 11-29 and shown diagrammatically in Fig. 11-30. Vertical tool forces F_v will act to compress all four rings equally. Horizontal tool forces F_h set up a moment $(b/a)F_h$ which tends to extend rings 1 and 2 while compressing rings 3 and 4. Because of this action, it is possible to mount four strain gages on each ring and connect them electrically in two different bridge circuits so that horizontal and vertical forces on the planer tool can be recorded at the same time.

The strain gages are mounted on the sides of the rings (Fig. 11-31) and oriented with their major axes circumferential. This orientation minimizes the effects of axial strain in the ring and makes the gages highly sensitive to the bending strains which accompany compression or extension. The gages on the inside of the rings naturally sense a strain opposite in sign to that of the outside gages and thus can be employed for temperature compensation as well as augmentation of the circuit output. It should be noted that except in the case of thin-walled rings (ratio of thickness to radius equal to 0.10 or less) the stress on the inner surface cannot be considered equal to that on the outer surface. This fact need not prohibit the use of thick-walled rings so long as they are calibrated for bridge output versus load. The strain at any point on the ring still varies linearly with load at stresses below the proportional limit.

FIG. 11-29. MIT planer dynamometer. (*Courtesy of E. G. Loewen, Massachusetts Institute of Technology.*)

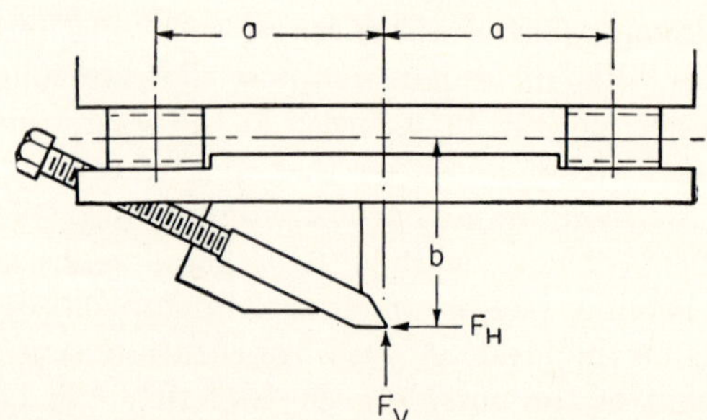

FIG. 11-30. Mechanical arrangement of the MIT planer dynamometer. (*Loewen, Marshall, and Shaw.*)

The method of connecting gages for separate indication of vertical and horizontal forces will be evident from a study of Fig. 11-31. Analysis becomes quite simple when it is remembered that for adjacent legs of the bridge the output varies as the difference in resistance changes and for opposite legs as the sum. In the case of the bridge circuit for vertical forces, gages R_{1a}, R_{1b}, R_{3a}, and R_{3b} will all be strained in tension, and

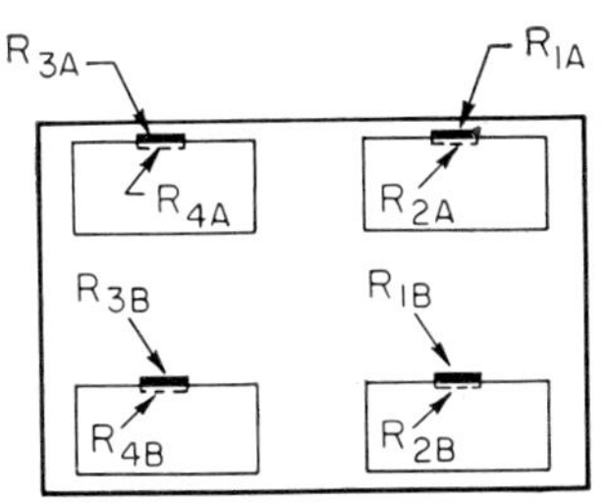

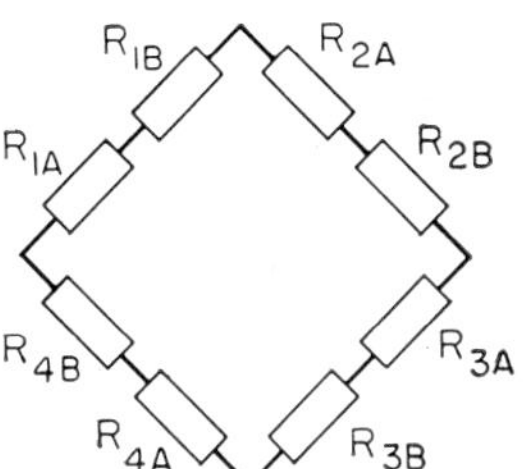

PLAN VIEW OF RINGS SHOWING GAGE LOCATIONS FOR MEASURING THE HORIZONTAL COMPONENT OF TOOL FORCE.

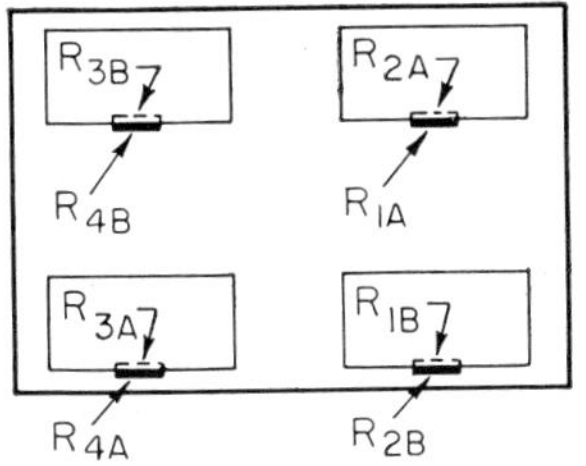

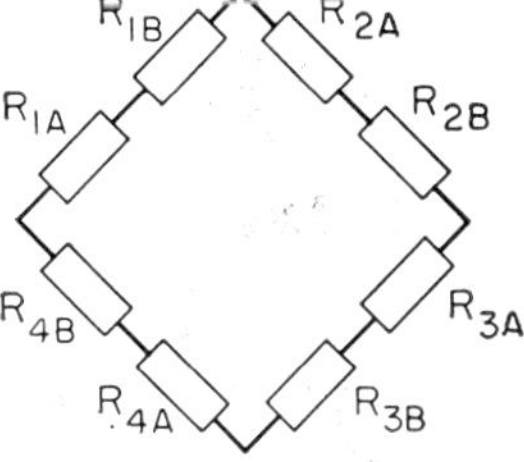

PLAN VIEW OF RINGS SHOWING GAGE LOCATIONS FOR MEASURING THE VERTICAL COMPONENT OF TOOL FORCE.

Fig. 11-31. Bridge circuits and strain gage arrangement of the MIT planer dynamometer. (*Loewen, Marshall, and Shaw.*)

their effects will be additive. Gages R_{2a}, R_{2b}, R_{4a}, and R_{4b} will be strained in compression, and their effects will add to the output of the bridge circuit since the resistance changes are of opposite sign. It can readily be shown that the reactions produced by the horizontal force will have no effect on the vertical-force circuit. The moment of the horizontal tool force will strain R_{1a}, R_{1b}, R_{4a}, and R_{4b} in compression and R_{2a}, R_{2b}, R_{3a}, and R_{3b} in tension, thus producing no bridge unbalance. The bridge circuit for measuring the horizontal force parallels that for the vertical force except for reversing the physical positions of the strain gages which make up the lower half of the bridge circuit. Dynamometers for drill presses, surface grinders, and lathes have been developed at the Massachusetts Institute of Technology employing these same general principles. In Fig. 11-32 is shown a commercial torque meter adapted for use as a drill-press dynamometer. The system as pictured does not measure drill thrust, which may also be important. Some drill-press

Fig. 11-32. Commercial torque meter used as a drill-press dynamometer to measure thread-tapping torque. (*Courtesy of Baldwin-Lima-Hamilton Corporation.*)

dynamometers, therefore, are mounted on the worktable and designed to sense both torque and thrust. Figure 11-33 shows a lathe dynamometer of slightly different form, whose operation can be understood from the previous examples.

Strain gages have also been used to study various drawing and forming operations in presses. The load-sensitive member can be located at any point in the press or die assembly where it carries the full load of the operation. An example of this technique is shown in Fig. 11-34. A small load-sensitive column has been incorporated in the die assembly so that drawing forces are applied to the bolster plate through this column. The design of the column is standard for axially stressed strain gage transducers. Four gages, two oriented along the column axis and two circumferentially in the Poisson arrangement, are used to detect the load. Fig-

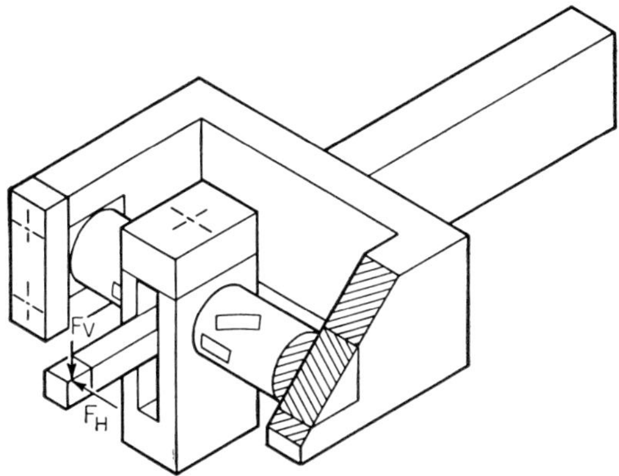

FIG. 11-33. Schematic drawing of the MIT lathe dynamometer. Eight strain gages measure bending and torsion in the circular member. (*Loewen, Marshall, and Shaw.*)

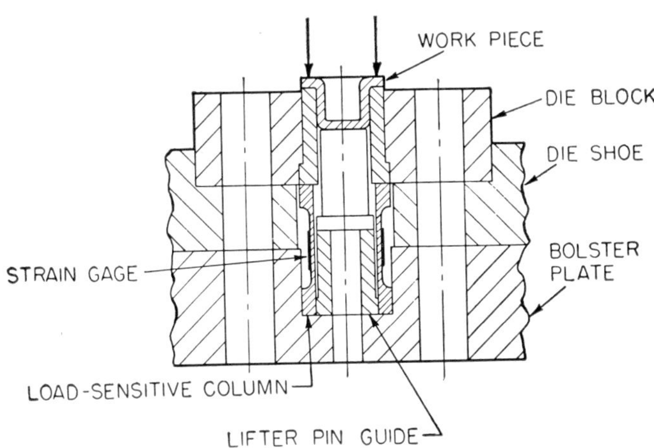

FIG. 11-34. Load column mounted in a die set for measuring drawing forces. (*Kimbell.*)

ure 11-35 shows oscillograms obtained from the above system during cupping and redrawing operations.

Figure 11-36 shows the Strainsert load-sensitive bolt for measuring tightening loads. The hollow shank of the bolt has two strain gages mounted along the bolt axis and 180° apart on the periphery of the hole. The orientation of the gages renders them insensitive to torsion stresses,

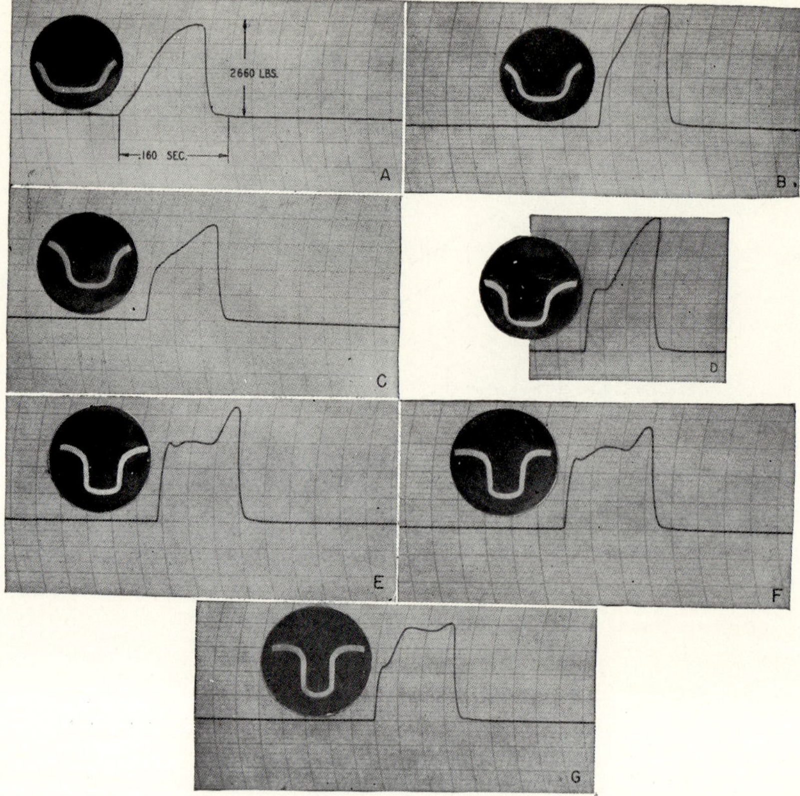

Fig. 11-35. Load oscillograms for sheet-metal cupping and redrawing operations: (*A*) cupping, (*B*) first redraw, (*C*) second redraw, (*D*) third redraw, (*E*) fourth redraw, (*F*) fifth redraw, (*G*) sixth redraw. (*Courtesy of United-Carr Fastener Corporation.*)

and their opposing locations act to cancel bending stresses. The bolt is thus sensitive to axial load only.

THE USE OF STRAIN GAGE TRANSDUCERS WITHOUT AMPLIFIERS

It is possible to design most strain gage force transducers so that a full bridge circuit of four active gages can be employed. Since the output of this type of system is four times that of a single gage, a sensitive microammeter will often be sufficient for load indication. The output can also be increased by using high-resistance gages and, if necessary, two gages in series in each bridge leg. The bridge supply voltage should also be made as high as is compatible with the heat-dissipating characteristics of the gages mounted on the strain-generating members. Piezoresistive strain gages on the transducing element will produce output signals of sufficient amplitude so that a common "1-mil" meter can be used directly, without amplification, to indicate the load. Equation (4-10) can be used to design the circuit parameters for these systems.

A typical transducer which has enough output to drive a microammeter directly is the brake-pedal force indicator (Fig. 11-37) developed by the Vehicle Testing Laboratory of the Ford Motor Company. The

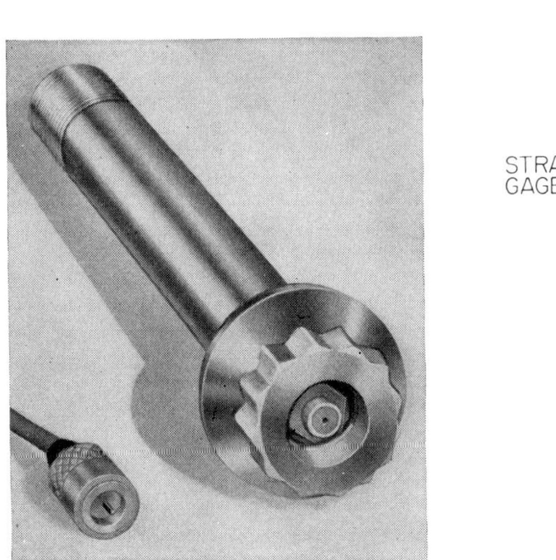

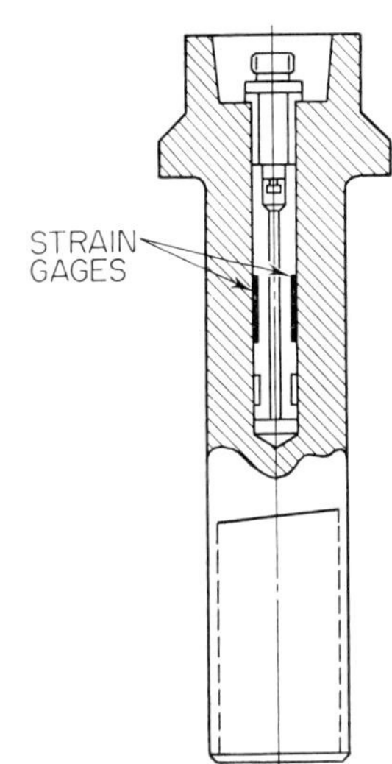

Fig. 11-36. Strainsert load-sensitive bolt. Two strain gages connected in series and mounted diametrically opposite on the periphery of the hole measure tightening loads. (*Courtesy of Strainsert Company.*)

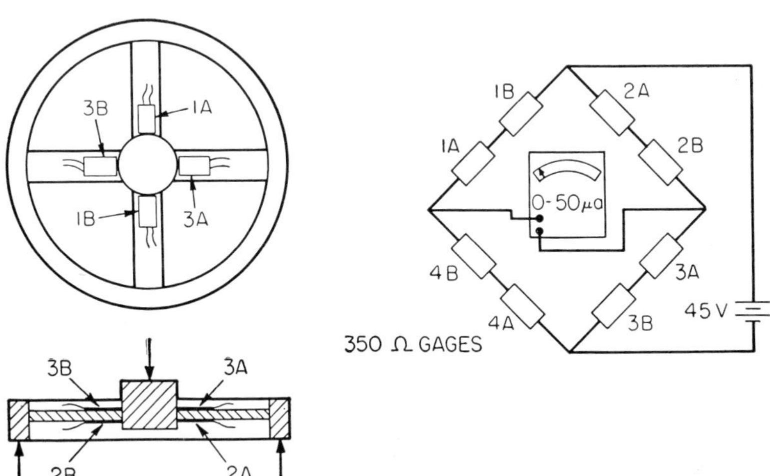

Fig. 11-37. Transducer and circuit for direct indication of force with a microammeter.

elastic element of this device is composed of four beams attached radially to a hub and a rim in the general form of a wheel. On the beams are mounted a total of eight 350-ohm strain gages, resulting in a bridge circuit with two gages in series in each leg. A 45-volt battery and a meter of 50 micro-amperes full-scale reading complete the circuit. The meter can, if desired, be calibrated so that the force magnitude is indicated directly in the proper units. This equipment makes a very convenient portable system for general-purpose field and mobile testing where accuracy requirements are not too high.

A further advantage of the type of transducer described here is that its electrical output is independent of the point of load application. This property occurs as a result of the same general considerations previously described for separating forces and moments with strain gage circuits.

ACCELEROMETERS

Like the foregoing force-measuring units, strain gage accelerometers have been built in a variety of forms. One of the simplest of these consists of a cantilever beam with a mass attached to the free end as sketched

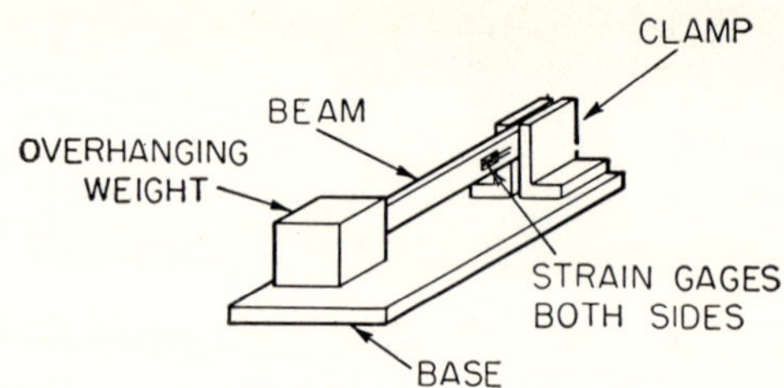

Fig. 11-38. Beam accelerometer employed by the Cramp Shipbuilding Company for measuring ship-launching accelerations.

in Fig. 11-38. This accelerometer was used by the Cramp Shipbuilding Company for investigating the accelerations which occur during the launching of a ship. Since such accelerations are very low in magnitude, a long, thin beam and a heavy weight were employed for sensitivity. Such a unit would, of course, be characterized by a low natural frequency. In this particular instance the low natural frequency is not a handicap because of the acceleration characteristics met in ship-launching practice.

A similar unit developed at the Naval Air Experimental Station in Philadelphia has been widely used for measuring aircraft accelerations during flight maneuvers. This unit consists of a fluid-damped double-cantilever arrangement with two strain gages at the root of each of the beams. The accelerometer is shown in Fig. 11-39. As built, the unit exhibits a natural frequency of 20 cps and has a range of $\pm 10g$ and a flat frequency response to 10 cps when damped with a 250-centistoke fluid. An interesting result of the double-cantilever construction is its freedom from the effects of transverse accelerations. This again is brought about by the respective sum and difference characteristics of opposite and adjacent Wheatstone-bridge legs.

A mechanically different accelerometer designed at the Naval Research Laboratory is shown sectionally in Fig. 11-40. This accelerometer has a range of $\pm 5{,}000g$ at frequencies up to 5,000 cps. In this instrument

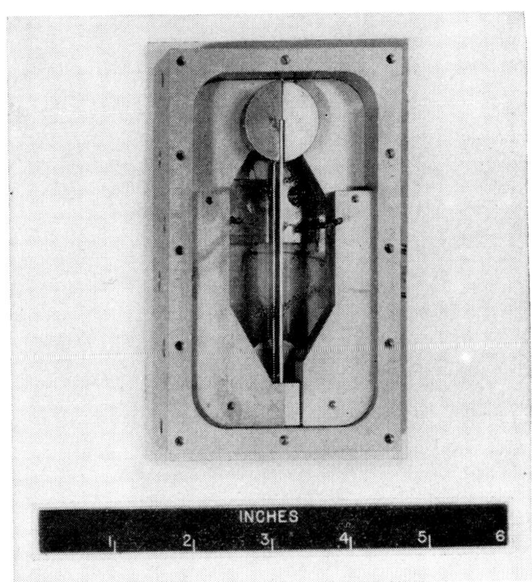

Fig. 11-39. Double-cantilever strain gage accelerometer developed by Weiss and Towle at the Naval Air Experimental Station, Philadelphia, Pa. (*United States Navy photograph.*)

two thin-walled dural cups act as the elastic members. The rims of the cups seat on the shoulders of the accelerometer body so that the thick-walled bottoms of the cups do not touch one another. Thick monel weights are then placed in each cup and the assembly tightened together with the center bolt. As a result, both dural cups are in initial tension (1,400 micro-inches per in. or so). Four strain gages are placed on each cup and connected as shown in Fig. 11-40. When subjected to velocity changes in the plane of the accelerometer centerline, the tensile strain in the wall of one cup increases, while that in the other decreases. With rated acceleration neither cup ever goes into compression. In this case a low-modulus-of-elasticity material is desirable for the cups so that maximum lateral or radial stiffness can be obtained for a given longitudinal elasticity. The gages, as indicated by the circuit diagram, are automatically temperature-compensated as well as being arranged for minimum sensitivity to transverse acceleration. Figure 11-41 shows an exploded view of the accelerometer.

The Statham Company manufactures a line of seismic accelerometers employing the unbonded strain gage principle. In the Statham instruments the inertia load of the mass is applied directly to several

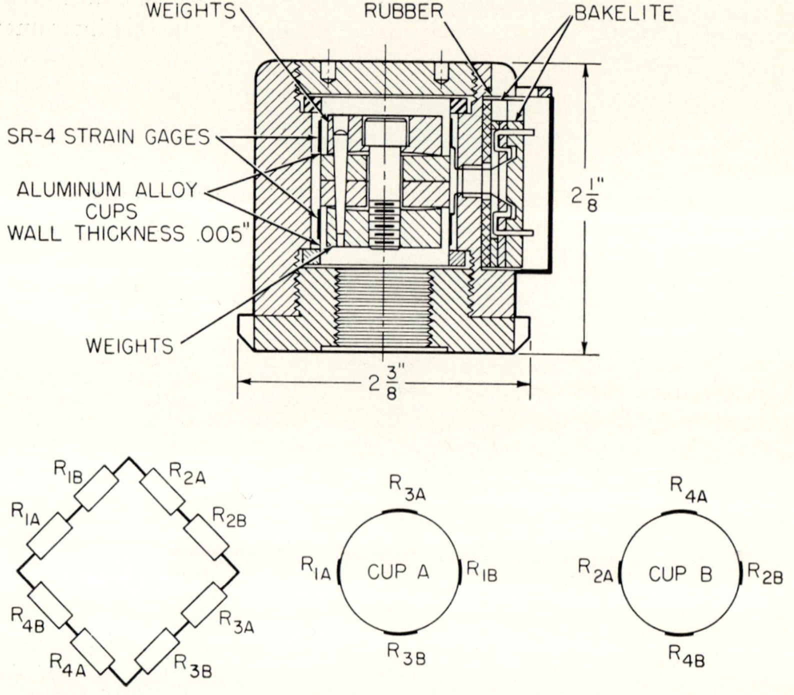

FIG. 11-40. Mechanical and electrical arrangement of strain gages in the NRL cup-type accelerometer. (*Naval Research Laboratory.*)

strands of supporting strain-sensitive wire. These accelerometers are built with ranges as high as $\pm 500g$ and natural frequencies as high as 4,500 cps.

It can be seen that strain gage accelerometers are all quite similar in consisting of a strain gaged elastic member supporting a mass. The design of accelerometers is considerably more complex than that of the load cells and force links previously described. The latter devices need be designed only for strength considerations and optimum gage location and orientation. Accelerometers, however, become involved with the field of vibrations, and for precise determination of accelerations it will be necessary to consider natural frequency, damping, applied frequency,

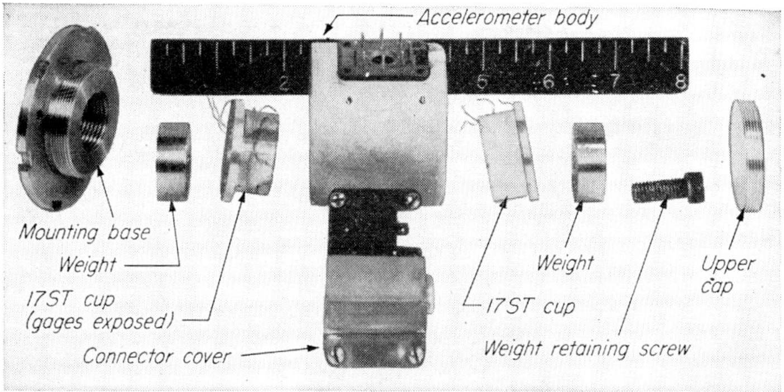

FIG. 11-41. Exploded view of the NRL cup-type accelerometer. (*Courtesy of Naval Research Laboratory, United States Navy photograph.*)

phase distortion, and similar ramifications as well as maximum sensitivity. Before attempting to design a strain gage accelerometer a study should be made of the references given at the end of this chapter.

STRAIN GAGE PRESSURE PICKUPS

Because of the versatility of the strain gage, pressure pickups based on this principle take a variety of configurations. One of the simplest ways to make a strain gage-type pressure element is merely to thin down a portion of the wall of a short length of tubing and bond a strain gage to the thinned surface. Actually, a second gage should be placed on an adjacent section of the full-thickness tube for temperature compensation. This technique is perfectly usable for measuring static or slowly varying pressures. If the pressure is pulsing or varying rapidly, however, the fluid column in the tube may affect the accuracy of the results.

Diaphragm-type pressure cells have generally been the most popular. These usually operate on one of two principles. The strain gages are mounted either directly on the diaphragm or on an elastic supporting member which is strained by diaphragm displacement. The Control Engineering Corporation manufactures a pressure transducer of the latter type employing a "catenary" diaphragm. Figure 11-42 is a sectional view of this pressure pickup. The manufacturer claims virtually complete insensitivity to engine temperature, vibrations, and similar variables. Low-pressure air cooling is employed in the pickup specifically intended for engine-indicator applications. The latter pickup has a natural frequency of approximately 45,000 cps and a range of -10 to $+2,000$ psi dynamically or -10 to $+3,000$ psi for static pressures.

Mounting the strain gages directly on the diaphragm is apt to lead to a smaller, more compact installation. A reference to Timoshenko's

"Strength of Materials," Part II, will confirm that the stress distribution in a uniformly loaded thin plate is as shown in Fig. 11-43. Since there are both tensile and compressive strains present, the opportunity of securing temperature compensation in adjacent bridge legs suggests itself. The two strain gages might be mounted on the diaphragm as indicated in Fig. 11-44 so that gage R_1 is subjected to tensile strain, while gage R_2 is strained in compression. Figure 11-45 illustrates a pressure pickup

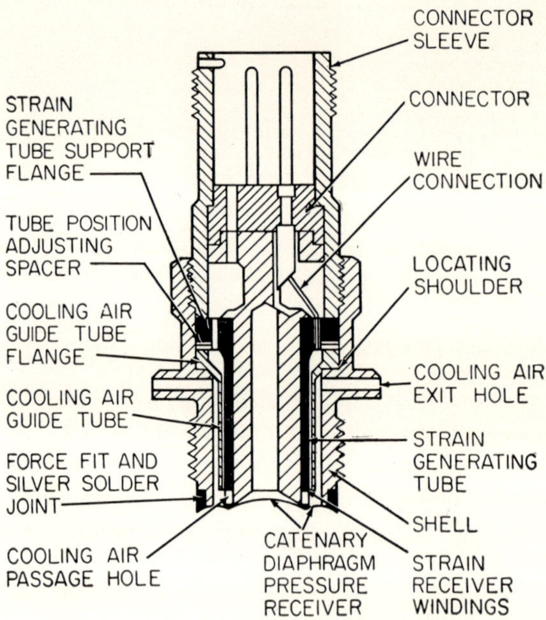

FIG. 11-42. Cross section of the "catenary" diaphragm pressure transducer. The diaphragm force is transmitted to a strain-generating tube upon which a strain gage is mounted. (*Courtesy of Control Engineering Corporation.*)

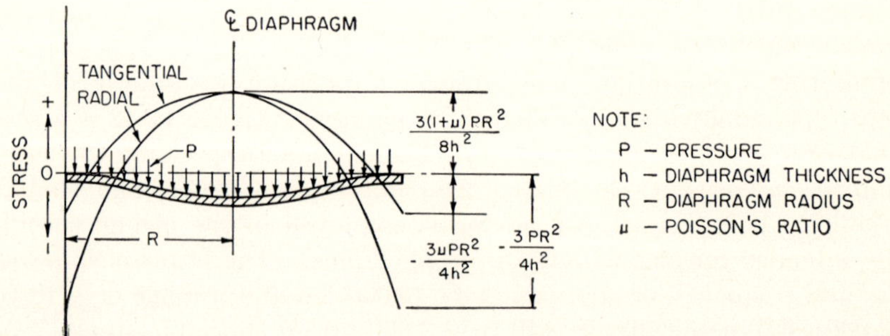

FIG. 11-43. Stress distribution in a uniformly loaded diaphragm with clamped edges. (*Timoshenko.*)

based on this principle built by the David Taylor Model Basin. As an alternative, a strain gage with a spiral grid (Fig. 11-46) can be employed. Self-temperature-compensated foil spiral grid gages are available in ½- and ¼-in.-diameter sizes from the Baldwin-Lima-Hamilton Corporation.

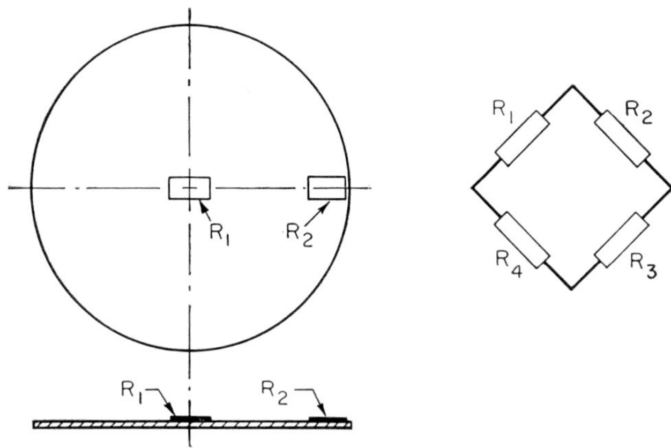

Fig. 11-44. Disposition of strain gages on a diaphragm for temperature compensation and maximum output.

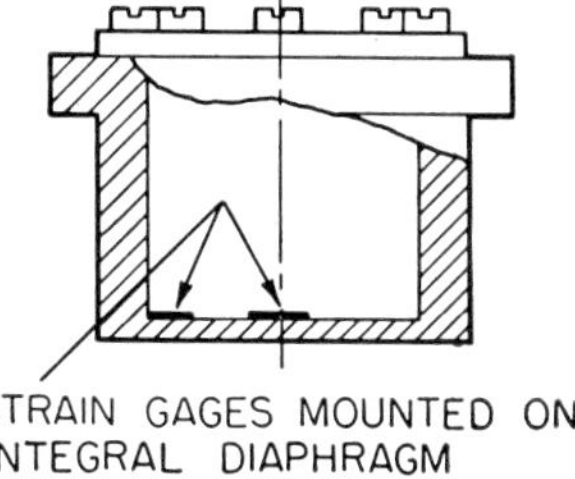

Fig. 11-45. Integral diaphragm-type pressure transducer developed at the David Taylor Model Basin. Sensitivities of these transducers (varying with materials and dimensions) range from 10 to 40 micro-inches per in. per psi. (*Wenk.*)

Fig. 11-46. Spiral grid foil gage for use on diaphragm-type pressure transducers. (*Courtesy of Baldwin-Lima-Hamilton Corporation.*)

The authors have constructed a number of miniature pressure transducers of the type having strain gages bonded directly to the diaphragm. Because the size and weight were major considerations and the assemblies were originally intended for instrumenting dynamic pressures, only one gage was used on each diaphragm. A C-19 gage of $\frac{1}{16}$ in. gage length was bonded to the center of a 0.205-in.-diameter diaphragm after trimming the gage down to the bare essentials. This is shown in Fig. 11-47. The diaphragm is clamped to a shoulder in the pickup body as illustrated in Fig. 11-48 by tightening the nut down on the compression sleeve. This has been found to create a satisfactory seal for the pressures at which the gages have been tested to date, that is, up to 1,000 psi. Lead wires are brought out through a central hole in the nut which

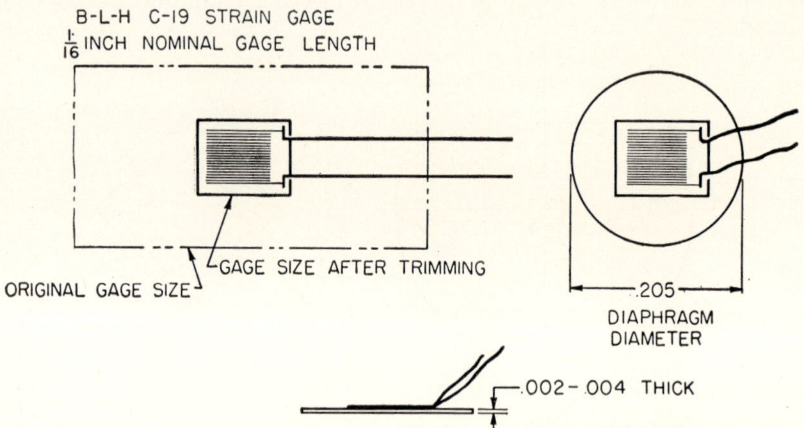

FIG. 11-47. Manner of trimming and mounting a strain gage on the diaphragm of the Wayne State University miniature pressure transducer.

is later filled with some sealing compound such as Glyptal or epoxy cement. Figure 11-49 shows the component parts and a completely assembled unit alongside a scale for size comparison. Since the pickup shown in Fig. 11-48 uses only a single strain gage, the gage should, of course, be self-compensating. Another means of incorporating temperature compensation in these transducers involves cementing an additional gage to the inner surface of the compression sleeve. The entire pickup is small enough so that temperature differentials should ordinarily not be very great except when subjected to rapid temperature fluctuations. The second gage can also be useful in assembling the unit. If the gages are connected as adjacent legs in the Wheatstone bridge and the bridge balanced before tightening the retaining nut, the load in the compression sleeve, and hence the sealing pressure, can be measured as the nut is tightened.

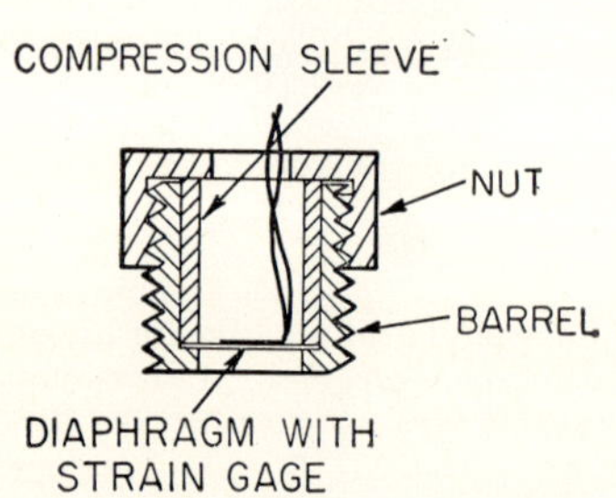

FIG. 11-48. Cross section of the Wayne State University miniature pressure transducer.

In constructing pickups of such small size it will be found that paper or epoxy gages are much easier to mount than bakelite gages. Installations employing bakelite gages can be made, however, if one has a sufficient supply of patience—and bakelite strain gages. A diaphragm-type pressure pickup has also been devised for the measurement of blood pressures. In this particular case the diaphragm is an integral part of the stainless-steel body, and the temperature-compensating gage is mounted on the inner surface of the pickup cover.

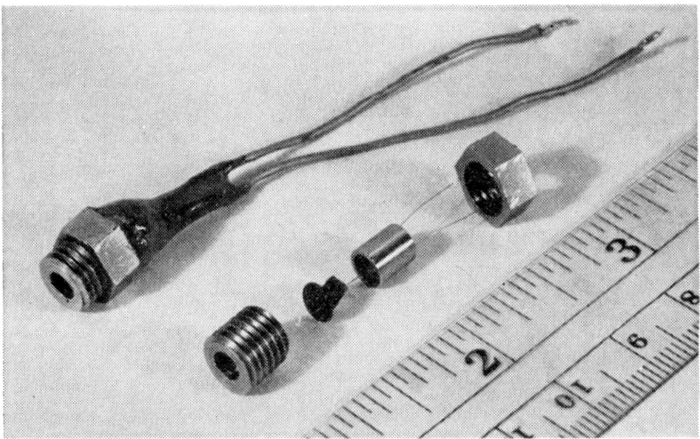

FIG. 11-49. Component parts and assembly of the Wayne State University miniature pressure transducer.

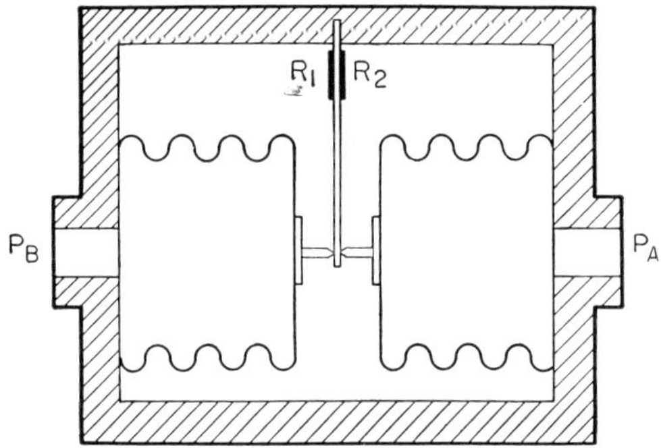

FIG. 11-50. Strain gage transducer for measuring differential pressures with double bellows and cantilever beam.

Still another type of pressure transducer is to be found in the bellows construction indicated in Fig. 11-50. A light cantilever beam is deflected by the bellows and the beam strain measured as an indication of pressure. This construction has the advantage of capability for measuring differential pressures. There are also no sealing problems, and temperature compensation can be obtained by methods discussed several times earlier in this book. The Taber Instrument Corporation manufactures a pressure transducer which contains a ring supporting a diaphragm assembly. The strain gages are mounted on the ring surface as shown in Fig. 11-51. These units are available in capacities ranging from 50 to 10,000 psi.

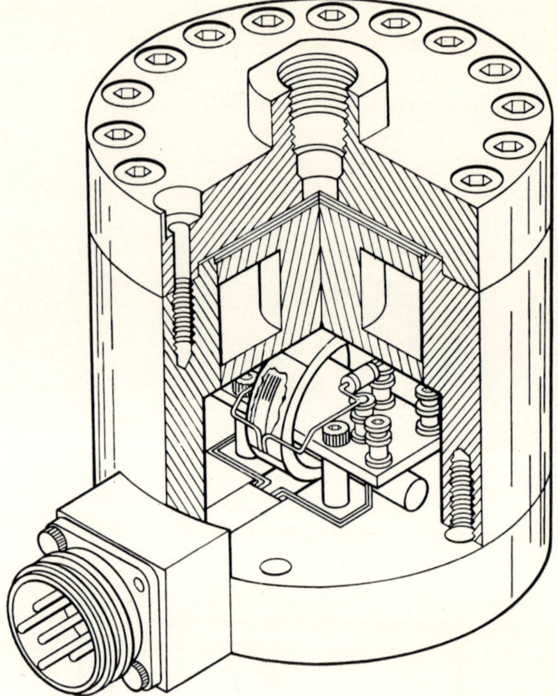

Fig. 11-51. Commercial pressure transducer in which the diaphragm force deforms a ring upon which strain gages are mounted. (*Courtesy of Taber Instrument Corporation.*)

DISPLACEMENT INSTRUMENTATION

Measurements of displacement, dimensional deviation, or deformation are accomplished very easily with strain gages. The basic technique is to mount the strain gages on an elastic member so arranged that it will be strained in following the significant deflections. Suppose, for example, one wishes to design an electrical gage for dimensional inspection of production parts. This might consist of nothing more than the ubiquitous cantilever beam supported so that the parts to be inspected can deflect the free beam end as illustrated in Fig. 11-52. The strain gages are connected in the conventional manner for the cantilever beam. The meter of the strain indicator might be calibrated in 0.0001-in. increments of deviation from the nominal dimension, although one could obviously design this system so that it would automatically reject and separate the parts which are over or under the limit. The same principle can be applied to continuous measurement or control of sheet width or thickness in, say, a rolling-mill or other strip process.

The Research Department of the Ford Motor Company has used the same technique in a somewhat more dynamic manner. Figure 11-53 illustrates a strain gage "lashometer," employed by the above organization to study the valve lash or clearance in L-head internal-combustion engines. The solid base of the fork is pivoted in an anchor so that the free end can travel up and down with the valve. Since the spring load to close the cantilever prongs is much lower than that of the valve

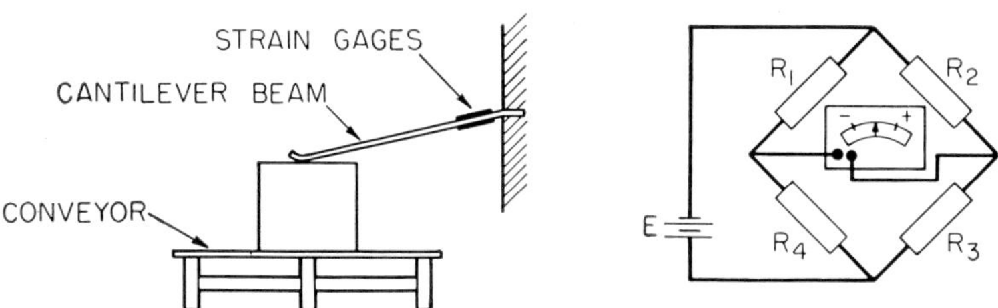

FIG. 11-52. Method of dimensional inspection with a strain gage instrumented thin cantilever feeler.

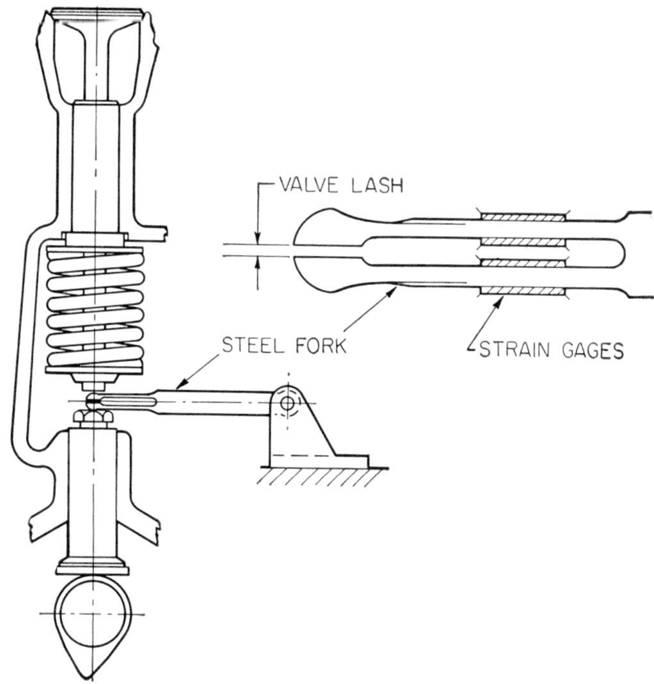

FIG. 11-53. Working diagram of the strain gage lashometer. (*Courtesy of Ford Motor Company.*)

spring, the prongs will be closed whenever the valve is off its seat. When the camshaft rotation is such that the valve lifter is riding on the base circle of the cam, the valve will be on its seat and the prongs of the fork will open as far as possible. The amount the fork opens is a direct measure of the valve lash. Two strain gages are mounted at the root of each prong and connected in the usual manner. The completely assembled lashometer is shown in Fig. 11-54.

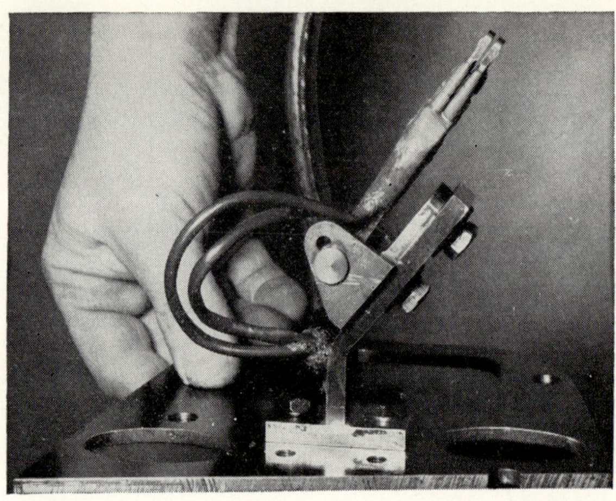

Fig. 11-54. Strain gage lashometer and mounting-bracket assembly. (*Courtesy of Ford Motor Company.*)

The discussion of strain gage transducers could be extended indefinitely if one wished to describe in detail each of the many applications of this technique. The basic methods reported in this chapter should, however, indicate the remarkable versatility of the strain gage transducer and establish the general principles from which instruments for almost any purpose can be designed. It should also be apparent that, by merely constructing a closed-loop system in which the strain gage output is fed back to some corrective device, strain gages can be employed to regulate or control any quantity which they are able to measure. The strain gage transducer can therefore regulate forces, deformations, pressures, accelerations, and similar physical variables.

BIBLIOGRAPHY

General

Baldwin-Lima-Hamilton Corp., *Bulls.* 274, 306, 307, and 325.

Busch, C. D.: Mechanical Mouse Aids Research in Subsurface Drainage, *Agr. Eng.*, vol. 39, no. 5, pp. 292–293, May, 1958.

Cleveland, A. E.: Strain-gage Method of Determining the Running Lash of L-head and Overhead-valve Engines, *SAE J.*, vol. 59, pp. 34–36, July, 1951.

Flax, A. H., and M. C. Wardle: Application of Electric Strain Gages to Aircraft Design Problems, *Proc. SESA*, vol. 2, no. 1, pp. 50–66, 1944.

Frederick, C. L.: Aircraft Instruments for Radio-telemetering and Television-telemetering, *Proc. SESA*, vol. 4, no. 2, pp. 103–121, 1947.

Fyffe, R. J., and A. Arobone: Strain Gage Transducers for Measurement and Control, *Product Eng.*, vol. 23, pp. 121–148, November, 1952.

Guins, S. G.: Strain Gages in Design, *Machine Design*, vol. 23, no. 1, pp. 145–146, 186, January, 1951.

Hizer, R. C.: Testing Vehicle Components with Strain Gages, *Product Eng.*, vol. 20, no. 4, pp. 134–137, April, 1949.

Kramer, E. H., and E. J. Lunney: Dynamic Measurements during Aircraft Landings, *Proc. SESA*, vol. 7, no. 1, pp. 82–102, 1949.

Lebow, M. J.: Some Principles of Transducer Design, ISA Summer Instrument Automation Conference, Toronto, Ontario, June 5–8, 1961, Preprint no. 5-TC-61.

Magee, G. M., and R. Ferguson: Applications of Electric Measuring Equipment in Railroad Research, *Proc. SESA*, vol. 2, no. 1, pp. 1–8, 1944.

McConnell, W. A.: New Ways of Measuring Vehicle Performance on Road, *SAE J.*, vol. 57, no. 7, pp. 27–30, 1949.

Partington, E. J., and S. E. Westman: Transient Recording Pickup Methods, *Automotive and Aviation Inds.*, vol. 93, no. 9, pp. 20–24, 64, Nov. 1, 1945.

Rankine, J., W. H. Bailey, and F. P. Stanton: Resistance Strain Gages for the Measurement of Pull Force, Torque and Strip Tension, *J. Iron Steel Inst.*, vol. 160, pp. 381–387, December, 1948.

Stein, P. K.: Strain Gage Transducers, *Product Eng.*, vol. 27, pp. 196–198, March, 1956.

Symposium: Toepassing van rekstrookjes in meetinstrumenten, *Ingenieur*, vol. 67, nos. 26, 29, 33, 35, pp. 89–100, July 1, 1955; pp. 103–110, July 22, 1955; pp. 111–120, Aug. 19, 1955; pp. 121–130, Sept. 2, 1955.

Thompson, J. L.: Wire Strain-gauge Transducers for Measurement of Pressure, Force, Displacement, and Acceleration, *J. Brit. Inst. Radio Engrs.*, vol. 14, no. 12, pp. 583–600, December, 1954.

Tiffany, A., and J. Wood: Precision Strain Gauge Techniques, *Electronic Eng.*, vol. 30, no. 367, pp. 528–535, September, 1958.

Load and Force Measurement

Anderson, A. R.: A Three-component Force Recorder, *Proc. SESA*, vol. 5, no. 2, pp. 42–48, 1948.

Brewer, G. A.: Analysis of Press Performance, *Product Eng.*, vol. 19, no. 10, pp. 81–85, October, 1948.

Clyde, A. W.: Drawbar Dynamometer Using Strain Gages, *Agr. Eng.*, vol. 36, no. 8, pp. 521–522, August, 1955.

Conover, R. E.: Strain-gage Dynamometers and Indicators, *Instruments*, vol. 23, pp. 445–448, May, 1950.

Cunningham, D. M., and G. W. Brown: Two Devices for Measuring the Forces Acting on the Human Body during Walking, *Proc. SESA*, vol. 9, no. 2, pp. 75–90, 1952.

Dearinger, J. A.: Dynamic Weighing of Vehicles, *Public Roads*, p. 200, October, 1961.

Eisenberg, P., M. S. Macovsky, and W. L. Stracke: A Six-component Dynamometer for the Measurement of Forces and Moments on Models of Ship Appendages, *David Taylor Model Basin, Rept.* 692, 1949.

Kaufman, A. B.: Strain Gauge Link, *Radio and Television News*, vol. 43, no. 3 (*Radio-Electronic Eng.*, vol. 14, no. 3), pp. 7–9, 26–27, March, 1950.

Kaufman, A. B.: Strain Gauge Load Rings, *Radio and Television News*, vol. 44, no. 2 (*Radio-Electronic Eng.*, vol. 15, no. 2), pp. 9A–11A, 30A, August, 1950.

Kececioglu, Dimitri: Force Components, Chip Geometry, and Specific Cutting Energy in Orthogonal and Oblique Machining of SAE 1015 Steel, *Trans. ASME*, p. 149, 1958.

Kimbell, A. R.: Experimental Determination of Metal Drawing and Forming Forces, *Proc. SESA*, vol. 7, no. 4, pp. 51–60, 1949.

Lebow, M. J.: An Autographic Wind Tunnel Balance, Wayne State University master's thesis, 1949.

Loewen, E. G., E. R. Marshall, and M. C. Shaw: Electric Strain Gage Tool Dynamometers, *Proc. SESA*, vol. 8, no. 2, pp. 1–16, 1951.

Loewen, E. G., and M. C. Shaw: Dynamometer for Measuring Forces on Drill, *Instruments*, vol. 23, no. 6, pp. 560–561, June, 1950.

Lundquist, E. C.: Electrical Resistance Strain Gages Applied to Wind Tunnel Balances, *Inst. Aeronaut. Sci. Special Pub.* no. 102, 1946.

Mains, R. M.: A Strain-gage Balance System for a Supersonic Wind Tunnel, *Proc. SESA*, vol. 5, no. 2, pp. 100–114, 1948.

Meier, J. H.: Some Phases of the Technique of Recording Performance Data on Large Machines, *Proc. SESA*, vol. 10, no. 1, pp. 35–52, 1952.

Newberry, C. W.: A Squat Load-measuring Gauge, *Engineering*, vol. 177, no. 4598, pp. 339–341, Mar. 12, 1954.

Pavlov, N. N., *et al.*: Application of Strain Gages to the Study of (Tire) Cord at High Elongation Rates, *Rubber Chem. & Tech.*, vol. 32, pp. 907–914, July, 1959.

Perkins, P. J., Jr., and M. B. Millenson: An Electric Thrust Meter Suitable for Flight Investigation of Propellers, *NACA*, *Research Mem.* E9C17, 1949.

Rottersman, H., *et al.*: Strain Gage Dynamometer for Measuring Cutting Tool Loads, *Iron Age*, vol. 164, pp. 55–61, Sept. 29, 1949.

Sanks, R. L.: Two Useful Gages Measure Bolt Tension and Slip in a Joint, *Civil Eng.*, vol. 26, pp. 754–755, November, 1956.

Wolfe, H., and R. W. Powell: Device for Measuring Tip Force and Current in Spot Welding, *Welding J.*, Welding Research Supplements, pp. 293–296, June, 1942.

Pressure Measurement

Bierman, H. R.: A Device for Measuring Physiological Pressure Phenomena Using the Bonded Wire Strain Gauge, *Rev. Sci. Instr.*, vol. 19, no. 10, pp. 707–710, October, 1948.

Bierman, H. R., and R. Jenkins: Hypodermic Pressure Manometer Utilizing the Bonded Wire Resistance Strain Gauge, *Rev. Sci. Instr.*, vol. 22, pp. 268–269, April, 1951.

Carter, B. C., J. C. Ghosh, M. V. C. Sastri, and K. V. Chinnappa: Measurement of Surface Strains in Diaphragms, *Engineering*, vol. 168, pp. 581–583, Dec. 2, 1949.

Dimeff, J., J. A. Carson, and A. C. Charters: Piston-type Strain Gauge for Measuring Pressures in Interior Ballistics Research, *Rev. Sci. Instr.*, September, 1955, vol. 26, pp. 879–883.

Draper, C. S., and Y. T. Li: New High-performance Engine Indicator of the Strain-gage Type, *J. Aeronaut. Sci.*, vol. 16, pp. 593–610, October, 1949.

Warshaw, H. D.: A Gauge for Indicating Pressure Transients in a Combustion Chamber, *Rev. Sci. Instr.*, vol. 23, no. 9, pp. 493–496, September, 1952.

Wenk, E., Jr.: A Diaphragm-type Gage for Measuring Low Pressures in Fluids, *David Taylor Model Basin, Rept.* 665, 1950.

Wenk, E., Jr.: An Elastic Tube Gage for Measuring Static and Dynamic Pressures, *David Taylor Model Basin, Rept.* 627, 1948.

Werner, F. D.: The Design of Diaphragms for Pressure Gages Which Use the Bonded Wire Resistance Strain Gage, *Proc. SESA*, vol. 11, no. 1, p. 137, 1954.

Accelerometry

Anderson, A. R., and C. R. Nevitt: Application of Electric Strain Gages to Shipbuilding Problems, *Proc. SESA*, vol. 1, no. 1, pp. 1–9, 1943.

Boggis, A. G.: An Accelerometer for Measuring Ship Hull Vibrations, *J. Sci. Instr.*, vol. 27, pp. 212–214, August, 1950.

Kammer, E. W., and S. Holt, Jr.: A Bonded Wire Strain Gage Type Accelerometer, *Proc. SESA*, vol. 6, no. 2, pp. 53–60, 1948.

Weiss, D. E.: Design and Application of Accelerometers, *Proc. SESA*, vol. 4, no. 2, pp. 89–102, 1947.

EXERCISES

11-1. Construct a simple tension load cell. Calibrate the cell by applying loads incrementally to the rated load and back to zero again. Plot the results and determine the calibration constant and a measure of the precision and repeatability of your transducer.

11-2. Describe the steps you think might be taken by a commercial transducer manufacturer in producing an instrument guaranteed to exhibit 0.1 per cent accuracy and linearity.

11-3. Select a transducer application and design the appropriate circuitry for use in conjunction with piezoresistive strain gages. The transducer is to be direct-reading on a sensitive meter without amplification.

11-4. Design a pair of surgical forceps that will respond to lateral pressure at the tips of the forceps only.

11-5. Build a transducing screw driver with strain gages, and test for the ratio of torque to axial force needed for driving screws in wood. Conduct comparative tests on hard and soft woods and with slotted and Phillips head screws.

11-6. Design and build a transducer to be used for measuring the gripping force of a hand.

11-7. Build a dynamometer to be attached to the heel of a shoe for measuring the magnitude of the force incurred in walking, running, and jumping. The transducer should separate the horizontal and vertical components of the force produced.

11-8. Design a transducer to measure the torque produced in the use of an automobile steering wheel. This ought to be a wheel-like device which clamps on the existing steering wheel for maneuvering the automobile.

11-9. Design a brake-pedal dynamometer that will fit on the brake pedal to measure the pedal force applied by the foot in normal braking operations.

11-10. Design and build an accelerometer that will respond to accelerations of $\pm 1g$ and will respond properly to a rise time of $100g$ per second. Test the accelerometer for its performance with respect to these specifications.

11-11. Design and build a static pressure transducer using strain gages mounted on a length of steel tubing.

11-12. Conceive, design, and construct a strain gage velocity pickup for use on an automobile or boat.

11-13. Using a spark plug as the primary member, design and construct a pressure transducer for measuring the pressures developed in the cylinder when the engine is running.

12 SPECIAL PROBLEMS, TECHNIQUES, AND APPLICATIONS

PHASE BALANCING OF STRAIN INDICATORS

In the description of strain-indicating instruments up to this point it has been assumed that all the Wheatstone-bridge elements were pure ohmic resistances. Exceptions to this include certain direct-reading and self-balancing strain indicators which use variable capacitors for one or more legs of the bridge and additional capacitors in parallel with the strain gages for phase balancing. Returning to conventional strain indicators, whenever one or more strain gages are being supplied with a-c electrical energy through leads of over a few feet in length, the capacitance between the leads, in combination with the resistances of the leads and the gage, produces a *reactive impedance*. As a result, the voltage across the gage terminals of the strain indicator is somewhat out of phase with the applied bridge voltage. If the leads are not too long, say, 50 ft or less, and if the active and compensating gages have leads of the same length, the voltages across these two legs of the bridge will be essentially in phase with one another and the bridge may operate normally. It sometimes happens, however, that the leads to the active gage are much longer than those to the compensating gage, or for other reasons the capacitances are quite unequal. In this case the voltages of the two legs will be out of phase, and it will be found that the sensitivity of the strain-indicator balancing control is greatly reduced. In extreme instances it may be impossible to balance the indicator at all. The remedy for such a condition is ordinarily quite simple and consists in placing capacitance in parallel with one of the legs until phase balance is achieved.

The proper value of shunt capacitance is commonly determined by a trial-and-error process. A 0- to 5,000-micro-micro-farad capacitor decade is first connected in parallel with the gage suspected of having the least shunt capacitance. With the decade set at zero the strain indicator is then balanced, after which the balance control sensitivity is determined by noting the meter indication for a given movement of the control. A shunt capacitance of 300 micro-micro-farads is then introduced with the decade and the indicator again balanced and checked for sensitivity. This process is repeated, greater shunt capacitance being added until maximum sensitivity is reached, at which time it can be assumed that the active and compensating bridge legs are in phase.

Phase, or capacitive, balancing can also be accomplished by measuring the amplifier output voltage with an oscilloscope or a-c vacuum-tube voltmeter as the indicator is balanced and shunt capacitance added. The oscilloscope or voltmeter should be connected to the amplifier output ahead of the detector circuit or to the output jack for dynamic indication and recording if one is provided. If a voltage is observed at the amplifier output when the meter on the strain indicator shows a balance, lack of phase balance is evident. As capacitance is shunted across the proper gage, the amplifier output should decrease. The shunt capacitance is increased until no further reduction of amplifier output is detected, at which time it can again be assumed that the active and compensating legs are in phase. It will ordinarily be impossible to reduce the amplifier output completely to zero because of harmonics present. Phase unbalance can also occur as the result of inductance from coiled lead wires. The procedure for balancing is the same as that described for capacitive unbalance.

EFFECT OF LEAD-WIRE RESISTANCE ON STRAIN-INDICATOR ACCURACY

For most strain measurements the resistance of the lead wires from the instrument to the gage is small enough to be insignificant. When long or small-diameter leads are used, however, an error will be introduced. The magnitude of the error can be readily calculated and corrected for by noting that the lead resistance is in series with the gage resistance and hence acts to reduce the effective gage factor accordingly. As an example, assume a 120-ohm strain gage connected to the strain indicator by 75-ft leads of No. 20 copper wire (approximately 10 ohms per 1,000 ft). The total lead-wire resistance in series with the gage (150 ft) is 1.5 ohms. This will reduce the effective gage factor by the ratio of 1.5:120, or 1.25 per cent. The correction can be made either by setting the gage factor adjustment of the strain indicator to the manufacturer's value (shown on the package of gages) and multiplying the measured strain by 1/0.9875 or by setting the gage-factor control to a value which is 98.75 per cent of that for the gage alone.

If calibration is accomplished by connecting a calibration resistor across two of the leads in order to shunt one leg of the Wheatstone-bridge circuit, an additional error is introduced. This situation is shown schematically in Fig. 12-1, where R is the nominal resistance of each leg of the Wheatstone bridge, R_L the resistance of the lead wire, and R_C the value of the calibration resistor.

It has been shown by Perino that under these conditions the output signal to the instrument caused by strain in any gage is attenuated by approximately $2R_L/R$ as indicated above, while the signal due to connecting the calibration resistor is increased by $2R_L/R$. These conditions produce a calibration signal which is in error with respect to the

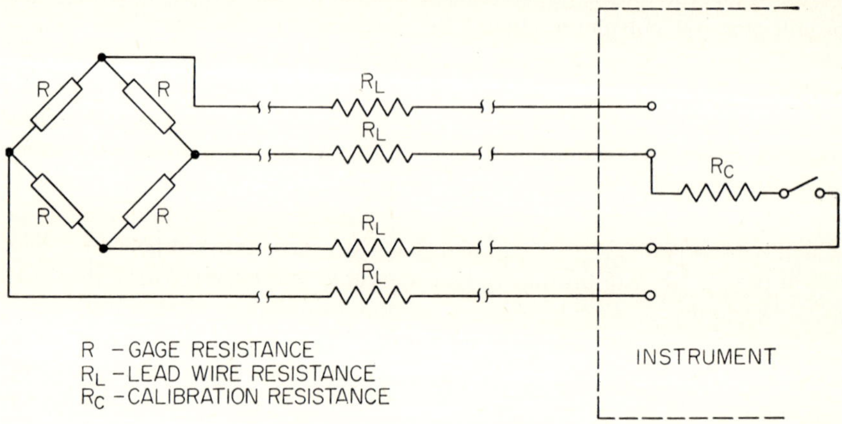

FIG. 12-1. Equivalent circuit for remotely located Wheatstone bridge with calibration resistor connected across instrument end of long lead wires. (*After Perino.*)

strain signal by a factor of $4R_L/R$. A correction for this error can be made by multiplying the apparent strain by

$$\left(\frac{R + 2R_L}{R}\right)^2 \frac{R_C + 0.5R}{R_C + 1.5R_L + 0.5R} \tag{12-1}$$

An alternative procedure described by Perino involves the use of six-wire circuitry between a full bridge and the instrument. This circuit effectively places the calibration resistor electrically adjacent to the bridge circuit and eliminates the error due to lead-wire resistance.

REDUCTION OF SPURIOUS NOISE FROM INSTRUMENT CABLES

It may sometimes occur in measuring strains on oscillating or reciprocating mechanisms that the cabled leads from the instrument to the strain gages must be subjected to rapid motion or vibration. This situation also arises in shock and impact studies. Under these circumstances one is apt to find that a great deal of electrical noise is generated in the cable. The noise signal can easily exceed and obscure the test signal unless countermeasures are taken.

The NBS has studied this problem and measured noise voltages as high as 500 millivolts peak-to-peak in standard microphone cables. The NBS investigation demonstrated that the noise in a coaxial cable is generated by relative motion between the conductors and the dielectric. It was also discovered that a conducting coating applied to the dielectric surfaces reduced the noise level to a negligible magnitude. As an outgrowth of this study, the NBS has established the design of a noise-free instrument cable. Commercial cables of this type should be employed for strain gage systems in which lead motion might be troublesome.

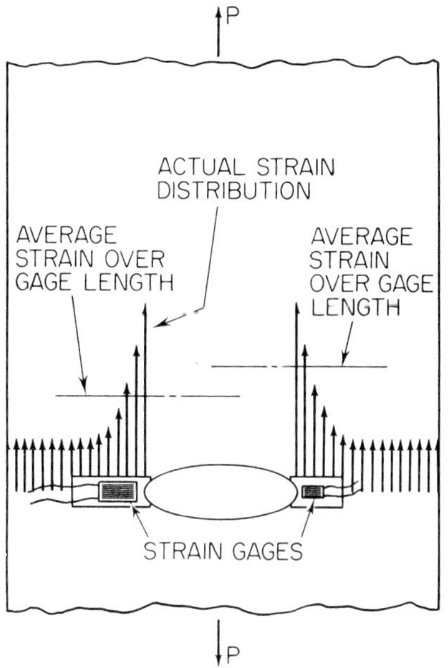

Fig. 12-2. Effect of gage length on indicated strain in the presence of a severe strain gradient. The shorter gage on the right indicates a higher strain. An infinitesimal gage length would be necessary to indicate the peak strain. (*Shock and Vibration Handbook, C. M. Harris and C. E. Crede, eds., vol.* 1, *p.* 17-7, *McGraw-Hill Book Company, Inc.,* 1961.)

STRAIN GRADIENT

Measurements made with strain gages bonded in a region of strain gradient will always be somewhat in error. The strain gradient may be in the plane of the strain gage or normal to that plane, that is, normal to the surface of the part.

Strain gradients normal to the plane of the strain gage occur most frequently when the test member is subjected to bending or torsion. The strain-measurement error in such cases arises because the gage is mounted a finite distance above the surface of the part. It is evident that the error can be minimized by having the gage filaments as close as possible to the material surface. This requires a gage with a thin backing (or no backing), as well as a thin layer of cement between the gage and surface. A bending separator gage, described elsewhere in this chapter, can sometimes be used to determine the gradient and correct for it.

When the strain gradient is in the plane of the gage, a different approach is required. This is a very common situation, since the point of maximum strain usually coincides with a stress concentration, and the strain field in the neighborhood of such a discontinuity is naturally characterized by a gradient. The gradient often increases in steepness near the edge of the discontinuity. The resistance strain gage has a finite gage length, and thus produces a signal corresponding to the average strain over the gage length. It is this fact which has led to the manufacture of gage lengths as small as $\frac{1}{64}$ in. Figure 12-2 illustrates that the shorter the gage length, the more accurately the peak strain in the vicinity of the discontinuity will be indicated. Unfortunately, the very short gages seldom exhibit the stability characteristics available with longer gages, and a compromise may be necessary in order to obtain precision.

THE USE OF STRAIN GAGES ON CAST IRON, MAGNESIUM, AND OTHER MATERIALS HAVING NONLINEAR STRESS-STRAIN CHARACTERISTICS

In conducting stress-analysis studies of members made from nonlinear materials, it is imperative that the peculiar properties of the material be kept in mind. Such materials, unlike steel, do not exhibit constant values of the modulus of elasticity and Poisson's ratio. These properties vary with strain, and the variations must be considered in converting strain data to stresses. Thus, it is not possible, even in the case of a simple tension member, to multiply the measured strain by a fixed modulus of elasticity and obtain the correct stress. The only accurate method involves initial determination of the stress-strain properties of the particular material on a testing machine. These data, which must include Poisson's ratio, can subsequently be used for calculating stresses from observed strain data.

STRAIN GAGES APPLIED TO NONMETALLIC SURFACES

Bonded strain gages find their greatest use on steel, aluminum, and other metals. Because of this fact, most of the experience and technology in bonding methods which have been reported are related specifically to use on metallic surfaces. The strain gage, however, offers so many inherent advantages as a strain transducer that it is only natural for investigators to utilize the same device on nonmetallic surfaces wherever possible. A number of difficulties arise in attempting to employ bonded strain gages on such materials. Concrete, for example, is characterized by a rough surface and a heterogeneous and not completely isotropic structure; in addition, the probability of moisture reaching the underside of the strain gage is very great. Wood is another material which can cause difficulties due to anisotropy and moisture permeability. Substances with extremely porous and granular surfaces as well as those of the opposite extreme—glass-smooth surfaces—may also resist attempts to obtain a strong bond and stable gage operation.

It is known that adhesive phenomena are related not only to surface roughness and porosity but also to the molecular structures of the bonding surfaces and the bonding agent. There is, in fact, a rapidly advancing science of adhesion, as evidenced by the recent growth of adhesive fastening methods in the fabrication of manufactured goods. The approach here, however, will be to treat the process of strain gage bonding as an art, rather than a science. Investigators in the field of stress analysis, when faced with a situation in which for some reason the conventional cements malfunction, merely experimented until they found a satisfactory bonding agent or technique. This has led to solutions of varying practicality and effectiveness for some of the more common problems, such as bonding to concrete. Representative techniques for various materials will be described, but the degree of refinement employed in an individual instance will depend upon the particular conditions affecting the application, including the accuracy and stability expected of the strain gage, as well as the length of time over which the gage must operate. A certain amount of trial-and-error experimentation may be necessary in evolving a satisfactory technique for some of the special bonding and moisture-proofing problems which are apt to occur.

GLASS AND CERAMICS

Glass and ceramic materials often present similar problems in strain gage bonding because of the smooth surfaces commonly associated with these substances. Some investigators have employed a light sandblast or etching to roughen the surface and increase the effective bonding area. This process, however, may often be unsatisfactory because of the resultant damage to the material surface. In general it will be found that adequate bonding can be secured by following a few common-sense practices. One of these is cleanliness. The presence of an oily film seems to have an especially inhibiting effect when smooth surfaces are to be bonded. Optimum adhesion will be obtained after thoroughly cleaning the glass or ceramic surface with acetone, carbon tetrachloride, dichloroethylene, or other volatile solvents. The underside of the strain gage should also be cleaned, but this must be done carefully in working with paper gages. A cloth dampened with acetone and wiped lightly over the undersurface of the gage will ordinarily suffice. If the cloth is too wet with acetone, the gage may be damaged. Once the gage and bonding surface are immaculately clean, the cement and gage should be applied immediately. The remainder of the bonding procedure is the same as for applying strain gages to metal surfaces.

A further helpful technique is that of precoating the glass or ceramic with a thin layer of cement which has been diluted slightly with solvent. The thin precoat seems to form a sound adherent base in preparation for the final coat and the strain gage. When the precoat has hardened, a layer of regular cement and the gage can be applied in the normal manner.

Some cements will be found to have a greater affinity for the glass or ceramic surface than others. Bakelite cement will bond well to these materials when conditions are such that the recommended curing cycle can be employed. deKhotinsky cement has also been used successfully on glass and ceramic surfaces, as has Cenco Sealstix, an adhesive similar in properties to deKhotinsky cement. Epoxy cements are generally excellent adhesives for this purpose.

WOOD

There are no particular problems associated with the actual process of bonding paper or epoxy strain gages to a dry wood surface. The wood surface is ordinarily cleaned with fine sandpaper, after which the cement and the gage are applied as on other surfaces. If the wood has been well dried and the tests are conducted in the laboratory where the humidity does not become excessive, the gages should function as satisfactorily as on metal surfaces. Any moisture in the wood, whether present at the time of bonding or absorbed later, may affect the accuracy and stability of the gage readings.

One method of controlling moisture absorption from the wood by the strain gage is to bond a thin layer of metallic foil to the wood underneath the gage. The foil will act as a moisture barrier and will greatly stabilize gage readings. It must be remembered that wood is characterized by a low modulus of elasticity and that the stiffness of the strain gage and moisture barrier could affect the strain of the wood when tested in thin sections.

Another important factor to be considered is that wood is far from isotropic in most of its physical properties. In particular, the Poisson's ratio is greatly different in a direction parallel to the grain from that in a direction normal to the grain. The modulus of elasticity is also different in these two directions. This lack of isotropy can result in significant errors when strains are translated into stresses. The gage factors for conventional strain gages are stated on the basis of the gage being cemented to steel or some material with a similar Poisson's ratio. When gages are cemented to materials with radically different Poisson's ratios, the calibration factor is no longer valid. There are many cases of two-dimensional strain in wood structures in which sizable errors could arise from the lack of isotropy in Poisson's ratio and modulus of elasticity.

CONCRETE AND ROCK

Concrete and rock offer their own peculiar problems of strain gage bonding and instrumentation. As in the case of other materials, comparative smoothness and rigorous cleanliness are essential to a strong bond.

In early attempts to employ bonded wire strain gages for studying concrete structures, difficulties were encountered with bonding, moisture in the concrete affecting the leakage resistance between gage and ground, and variation of physical properties with direction. One investigator reports having overcome the problems which center around the strain gage itself by the following techniques:

The concrete surface is first ground smooth and plane, after which the dust is removed and the concrete thoroughly dried. A coat of Duco cement is then applied to the concrete, and a piece of 0.010-in.-thick celluloid is pressed firmly in place as a base for the strain gage. The act of applying pressure to the celluloid is found advantageous in forcing cement down into the pores of the concrete. When the above installation has dried for 24 hr, the film is sanded smooth and a strain gage cemented to the celluloid by the standard technique. Hot Petrosene wax is applied over the gage area, and when this has set, the surface over and around the gage is covered with lacquer. These precautions are said to result in stable, accurate gage readings over long periods of time.

When the concrete being tested is out of doors or otherwise situated so that it can absorb moisture, it will usually be found that a metallic-foil moisture barrier gives much better results than the sheet celluloid employed in the foregoing technique. Since concrete is a heterogeneous substance, composed of coarse and fine aggregate, as well as a cement-water paste, the local strain distribution may be erratic and not representative of the gross strain distribution, which is ordinarily the object of instrumentation. This situation can be remedied by selecting a gage of sufficient length to average out the effect of nonuniform strain in the direction of the gage axis.

The NBS has developed a method for embedding strain gages directly in concrete during the fabrication of a test specimen or structural member. The strain gage is bonded to the inner surfaces of a rectangular metal-foil envelope made of 0.001-in.-thick brass shim stock. Brass was selected because its ductility was sufficient to withstand bending and folding without cracking. The metal-incased strain gage is embedded within a concrete specimen by inserting it at the desired position and orienting it immediately after the fresh concrete has been poured. The cement-water paste in the concrete adheres to the brass envelope, so that a complete transfer of strain is obtained. A commercial form of this gage is available from the Baldwin-Lima-Hamilton Corporation in several varieties, including one which is self-temperature-compensated. Known as the Valore-Brass Foil Envelope gage, it is manufactured in a 3-in. gage length and with a resistance of 300 ohms.

The problems of bonding strain gages to rock are very similar to those encountered with concrete. If the rock is out of doors, it will usually be necessary to employ a piece of metallic foil under the strain gage, primarily as a moisture barrier, although some investigators have observed what appear to be earth-current effects in such gages and have found that the electrostatic shielding provided by the metallic foil improves gage stability. The embeddable strain gage can also be used on rock very successfully by cementing the unit to a prepared surface of the rock. Prewaterproofed strain gages are, in fact, very useful for outdoor installations on any kind of surface. One laboratory incases their strain gages in metallic foil in the laboratory and then solders them with low-melting-point solder to metallic surfaces which are exposed to high humidity.

MISCELLANEOUS MATERIALS

Strain gages have been applied to almost every conceivable solid material. One of the more unusual applications is that to bone, both human and animal. No particular difficulties occur in bonding paper or epoxy strain gages to dry, "lifeless" bone. The surface of the bone is cleaned well with ether or acetone, after which the cement and gage are applied as usual. Elastic properties of the bone, such as Poisson's ratio and the modulus of elasticity, must be kept in mind in translating strains to stresses. Experience in attempting to bond strain gages to live bone has been much less successful. It has been found that most air-drying cements are too hygroscopic to retain their adhesive properties for more than a few hours. Several experiments were conducted at Wayne State University to determine the strain in the leg bone of a dog while the animal was walking. In preparation for applying the strain gage, the skin and muscle on the dog's leg were cut and opened to bare the bone for an area large enough to allow cementing a Baldwin C-7 gage in place. The wound was then left open for several days (covered by a guard to prevent irritation) for the purpose of reducing seepage around the cut.

When the investigators were ready to apply the strain gage, they first scraped the bone lightly and coated the area with a thin layer of collodion. When this had dried, a second coat of collodion and the strain gage were applied. The collodion dries very rapidly, and within a few minutes it was possible to place the dog in a treadmill to record strain variations due to walking. Figure 12-3 shows the incision with the gage applied. It was found in these tests that the strain gages loosened and became useless after approximately 36 hr because of moisture penetration from the bone.

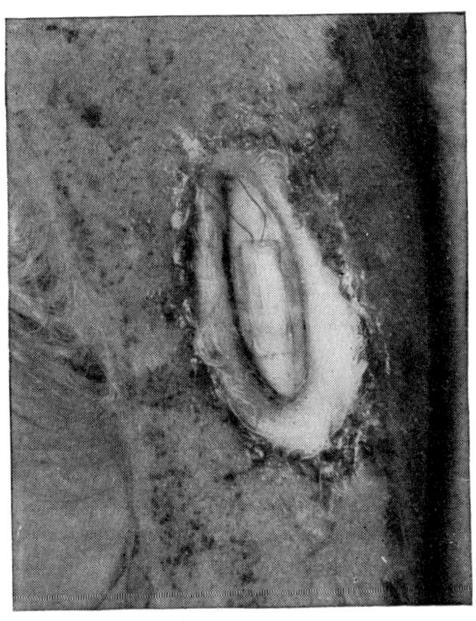

FIG. 12-3. Strain gage mounted on the leg bone of a live dog for studying bone stresses during walking. (*Courtesy of Wayne State University.*)

For strain gage installations on the bones of intact cadavers, epoxy-backed foil gages, mounted with contact cement (cyanoacrylate), have performed very satisfactorily. After making an incision and locating the exact mounting site for the strain gage, the bone is scraped with a sharp woodchisel to remove the periosteum and leave a smooth surface, care being taken not to expose the spongy inner bone.

Moisture seeping into the wall is the greatest obstacle to a satisfactory gage installation. Openings in the sides and bottom of the incision should be packed with gauze or cotton to minimize seepage. Arteries must be tied. In extreme cases the walls can be coated with latex or embalmer's In-R-Seal. Immediately prior to installing the gage, the proper area should be cleaned with volatile solvents. Swabbing with acetone followed by a 1:1 mixture of ether and alcohol is recommended. Evaporation of the solvent can be accelerated by directing a jet from a compressed-air source or from a heated air blower such as a hair dryer at the incision. If the gage is not applied immediately, the cleaning process must be repeated just prior to installation.

The strain gage is ordinarily wired before mounting, and the soldered joints are moistureproofed with rubber cement and/or wax. Rubber-insulated lead wire must be used, since plastic insulation is commonly attacked by the embalming fluid.

The bonding procedure consists in coating the back of the gage with accelerator; applying a generous layer of contact cement to the bone surface and spreading it to cover an area somewhat larger than the gage;

setting the gage in place properly oriented; and exerting pressure through a piece of teflon tape by a rolling motion of the finger to precipitate hardening of the cement. The installation is completed by coating the gage and lead wires with wax. Strain gages applied in this manner have functioned normally for periods as long as several months.

Gages have also been applied to cadaver bone with F-88 dental cement. The procedure is essentially the same as the above. Both contact and dental cements should be satisfactory for use on living bone as well. Strain gages have been bonded to living bone with epoxy cements by investigators at the Orthopedic Research Associates, Inc., at Allentown, Pa.

PLASTIC MATERIALS

The use of strain gages on the surface of plastics can also give rise to difficulties. One of these stems from the fact that the strain gage cement solvent may react chemically with the plastic, resulting in actual deterioration, surface crazing, or at least modifying the physical properties of the plastic. The only remedy is to seek out a cement which will not affect the particular plastic being investigated. Since plastics vary so widely in chemical composition and since the cements commonly used with strain gages are themselves plastics, it is imperative that the cement be tested for chemical inertness with the plastic on which it is to be used.

It is further necessary that the cement be capable of extended elongation without cracking or slipping. This need arises from the low elastic moduli (½ million psi is a typical value) common to many plastics.

The latter characteristic of plastics is also important in testing thin sections. It will be necessary to make certain that the presence of the strain gage does not increase the rigidity of the plastic member and as a result give erroneous strain readings. As a matter of interest, it has been found at the David Taylor Model Basin that a load of 3.9 lb is required to elongate a pair of SR-4 A-5 strain gages 1,000 micro-inches per in.

MEASURING LARGE STRAINS

There are occasional problems which require the measurement of very large strains, such as those encountered in the plastic range of metals. One such case is in observing fundamental data on the strength of materials. Another occurs in the field of activities associated with limit design. Standard strain gages will ordinarily withstand strains of from 1.5 to 4 per cent (15,000 to 40,000 micro-inches per in.), depending upon the type of gage and the manufacturing procedures. In general, the larger, lower-resistance gages are superior in this characteristic. While the above strain range is beyond the elastic limit for all metals, it is not sufficient to study the plastic strains which can occur between the yield point and actual rupture of ductile metals. For the latter purpose, strain gages which will measure strains up to 10 or even 20 per cent are required. The principal strain gage manufacturers offer post-yield strain gages capable of accurately indicating strains as great as 10 to 15 per cent.

A strain gage for indicating such large strains must be special in several respects. The strain-sensitive wire must be ductile and must have a plastic gage factor equal to its elastic gage factor. The cement used must be strongly adherent to prevent slip and ductile enough not to crack. Finally, a special type of backing material is required since many papers rupture at strains of approximately 3 per cent and in so doing tend to break the strain-sensitive filament. These problems have been overcome both experimentally and commercially.

The David Taylor Model Basin has developed postyield strain gages capable of measuring strains up to 18 per cent. The gages were made of 0.001-in. Constantan wire (treated to a special annealing process), 0.001-in.-thick sheet nylon as a base for handling and bonding the gage, and two cements, Pliobond and Acryloid B-7. The Pliobond cement (a product of the Goodyear Tire and Rubber Company, Akron, Ohio) is used as a precoat on top of the nylon sheet before applying and cementing the wire in place and is also used to bond the completed strain gage to metal surfaces. The Acryloid B-7 (made by the Rohm and Haas Company, Philadelphia, Pa.) is applied over the Pliobond in cementing the wire to the nylon. The two cements are necessary for this operation because acrylics will not bond directly to nylon, and yet the acrylics have excellent properties in terms of holding the strain-sensitive wire firmly in place.

An entirely different technique for measuring large strains or deformations involves use of the "clip gage." This gage is constructed by bonding strain gages to the upper and lower sides of a piece of channel-shaped spring steel, as shown in Fig. 12-4. The assembly is then clipped or otherwise mounted on the test specimen so that the legs deflect as the specimen is strained, thus straining the backbone of the clip gage to a greater or lesser degree. Any desired reduction in strain magnitude can be obtained in this manner by merely altering the proportions of the clip gage.

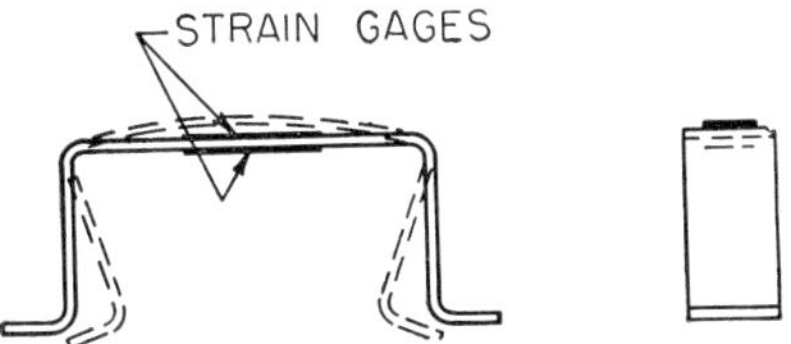

FIG. 12-4. Clip gage for measuring very large strains or displacements.

When strain gages undergo cyclic straining, as, for example, in monitoring fatigue tests, the allowable strain is greatly reduced because the strain gage itself is subject to fatigue failure. Considering the statistical scatter which is characteristic of all fatigue phenomena, and the fact that the fatigue durability varies widely with gage construction and proportions, no fixed strain limit can be specified. A further factor which modifies the endurance limit of a strain gage is the manner of lead attachment. The soldered connections to the external leads act as stress concentrations. Because of this the connections should be made with a minimum of solder. Properly applied foil or dual-lead wire strain gages of intermediate lengths should be capable of withstanding a million or more cycles at a strain of 1,500 micro-inches per in. The shorter strain gages may fail after a few thousand cycles at this strain.

There are many instances, including the problem of monitoring fatigue tests, in which the directions of the principal axes are known before applying the strain gages. Under these circumstances a very simple method of extending the effective strain range of the gage is available. If the stress field is uniaxial, a single strain gage can be mounted at any convenient angle away from the principal axis to provide the desired attenuation in strain. The principal strain is then proportional to the indicated strain through the attenuation factor. In a biaxial stress field, two gages will be required unless the ratio of the principal strains is known from other considerations. The two gages can be mounted at angles with respect to the principal axes such that the strains are attenuated to within the allowable range. This technique is also applicable to strain measurements on low-modulus plastics when the directions of the principal axes are known.

A unique mercury strain gage for measuring very large strains was reported by R. J. Whitney in connection with the study of forearm blood flow.

The same technique, employed by D. E. Strandness, Jr., and others, involved the use of a 2-in.-long rubber tube having an inside diameter of 0.014 in. and filled with mercury. Silver electrodes in the ends of the tube make contact with the mercury. With this type of gage a strain of 35 to 50 per cent can be measured, and the resistance change is linear with strain since the volume of the mercury remains constant and the gage factor is 2.

A gage of any convenient length may be employed, but the gage resistance is very low, varying from a fraction of an ohm to 3 or 4 ohms, depending on the length. Since conventional strain gage instruments are designed for gages having a resistance of 120 ohms, the Wheatstone-bridge circuit must be modified to match the impedance of the strain gage amplifier. Such an impedance-matching circuit for the mercury strain gage, credited to R. W. Elsner, C. J. Eagan, and S. Andersen (an unpublished report) by Strandness in his paper on the plethysmograph, is shown in Fig. 12-5. This was designed for use with a conventional Sanborn strain gage amplifier.

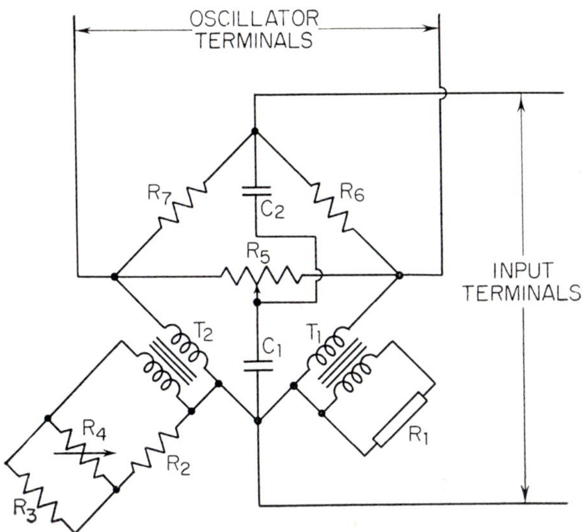

FIG. 12-5. Impedance-matching circuit for adapting the low-resistance mercury strain gage to the Sanborn strain amplifier. (*After Strandness.*)

In actual use Strandness found that a strain of about 40 micro-inches per in. produced a deflection of 1 millimeter on the Sanborn recorder.

SEPARATION OF BENDING AND AXIAL STRAINS

There is another interesting strain-measurement problem which requires the construction of a special fixture similar to the clip gage. The determination of stresses in large flat plates is often complicated by local bending of the plate. It is common practice in such instances to measure strains from both sides of the plate and take the average of these as the strain at the center, or neutral, plane. This method is satisfactory when the plate is so mounted that both sides are accessible for installation of strain gages. There are cases, however, in which one side of the plate is inaccessible, and the necessity arises for taking all strain measurements from the open side. This calls for some method of detecting bending as well as direct strains if the true strain at the neutral plane is to be determined.

The problem was first solved by Boodberg and Howe, who took strain readings on the open side of the plate and simultaneously at a known distance above its surface by means of a mechanical bridge arrangement. More recently, the Budd Company has introduced a commercial gage known as the Flexagage, which performs the same function much more conveniently.

The Flexagage consists of two strain gages mounted back to back on a plastic separator (Fig. 12-6). When this assembly is bonded to a

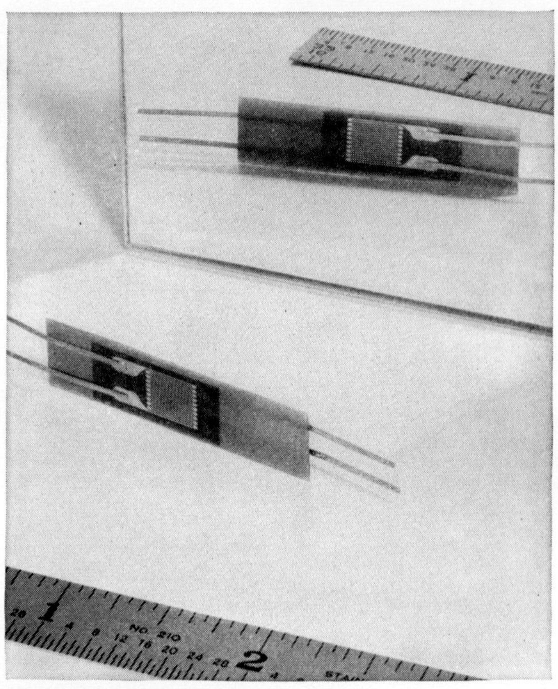

FIG. 12-6. Direct and mirror view of Flexagage, showing two strain gages mounted back to back on a plastic separator. This transducer allows separate measurement of bending and axial strains from one side of a plate. (*Courtesy of The Budd Company.*)

plate as shown in Fig. 12-7 the readings from the two strain gages supply sufficient information to allow determining both the bending and axial strains in the plate.

It is evident from the figure that by virtue of similar triangles,

$$\frac{\epsilon_b}{t/2} = \frac{\epsilon_1 - \epsilon_2}{h} \qquad (12\text{-}2)$$

or

$$\epsilon_b = \frac{t}{2h}(\epsilon_1 - \epsilon_2) \qquad (12\text{-}3)$$

where ϵ_b = bending strain at plate surface
ϵ_1 = indicated strain in uppermost gage
ϵ_2 = indicated strain in gage adjacent to plate surface
t = thickness of plate
h = thickness of plastic separator

The axial strain ϵ_a is then

$$\epsilon_a = \epsilon_2 - \epsilon_b$$

$$\epsilon_a = \epsilon_2 - \frac{t}{2h}(\epsilon_1 - \epsilon_2) \tag{12-4}$$

Flexagages are available with different thicknesses of plastic separator for use on a range of plate gages. Equation (12-3) demonstrates that for a given bending strain, the difference indication, $\epsilon_1 - \epsilon_2$, is proportional to h/t, the ratio of plastic to plate thickness. However, the reinforcing effect of the plastic also increases with this ratio. A practical

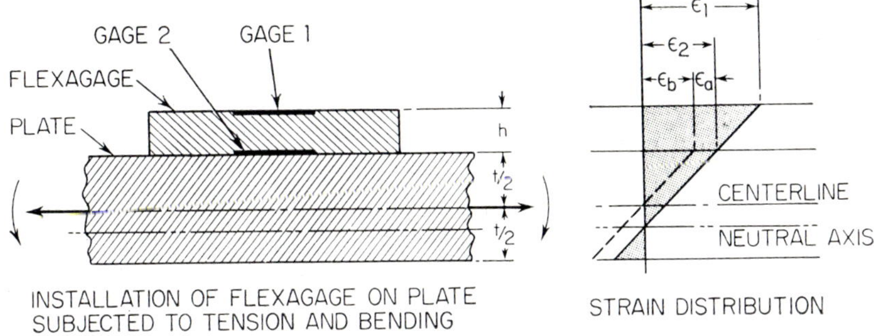

FIG. 12-7. Strain distribution in Flexagage installed on plate subjected to combined tension and bending. (*Courtesy of The Budd Company.*)

compromise is obtained for most metals by keeping the plastic thickness between one-fourth and one-half of the plate thickness.

MAGNETOSTRICTIVE EFFECTS

The strain-sensitive wire or foil grids in gages intended for dynamic strain measurement are often made from Iso-elastic alloy, a cold-worked Elinvar (36 per cent Ni, 8 to 12 per cent Cr, a few per cent Mn, and the remainder iron). Such gages may produce erroneous signals due to magnetostrictive effects.

Vigness has demonstrated that Iso-elastic strain gages are subject to two types of anomalous performance. First, the resistance of the gage is affected by a magnetic field. Resistance changes as large as 0.02 per cent (corresponding to a strain of approximately 60 micro-inches per in.) were observed for strong magnetic fields, and gage factors were correspondingly in error. In addition, the Iso-elastic gage exhibits self-generated voltages with dynamic strain. Spurious voltages in the order of 1 millivolt were recorded under impact conditions. The self-generated voltage is proportional to the rate of change of strain and, of course, appears whether or not the strain gage is supplied with excitation voltage. Constantan and other nonferromagnetic gage materials are not subject to magnetostrictive effects.

RESIDUAL-STRESS MEASUREMENT

Residual stresses can be measured with strain gages by any of several techniques. These generally consist in relaxing the stresses in the gage region through cutting, drilling, etching, or otherwise removing the adjacent or opposing material. The strains produced as a result of relaxation can be interpreted in terms of the original residual stresses in the piece. All such methods are, of course, destructive of the test piece.

For cylindrical specimens and assumed axisymmetric stress distribution, the Sachs turning or boring-out method is most commonly applied. In this technique successive concentric layers of material are removed either from the outer surface or from a bored hole in the piece. The changes in longitudinal and tangential strains accompanying the removal of each layer are recorded. The initial residual stresses in the longitudinal, tangential, and radial directions, as functions of the radius of the cylinder, can then be calculated numerically.

In the case of a solid cylindrical specimen, one approach is to mount strain gages in the longitudinal and tangential directions on the surface (often in three sets of two gages each, located at 120° intervals around the periphery of the cylinder for greater accuracy). A hole is then drilled along the axis of the cylinder, removing about 5 per cent of the cross-sectional area. The remaining area is subsequently removed in, say, 5 per cent increments by boring or grinding, and the strain gage indications recorded after each operation. The equations developed by Sachs for calculating the longitudinal, tangential, and radial stresses from the observed longitudinal and tangential strains after each layer removal are:

$$\begin{aligned}
\sigma_l &= \frac{E}{1-\mu^2}\left[(F_b - F)\frac{d\varphi}{dF} - \varphi\right] \\
\sigma_t &= \frac{E}{1-\mu^2}\left[(F_b - F)\frac{d\theta}{dF} - \frac{(F_b + F)\theta}{2F}\right] \qquad (12\text{-}5) \\
\sigma_r &= \frac{E}{1-\mu^2}\left[\frac{(F_b - F)\theta}{2F}\right]
\end{aligned}$$

where $\sigma_l, \sigma_t, \sigma_r$ = longitudinal, tangential, and radial stresses at diameter corresponding to area F

μ = Poisson's ratio

$\theta = \epsilon_t + \mu\epsilon_l$

ϵ_l = strain in longitudinal direction

ϵ_t = strain in circumferential direction

$\varphi = \epsilon_l + \mu\epsilon_t$

F_b = cross-sectional area of original cylinder $= \pi D_0^2/4$

$F = \pi D_i^2/4$ calculated from inside diameter D_i after boring each layer

From the strains corresponding to each layer removal the quantities φ and θ are calculated. These are plotted against the area F, and smooth curves are drawn from which values of φ, θ, $d\varphi/dF$, and $d\theta/dF$ are obtained for substitution into Eqs. (12-5).

The accuracy of the results can be checked by noting that the area under the compression portion of the stress curve should equal that under the tension portion for both the longitudinal and tangential stress distributions. While the same criterion does not exist for the radial stress, the latter stress should, of course, be zero at the inner and outer boundaries.

A serious limitation on the method described above is that the metal-removal process can never be carried all the way to the outside surface. Practical machining considerations will ordinarily necessitate stopping approximately 0.030 in. short of the outside. The stress in this last increment of material must be extrapolated from the preceding data or deduced from other techniques, such as slitting the remaining tube in a manner which will release the tangential and longitudinal stresses.

The latter procedure is not always satisfactory and, at best, introduces a discontinuity in the method and an uncertainty in precision right at the most significant step in the entire process. Since the surface residual stresses are apt to be of the greatest importance, it is in this region that maximum accuracy is appropriate. One method of overcoming the above problem is to stop the boring process at a diameter large enough for mounting additional strain gages in the bore. The gages can now be removed from the outer surface, and the part turned or ground on its outside diameter in steps as before. The questionable region now occurs in the body of the cylinder, and the curves for the stresses on both sides of this region can be joined smoothly by interpolation.

The equations for calculating the stresses from the strains observed at each step in the turning-down process are identical with those for boring out except for the area terms:

$$\sigma_l = \frac{E}{1-\mu^2}\left[(F - F_a)\frac{d\varphi}{dF} - \varphi\right]$$

$$\sigma_t = \frac{E}{1-\mu^2}\left[(F - F_a)\frac{d\theta}{dF} - \frac{(F + F_a)\theta}{2F}\right] \tag{12-6}$$

$$\sigma_r = \frac{E}{1-\mu^2}\frac{(F - F_a)\theta}{2F}$$

where F_a = original cross section of bore

$F = \pi D_0^2/4$ calculated from outside diameter D_0 after turning off each layer

When boring out is followed by turning down in the same specimen, the net stresses relieved by the boring operation must be combined properly with those from the turning operation in the manner described by Hanslip.

If it can be safely assumed for a particular test specimen that the tangential and radial stresses are of negligible magnitude throughout the piece, Eqs. (12-5) and (12-6) reduce to the following, respectively:

$$\sigma_l = E\left[(F_b - F)\frac{d\epsilon_l}{dF} - \epsilon_l\right] \tag{12-7}$$

$$\sigma_l = E\left[(F - F_a)\frac{d\epsilon_l}{dF} - \epsilon_l\right] \tag{12-8}$$

In all the above cases the length of the cylinder should be at least three times the initial diameter for accurate results.

Residual stress measurement in a plane specimen can be accomplished by attaching strain gages to one surface of the specimen and removing material in layers from the opposite surface. The removal of a layer of stressed material results in a bending moment, causing flexure of the specimen and corresponding strain on the reverse face. Material can be removed by etching, electropolishing, grinding, or even milling if carefully done. After each layer removal, the strains indicated by the gages are recorded, and the results used to calculate the initial stress distribution before the relaxing operation.

If it can be assumed that the residual stresses are primarily uniaxial, as is often the case, the stress is calculated from the following:

$$\sigma_n = \frac{1}{6}Et_n^2\frac{dC}{dt} - \frac{\sum_0^{n-1}\sigma\,\Delta t}{t_{n-1}} + \frac{1}{2}Et_{n-1}(C_0 - C_{n-1}) \tag{12-9}$$

where E = modulus of elasticity
t_n = thickness of specimen after removal of nth layer
t_{n-1} = thickness of specimen before removal of nth layer
C = curvature $1/\rho$ of specimen $= -2\epsilon/t$
ϵ = strain measured on reverse face of specimen
$dC/dt = (2/t_n)(\epsilon_n/t_n - d\epsilon/dt)$
$C_0 - C_{n-1} = 2(\epsilon_{n-1}/t_{n-1})$

The value of $d\epsilon/dt$ for calculating dC/dt is obtained by plotting measured strain versus thickness for all layers, drawing a smooth curve through the data points, and differentiating graphically.

When only the surface residual stress is of interest, a single layer of material can be removed, and Eq. (12-9) reduces to

$$\sigma = \tfrac{1}{3}Et\left(\frac{\epsilon}{t} - \frac{\epsilon}{\Delta t}\right) \qquad (12\text{-}10)$$

where t = thickness after removal of layer
ϵ = indicated strain after removal of layer
Δt = thickness of layer removed

Waisman and Phillips have developed similar, although somewhat more involved, equations for the general case of biaxial stress. Still another technique for measuring residual stresses involves relaxing the stresses by drilling a hole at a point surrounded by strain gages. In an extension of this technique, the entire region carrying the gages is removed by trepanning with a hole cutter.

EFFECTS OF NUCLEAR RADIATION ON STRAIN GAGES

Early attempts to utilize strain gages in the intense radiation fields associated with nuclear-reactor cores demonstrated the complete inadequacy of paper gages and nitrocellulose cements for this purpose. In general, any organic material in either the gage or cement will render it useless under severe radiation. It was also learned that soldered electrical joints are unacceptable for this service.

In subsequent experiments by Smith and Rendler of the Naval Research Laboratory, Constantan and Nichrome V foil gages (devoid of backing material) bonded with Allen P-1 ceramic cement were subjected to estimated thermal and fast (greater than 1 Mev) neutron fluxes of 10^{13} and 5×10^{11} neutrons per cm^2-sec, respectively, for a period of 2 weeks. Integrated thermal and fast neutron fluxes were estimated at 1.2×10^{19} and 6×10^{17} neutrons per cm^2.

These conditions produced 1 to 2 per cent increases in resistance in the Nichrome V gages and 0.1 to 0.5 per cent decreases in resistance in the Constantan gages. The reported resistance to ground through the ceramic cement decreased from 1,000 megohms to less than 100,000 ohms during the test. No data were taken on the effect of radiation on gage factor.

From the information currently available, the following tentative generalities can be made. Constantan strain gages can be used for static strain measurement in radiation fields for limited periods of time. Dynamic strain measurements are no problem as long as the gage remains functional (prior to excessive loss of insulation between the gage element and ground) and if the gage factor after irradiation is known. Strain gages should be used in pairs with a radiation-compensating dummy to cancel resistance changes. All electrical connections in the radiation field should be welded. Ceramic bonded Constantan gages containing no organic materials should perform satisfactorily for weeks or months in the radiation fields adjacent to a reactor where the fluxes are lower by factors of 10^3 to 10^6 than in the core.

WELDABLE STRAIN GAGES

Strain gage cements for use at temperatures above approximately 175°F generally require elevated-temperature curing cycles. One can readily envision gage installations on structural members for which it would be impracticable, if not impossible, to achieve the required curing temperature. A logical approach to circumventing these and similar problems of field installation involves premounting the strain gage in the laboratory on a thin metal carrier and then welding the assembly to the test structure. Under laboratory or production conditions the curing procedure is unhampered by limitations imposed by the physical circumstances at the test site. Instead, the gages can be bonded under clean, precisely controlled conditions, fully and properly cured, and exposed to postcure stabilizing treatments.

Commercial weldable strain gages have appeared as a result of these obvious advantages. One type of weldable gage as manufactured by the Baldwin-Lima-Hamilton Corporation is shown in Fig. 12-8. This

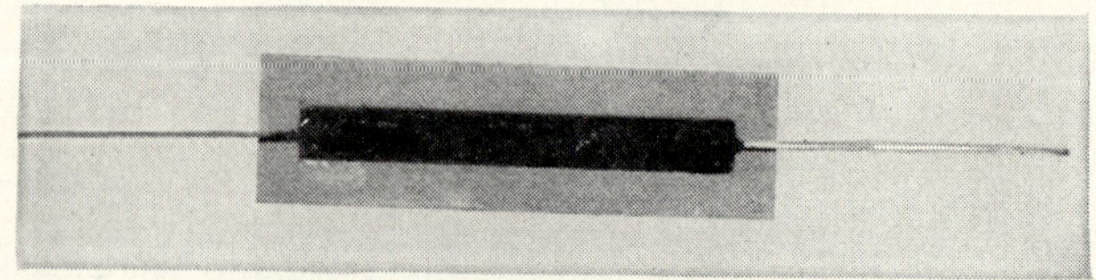

FIG. 12-8. Weldable strain gage consisting of conventional high-temperature strain gage bonded with ceramic cement to stainless-steel backing. Maximum rated operating temperature for static strain measurement—750°F. (*Courtesy of Baldwin-Lima-Hamilton Corp.*)

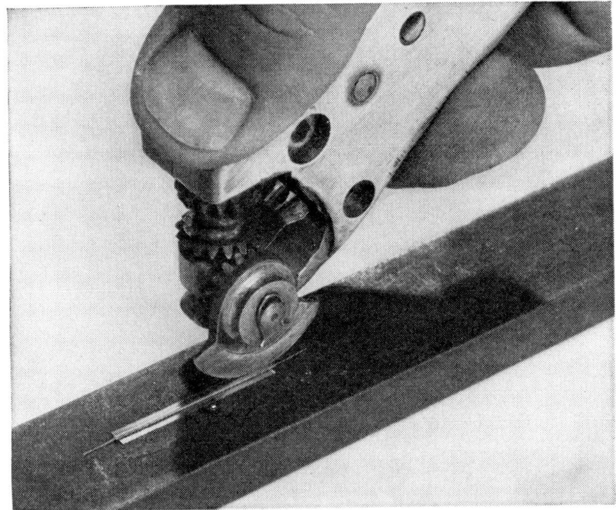

FIG. 12-9. Mounting Microdot weldable strain gage on metal specimen with special welding probe. (*Courtesy of Microdot, Inc.*)

gage embodies a standard foil element prebonded to a coupon of 0.005-in.-thick stainless steel. The gages are self-temperature-compensated. The Baldwin weldable strain gages are available in two different maximum temperature ratings, 500 and 750°F, determined by the element material and bonding agent. Installation of the gages is ordinarily effected by spot welding along the edges or flanges with a small condenser discharge welder.

Microdot, Incorporated, manufactures a series of weldable strain gages with the strain-sensitive filament surrounded by a metallic-oxide insulation and incased in a swaged stainless-steel tube. These strain gages have a maximum operating temperature of 750°F for stable static strain measurement and 1500°F for dynamic applications. In Fig. 12-9 a Microdot gage is being welded to a metal specimen using the Rollectrode, a special welding probe. Certain

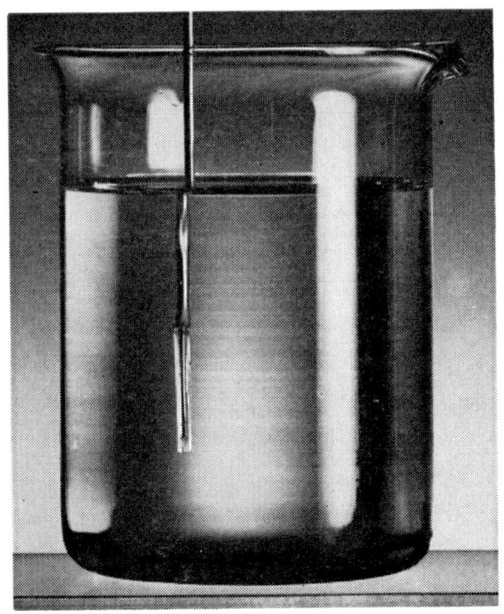

FIG. 12-10. Weldable strain gage with integral leads contained in a stainless-steel tube, permitting submerged operation of the gage. (*Courtesy of Microdot, Inc.*)

gage types are also available, with integral leads contained within a stainless-steel tube (Fig. 12-10) to allow immersion in water or other media.

Although weldable strain gages are limited to applications on flat or nearly flat surfaces, they offer a number of advantages, including a simple, quick installation procedure; immediate use after welding in place and connecting lead wires; standardized, properly cured and stabilized bond between the strain-sensitive filament and its carrier; and, in the case of the Microdot gages, an armored assembly which is highly resistant to damage from external factors such as mechanical impact and erosion.

PIEZORESISTIVE STRAIN GAGES

In 1954 Charles S. Smith published an article in *Physical Review* reporting an investigation on the piezoresistance effect in germanium and silicon at the Bell Telephone Laboratory. A paper in 1957 by W. P. Mason and R. N. Thurston in the *Journal of the Acoustical Society of America* reported on a continuation of the work, using these materials in the measurement of displacement, force, and torque. Since this time, rapid development has occurred, and piezoresistive strain gages are currently being marketed by several companies. Changes are occurring rapidly in the characteristics of the commercially available gages since this is a new development and competition is keen.

The gages consist of a filament cut from a single crystal of silicon which contains carefully controlled trace amounts of an impurity such as boron or arsenic. Lengths of the sensitive element vary from $\frac{1}{64}$ to $\frac{1}{2}$ in. A tab is fastened to each end of the sensitive element, to which leads may be attached.

The great advantage in using the semiconductor as the strain-sensitive element is that its gage factor may be as high as 175 compared with about 2 for conventional strain gage materials. This means that gage output is so large that much of the amplification required for conventional gage use can be dispensed with. Unfortunately, in addition to its high gage factor, the piezoresistive gage has a high temperature sensitivity and a nonlinear behavior at high strains, both of which characteristics are undesirable.

The first commercial gages were quite stiff, but gages now available can be bent to a radius of 0.125 in. The procedure for bonding the gage to the test area is the same as for the wire and foil gages, and the same cements are used. Piezoresistive gages have been used at temperatures up to 700°F, and they are capable of measuring tensile strains up to 3,000 micro-inches per in. In some gages, resistance change is linear with tensile strains up to 500 micro-inches per in., and then it becomes increasingly nonlinear until it varies by $2\frac{1}{2}$ per cent from linearity at

2,000 micro-inches per in. Greater nonlinearity occurs when the gage is used in compression. Gages are produced with resistances varying from 50 to 1,000 ohms, and they are also produced in weldable form.

Since both the resistance and gage factor vary with temperature, efforts are being made to reduce the effect. This can be done by adding impurities to the silicon crystal, but unfortunately the gage factor decreases as linearity and temperature effect are improved. Gage factors of gages as presently manufactured are about 120. Methods of reducing the effect of temperature and nonlinearity are available through the use of dummy gages and by taking advantage of the nonlinearity of the unbalanced Wheatstone-bridge circuit.

One advantage in using silicon as the sensitive element in the gage is that it can be manufactured with a negative gage factor as easily as with a positive one. Thus a full bridge using two positive and two negative gages may be used for tension as well as for bending. This not only provides temperature compensation, but also compensates for nonlinearity, since the gage-factor decrease in the compression gages is offset by its increase in the tension gages for the case of bending.

It is also suggested that the nonlinearity of the unbalanced Wheatstone bridge may be used to compensate for the nonlinearity of the gage factor at high-strain readings.

At present the semiconductor strain gage appears to be useful primarily for the measurement of very small strains (from 1 to 0.01 micro-inch per in.) and for use in transducers where compensating networks take care of the nonlinearity and temperature problems. Since resistance changes are very large, slip-ring resistance changes are negligible when used with semiconductor gages, and the high output also eliminates the necessity for high-gain amplifiers.

As an example of the application of semiconductor strain gages to transducers, Century Electronics and Instruments, Inc., supplies a pressure transducer, based upon these gages, which produces a full-scale signal of 4 volts for an input of 28 volts.

STRAIN MEASUREMENT AT CRYOGENIC TEMPERATURES

An early evaluation of strain gage performance at low temperatures was made by Day and Sevand. They conducted tests on strain gages at temperatures down to −300°F. Under these conditions the gages exhibited characteristics not radically different from those at room temperature.

More recently, tests at the Lewis Research Center of the National Aeronautics and Space Administration, reported by Chiarito, have demonstrated that at the boiling-point temperature of liquid hydrogen (−425°F), gages having filaments of Advance, Iso-elastic, Nichrome V, and similar strain-sensitive materials are subject to extensive drift and instability. In the same investigation it was found that foil gages made of Armour alloy (S-700—stabilized; source, Budd Instruments Division) were superior for this type of service. The Armour alloy also gave improved performance in measuring large strains (up to 1.2 per cent) at liquid-nitrogen temperature (−320°F).

ULTRA-HIGH-TEMPERATURE STRAIN MEASUREMENT

The use of bakelite-type SR-4 strain gages at temperatures up to 350°F has already been described in detail. There are, however, a number of occasions when it becomes necessary to measure strains on bodies subjected to much higher temperatures. One example of the need for high-temperature strain gages is in the strain analysis of high-pressure steam apparatus. Another is in studying the stresses and vibrations in gas-turbine disks and blades during operation. There is a constant demand for replacing turbine materials now in use with less strategic materials. This requires accurate knowledge of (1) the loads and stresses to which the blade and disk materials are subjected and (2) the properties of the materials themselves under operating conditions. Similarly, missiles, rockets, and space vehicles embody countless problems demanding high-temperature strain measurements. There is, in general, a rapidly increasing need for both static and dynamic strain measurements in the range of temperatures from 1000 to 2000°F. Strain gages to be employed at such elevated temperatures must be composed of filaments and cements especially selected for these severe conditions. Many of the strain-sensitive materials are, for one reason or another, unsuited to this type of operation. Similarly, the conventional gage-bonding agents are incapable of withstanding such temperatures.

At this point we might review briefly the requirements of strain gage filaments and bonding agents for elevated-temperature service. The strain-sensitive material should have the following characteristics:

1. As high a gage factor as possible.
2. Low thermal coefficient of resistance.
3. High resistance per unit length (in order to allow construction of physically small gages with high total resistance).
4. Consistent electrical properties over a wide range of temperatures.
5. Linear relationship between strain and resistance change.
6. Freedom from corrosion or chemical action by bonding agents at high temperatures.

A satisfactory bonding agent would be characterized as follows:

1. Mechanically and chemically stable at temperatures up to 1800°F or higher.

2. Strongly adhesive to metallic and ceramic surfaces.
3. Nonhygroscopic.
4. Electrically insulating at all temperatures.
5. Noncorrosive.
6. Free from checking, cracking, and other forms of failure due to straining at high temperatures.
7. Subject to easy and simple bonding procedures.

The wire materials that have been experimentally employed in ultra-high-temperature strain gages include Advance, Karma, Nichrome V, and several platinum-iridium alloys. Table 12-1 lists the approximate compositions and electrical properties of these materials.

TABLE 12-1. PROPERTIES OF STRAIN-SENSITIVE MATERIALS FOR HIGH-TEMPERATURE STRAIN GAGES*

Material	Composition	Gage factor	Resistivity,† ohms per cir-mil-ft	Temperature coefficient of resistivity,‡	Maximum operating temperature, °F
Advance.......	0.55 Cu, 0.45 Ni	2.1	294	±10	900
Karma........	0.74 Ni, 0.20 Cr, 0.03 Fe, 0.03 Cu	2.0	800	±10	1500
Nichrome V...	0.80 Ni, 0.20 Cr	2.0	650	60	2000
Platinum-iridium	0.80–0.90 platinum 0.10–0.20 iridium	6.0	200	440	2000

* The values in this table may vary appreciably with slight changes in composition or at elevated temperatures.

† At room temperature.

‡ Parts per million per degree Fahrenheit. Average over the range from room temperature to 212°F.

The platinum-iridium alloys are outstanding on the basis of gage factor, or strain sensitivity, having roughly three times that of the commercial strain gage materials. These alloys are also characterized by inherent chemical stability, even at high temperatures. The preceding advantages are partially discounted, however, by a low resistance and high thermal coefficient of resistance. The latter properties apparently limit the use of platinum-iridium alloys to dynamic strain applications in which the strain frequency is considerably higher than the frequency of any temperature fluctuations which may occur.

Nichrome V has a high resistance but is unfortunately similar to platinum-iridium in having a high thermal coefficient of resistance. This alloy is widely used for high-temperature measurement of dynamic strains. It is especially suited to the applications in which gage size is critical, since strain gages can be made quite small for a given total resistance.

Up to approximately 900°F the Karma alloy displays many of the characteristics of an ideal high-temperature strain gage wire. Although its gage factor is considerably less than that of the platinum-iridium alloys, it has a high resistance and low thermal coefficient of resistance, is stable in the presence of ceramic cements, and in general appears quite well suited to the measurement of static strains. Above 900°F, Karma undergoes metallurgical changes and develops a high and varying thermal coefficient of resistance. Advance, which is so commonly employed in conventional strain gage installations, disqualifies itself from high-temperature duty because it is subject to galvanic corrosion under these conditions.

From this brief summary of the high-temperature properties of existing strain-sensitive alloys, it becomes evident that precise static strain measurements above 1000°F are at present difficult to obtain. Some manufacturers employ Constantan in gages for use at temperatures up to 600°F. Others use Karma, recommending the gages for static strain measurements to 900°F. Gages with Nichrome V filaments are commonly rated at 1000°F for static strain and as high as 1800°F for dynamic strain. Special platinum alloys are used by one manufacturer and rated at 2000°F for dynamic strain measurements.

Many ceramic cements have been tested for bonding high-temperature strain gages. Cement evaluations conducted by the Baldwin-Lima-Hamilton Corporation have yielded the following information. Brimor[1] U-529 cement maintained adequate mechanical and electrical characteristics to a temperature of 1700°F. Allen[2] P-1 and Allen PBX cements, widely used for high-temperature strain gage bonding, were found to have acceptable properties to 1400°F. The Quigley[3] Triple-A high-temperature paints, which were originally used for the installation of custom-made high-temperature gages, exhibited objectionable hygroscopic characteristics. An additional cement, approximately equivalent in properties to Allen PBX, is Trans-Sonics[4] 64CP.

COMMERCIAL GAGES

Currently available high-temperature strain gages for duty at temperatures of 1000°F and above are usually supplied on some form of

[1] Morganite, Incorporated, Long Island City 1, New York.
[2] Robert A. Allen Company, Mechanicsville, N.Y.
[3] Quigley Company, Incorporated, New York 17, N.Y.
[4] Trans-Sonics, Incorporated, Burlington, Mass.

temporary carrier or backing. After removal from the backing, and welding of lead wires, the free filament is set in place on the test piece over a layer of ceramic cement which has previously been applied and cured. Additional ceramic cement is applied over the filament and cured to complete the bond.

Bonding procedures used by two of the principal gage manufacturers are shown in Figs. 12-11 and 12-12. It may be evident from these illustrations (which are greatly abridged summaries of the entire procedures) that high-temperature strain gage installation is far from a convenient routine.

The degree of precision and repeatability common to room-temperature applications cannot be expected from the high-temperature strain gages. Reasonably accurate static strain measurements at elevated temperatures will be achieved only by exercising a great deal of care and patience. Full temperature compensation for both gages and lead wires is, of course, an absolute necessity. For stable, repeatable strain indications the test member and gage installation should be cycled to the expected load and temperature several times. Corrections must also be made for changes in gage factor with temperature.

High-temperature dynamic strain measurement makes much less severe demands on the strain gage and the cement. Because of this, temperature compensation may be unnecessary, considerable loss in resistance to ground through the cement is acceptable, and thermal effects in lead wires are apt to be of no consequence.

Current high-temperature strain gage practice can be summarized as follows:

1. Up to 350°F: standard bakelite strain gages cemented according to the manufacturer's recommendations. Suitable for either static or dynamic strains.
2. Up to 500°F: bakelite strain gages cemented to ceramic precoated surfaces (using any of the previously mentioned high-temperature cements) to minimize effect of reduction in impedance of resin bonding agent. These gages can also be used for static or dynamic strain instrumentation.
3. Up to 600°F: strippable Constantan foil gages mounted with ceramic cement—static or dynamic applications.
4. 600°F to 1000°F: (*a*) strippable or free-handling Nichrome V foil gages mounted with ceramic cements—static or dynamic. (*b*) strippable Karma—dynamic only.
5. 1000 to 1500°F: strippable Nichrome V and platinum alloys mounted with ceramic cement—suitable for dynamic use only.
6. 1500 to 2000°F: Baldwin-Lima-Hamilton type HT platinum alloy free-wire filament gage mounted with ceramic cement supplied by the manufacturer—for dynamic strain measurement only.

FIG. 12-11. (*A*) Remove auxiliary strips from gage backing. (*B*) Separate gage connection tabs from backing material. (*C*) Cut plastic backing away with nippers. (*D*) Weld ribbon leads to gage tabs. (*E*) Strip gage from plastic backing. (*F*) Apply ceramic cement to cleaned specimen. (*G*) Install gage and tape in place. (*H*) Coat gage with ceramic cement. (*I*) Dry cement with ultraviolet lamp. (*J*) Remove handling tabs. (*K*) Form lead ribbons prior to making lead-wire connections. (*Courtesy of The Budd Company.*)

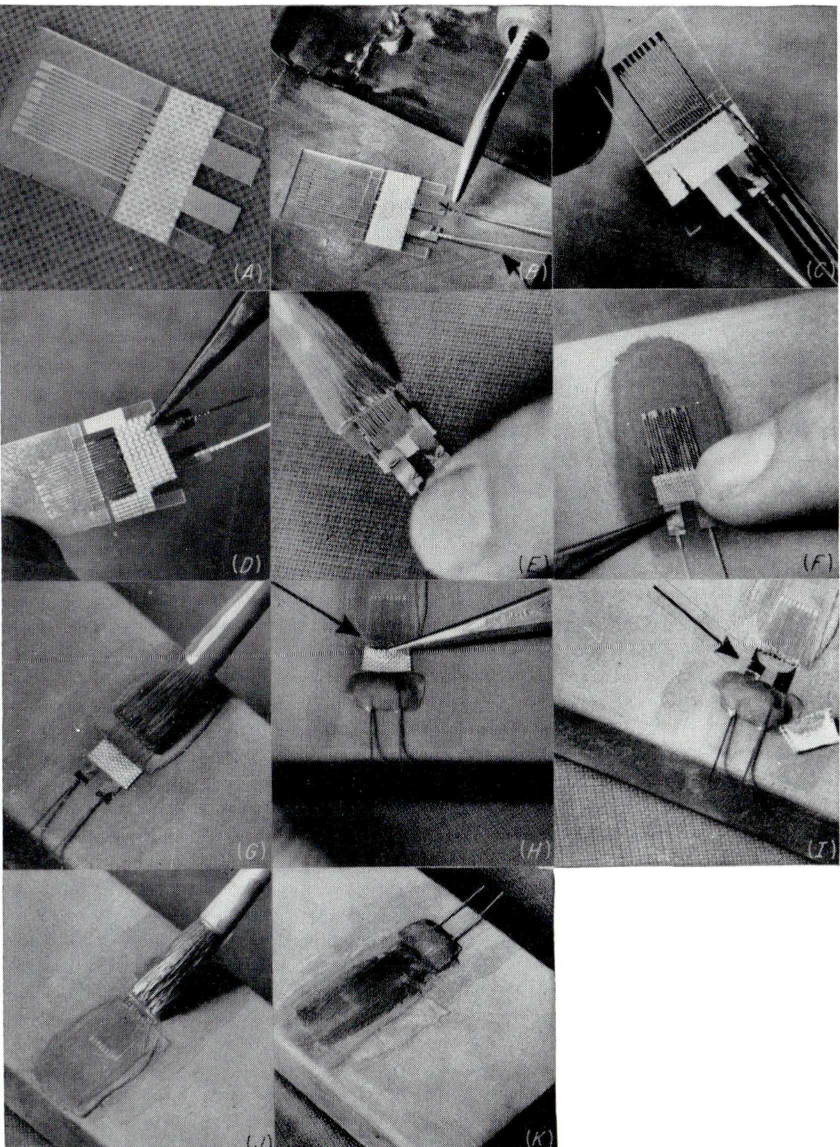

FIG. 12-12. (*A*) Free-handling high-temperature strain gage as received. (*B*) Weld leads to gage. (*C*) Cut glass tape with scissors. (*D*) Remove gage from handling envelope. (*E*) Wet undersurface of gage with ceramic cement. (*F*) Place gage on specimen. (*G*) Apply ceramic cement to grid area and to lead tabs. (*H*) Remove glass tape. (*I*) Remaining area to be cemented (indicated by arrow). (*J*) Final application of ceramic cement. (*K*) Installed gage. (*Courtesy of Baldwin-Lima-Hamilton Corporation.*)

SUMMARY

This chapter has described several techniques for the successful use of strain gages in out-of-the-ordinary applications. What is more important than the actual procedural details, however, is a philosophy of approach to such problems. Regardless of the number of particular cases which might have been presented here, someone would find that he did not have the specific instructions for the situation at hand, since all strain gage applications appear to have their own peculiar requirements. The techniques for special strain gage installations can be reduced to an essence consisting mainly of the willingness to experiment, combined with exactitude, care, and patience. When special problems arise, it is generally possible to experimentally develop procedures for obtaining satisfactory strain measurements. It is absolutely necessary to conduct control and evaluation tests to demonstrate that the new procedure does not introduce errors of its own.

BIBLIOGRAPHY

Ades, C. S., and L. H. N. Lee: Strain-gage Measurements in Regions of High Stress Gradient, *Experimental Mechanics*, vol. 1, no. 6, pp. 199–200, June, 1961.

Anderson, A. R.: How to Use Strain Gages in Concrete, *Eng. News-Record,* vol. 146, no. 10, pp. 46–47, Mar. 8, 1951.

Boodberg, A., and E. D. Howe: Method of Obtaining the Stress of the Mid-thickness by Measurements from Only One Surface of a Plate, *Proc. SESA*, vol. 5, no. 1, pp. 56–58, 1947.

Brosius, G. F., and D. Hartley: Evaluation of High Temperature Strain Gages, *Proc. SESA*, vol. 17, no. 1, p. 67, 1959.

Carlton, E. W., and J. H. Senne: Instrumentation and Strain Measurement in Welded Wire Fabric Reinforced Concrete Slabs, *J. Am. Concrete Inst.*, vol. 24, pp. 141–152, October, 1952.

Carpenter, J. E., and L. D. Morris: A Wire Resistance Strain Gage for the Measurement of Static Strains at Temperatures up to 1600°F., *Proc. SESA*, vol. 9, no. 1, pp. 191–200, 1951.

Chandler, R. L., and E. J. Dent: Temperature Compensated Strain Gauges, *Electronic Eng.*, vol. 32, pp. 414–421, July, 1960.

Chiarito, P. T.: Strain Measurements at Cryogenic Temperatures, Cryogenic Engineering Conference, University of Michigan, Ann Arbor, Michigan, Aug. 15–17, 1961.

Day, E. E.: Performance of Foil-type High-temperature Strain Gages up to 700°F, *Proc. SESA*, vol. 16, no. 1, p. 97, 1958.

Day, E. E., and A. H. Sevand: Characteristics of Electrical Strain Gages at Low Temperatures, *Proc. SESA*, vol. 8, no. 1, pp. 133–142, 1953.

DeMichele, D. J.: Wire Strain Gages for Elevated Temperature Service, *Product Eng.*, vol. 21, no. 10, pp. 115–117, October, 1950.

Demorest, D. J., and D. O. Leeser: A Study of Residual Stresses in Flat Beams by Electropolishing Methods, *Proc. SESA*, vol. 11, no. 1, pp. 45–54, 1954.

Dietz, A. G. H., and W. H. Campbell: Bonded Wire Strain Gage Techniques for Polymethyl Methacrylate Plastics, *Proc. SESA*, vol. 5, no. 1, pp. 59–62, 1947.

Dove, R. C.: Strain Measurement Errors in Materials of Low Modulus, *Proc. Am. Soc. Civ. Engrs.*, vol. 81, no. 691, p. 10, May, 1955.

Ernst, G. C.: The Use of SR-4 Strain Gages in the Testing of Wood and Wood-base Materials, *U.S. Dept. Agr., Forest Service, Pub. Forest Products Lab.* (Madison 5, Wis.), 1945.

Forst, J. J., and F. T. Geyling: Applications of Semiconductor Transducers in Strain Gages and Rigid Dynamometers, *Proc. SESA*, vol. 17, no. 1, p. 143, 1959.

Geiger, R. C., and I. Sherlock: External Strain-gage Instrumentation for Transient Elevated Temperatures, *Proc. SESA*, vol. 14, no. 2, p. 117, 1957.

Gorton, R. E.: Development and Use of High Temperature Strain Gages, *Proc. SESA*, vol. 9, no. 1, pp. 163–176, 1951.

Hannah, R. L., and A. M. Kinan: Measuring Strain to 1000°F, *Instruments & Control Systems*, vol. 33, pp. 1166–1168, July, 1960.

Hurry, J. A., and R. P. Woolley: New High Range Strain Gage, *Rubber Age*, vol. 73, no. 6, pp. 799–800, September, 1953.

Kemp, R. H.: Strain Gages for Jet Engine Research, *Elec. Ind.*, vol. 17, no. 5, pp. 52–57, 88, 90, May, 1958.

Kemp, R. H., W. C. Morgan, and S. S. Manson: The Application of High-temperature Strain Gages to the Measurement of Vibratory Stresses in Gas-turbine Buckets, *NACA, Tech. Note* 1174, April, 1947.

Leaf, W.: Techniques in Residual Stress Analysis, *Proc. SESA*, vol. 9, no. 2, pp. 133–140, 1952.

MacDonald, R. J., R. L. Carlson, and W. T. Lankford: An Apparatus for the Determination of Stress-Strain Properties at High Rates of Strain, *Proc. SESA*, vol. 14, no. 1, p. 163, 1957.

Marin, J.: A Biaxial Stress Machine for the Determination of Plastic Stress-Strain Relations, *Proc. SESA*, vol. 7, no. 1, pp. 71–82, 1949.

Mason, W. P.: Semiconductors in Strain Gauges, *Bell Labs Record*, vol. 37, no. 1, pp. 7–9, January, 1959; see also *Engineer's Digest*, vol. 20, no. 2, pp. 76, 96, February, 1959.

Mason, W. P., and R. N. Thurston: Use of Piezoresistive Materials in Measurement of Displacement, Force, and Torque, *J. Acoust. Soc. Am.*, vol. 29, no. 10, pp. 1096–1101, October, 1957.

Meitzler, A. H.: Effect of Strain Rate on the Behavior of Isoelastic Wire Strain Gauges, *Rev. Sci. Instr.*, vol. 27, p. 56, January, 1956.

Moyd, L.: Determination of the Coefficient of Linear Thermal Expansion of Rock Specimens by Means of Resistance Wire (SR-4) Strain Gages, *Mining Eng.*, vol. 187, no. 6, Transactions, pp. 603–604, June, 1950.

Perino, P. R.: The Effect of Transmission Line Resistance in the Shunt Calibration of Bridge Transducers, *Statham Instrument Notes*, House Organ of Statham Instruments, Inc., Los Angeles 64, California.

Pitts, J. W., and D. G. Moore: Development of High Temperature Strain Gages, *Natl. Bur. Standards (U.S.) Monograph* 26, Mar. 17, 1961.

Rendler, N. J., and R. C. Smith: Effect of Radiation upon Ceramic-bonded Strain Gages, U.S. Naval Research Lab., *NRL Report* 5450, Apr. 20, 1960.

Richards, Donald G.: A Study of Certain Mechanically-induced Residual Stresses, *Proc. SESA*, vol. 3, no. 1, pp. 40–61, 1946.

Sachs, G.: Evidence of Residual Stresses in Rods and Tubes, *Z. Metallog.*, vol. 19, pp. 352–357, 1927.

Sachs, G., and G. Espey: The Measurement of Residual Stresses in Metal, *Iron Age*, vol. 148, pp. 63–71, Sept. 18; pp. 36–42, Sept. 25, 1941.

Shoub, H.: Wire-resistance Strain Gages for the Measurement of Large Strains, *David Taylor Model Basin, Rept.* 570, March, 1950.

Smith, R. C., and N. J. Rendler: Transducers for Strain Measurement in Intense Radiation Fields, *Proc. SESA*, vol. 16, no. 2, p. 73, 1958.

Strandness, D. E., Jr.: A New Simplified Plethysmograph, *Surg. Gynecol. Obstet.*, vol. 112, no. 6, pp. 751–756, June, 1961.

Svensson, N. L.: A New Electric Resistance Strain Gauge for Large Strain, *Proc. SESA*, vol. 11, no. 1, p. 197, 1954.

Swainger, K.: The Measurement and Interpretation of Post-yield Strains, *Proc. SESA*, vol. 5, no. 2, pp. 1–8, 1948.

Teague, J. M., Jr., and H. H. Blau: Investigations of Stresses in Glass Bottles under Hydrostatic Pressure; Electric Strain Gauge and Brittle Coating Studies, *J. Am. Ceram. Soc.*, vol. 39, pp. 248–252, July 1, 1956.

Todd, J. D.: Waterproofing Electrical Resistance Strain Gages, *Engineering*, vol. 171, no. 4434, p. 67, Jan. 19, 1951.

Vigness, I.: Magnetostrictive Effects in Wire Strain Gages, *Proc. SESA*, vol. 14, no. 2, p. 139, 1957.

Vigness, I.: Magnetostrictive Electricity in Strain Gauges, *Rev. Sci. Instr.*, vol. 27, no. 12, pp. 1012–1014, December, 1956.

Waisman, J. L., and A. Phillips: Simplified Measurement of Residual Stresses, *Proc. SESA*, vol. 11, no. 2, pp. 29–44, 1954.

Whitney, R. J.: The Measurement of Changes in Human Limbs, *J. Physiol.* (*London*), vol. 121, no. 1, pp. 1–27, July, 1953.

Noise-free Instrument Cable, *Natl. Bur. Standards* (*U.S.*), *Tech. News Bull.*, vol. 36, no. 3, pp. 37–39, March, 1952.

Strain Gage Embedment in Concrete, *Natl. Bur. Standards* (*U.S.*), *Tech. News Bull.*, vol. 35, no. 9, pp. 137–139, September, 1951.

Symposium on Elevated Temperature Strain Gages, *ASTM*, *Spec. Tech. Publ.*, no. 230, 1958.

EXERCISES

12-1. Attach a strain gage to a cast-iron or magnesium tensile test specimen, and a dummy gage to an unstrained piece of the same metal. Load the test specimen incrementally to obtain data for plotting a stress-strain curve. From the resulting graph determine the initial-tangent modulus, the yield strength at 0.2 per cent offset, and the secant modulus of elasticity at this stress.

12-2. Connect active and dummy strain gages to a static strain indicator, first with short leads (say, 3 ft) and subsequently with very long leads (100 ft or more). Compare the indicated strain under both circumstances when the member with the active strain gage is subjected to the same load. Calculate the theoretical error due to lead-wire resistance, and compare with your observations.

12-3. With the long-lead-wire setup of Exercise 2, wind the active-gage lead wires tightly and closely around a small steel bar. Again observe and record the indicated strain due to the standard load on the test piece. Notice what has happened to the sensitivity of the strain indicator. Connect capacitors across the active-gage terminals of the strain indicator until phase balance is achieved.

A. With long leads connecting the strain indicator to the strain gage, connect a calibration resistor across two leads at the indicator to obtain a calibration reading.

Repeat the calibration by connecting the calibration resistor across the leads at the gage location. Compare the results obtained with the value computed by Perino's equation.

B. Shake the long leads between the strain gage and indicator violently and determine what effect, if any, this has on the meter reading.

12-4. Cement a strain gage to a light bulb. Record photographically from an oscilloscope trace the strain-time record which occurs when you break the bulb.

12-5. Attempt to measure the stress-strain characteristics of rubber using strain gages. Consider the problems you will encounter at very large strains, and select gages and cement accordingly.

12-6. Conduct an experiment to determine with strain gages the stress-strain characteristics of a sample of biological material (fingernail, ham bone, beef rib, fish scale, etc.).

12-7. Ice is becoming an increasingly important structural material. How would you bond strain gages to ice?

12-8. Derive an expression for the reinforcing effect of the Flexagage as a function of the elastic moduli of the plastic separator and the test material and of the dimensions of the Flexagage and the test specimen.

12-9. Design and construct a clip gage to be used as an extensometer for large strain measurements (to 100 per cent) on rubber. Gage length should be 1.0 in.

12-10. The gage factors of all metallic strain-sensitive materials tend toward 2.0 for plastic strains. What reasoning or analysis can you give to explain this fact?

12-11. Consult the literature on the technique of residual stress measurement by drilling a hole in a region surrounded by strain gages. Use this method to measure the residual stresses in a cold-worked steel member.

12-12. List as many electrical phenomena as possible which might be exploited for accurate static strain measurement at temperatures of 2000°F and above.

12-13. Make and calibrate a strain gage consisting of a mercury-filled rubber tube. Experiment with other electrolytes having a higher resistance than mercury. Note the effect of temperature change in these tests.

12-14. Observe the magnetostrictive effect in an Iso-elastic gage by impact straining of the material to which it is mounted.

12-15. Develop the required equations for determining the principal stresses and their directions when a suitable number of gages is embedded in a block of plastic subjected to a three-dimensional state of stress.

12-16. Set up an experiment by embedding strain gages in a block of plastic to confirm the equations developed in Exercise 15.

13 STRAIN INDICATION WITH BRITTLE COATINGS

The brittle-lacquer (Stresscoat) method of strain indication is an invaluable adjunct to the resistance strain gage as a tool for experimental strain analysis. This technique consists in little more than applying a coating of brittle lacquer to the structural member under test, loading the member, and analyzing the resultant lacquer cracks for information about surface strains. Stresscoat has a number of advantageous properties. Its effective gage length approaches zero; it gives an over-all picture of the strain distribution; it is applicable to any mechanical part or structure, regardless of material, shape, or mode of loading; and it gives principal strain and stress directions at every point on the surface of the object.

The properties particularly useful in conjunction with wire resistance strain gages are those by which Stresscoat indicates highly stressed areas, zones of stress concentration, and the directions of principal stresses. With this information strain gages can be located and oriented for reading the significant strains directly. Otherwise it will often be necessary to use large numbers of strain gage rosettes in an attempt to learn the magnitude and distribution of strains on a loaded member. Once the principal stress directions and the points of stress concentration have been determined with Stresscoat, two gages, mounted along the principal axes, can be used to determine the stresses at each point of interest. A single gage can also be used to obtain stress magnitudes directly, as described in Chap. 7. Stresscoat is also convenient in the relative ease with which it can be employed; that is, it requires no elaborate instruments or electrical wiring. The major limitation of Stresscoat is its lack of quantitative accuracy in indicating strain magnitudes. It is generally conceded that the accuracy is no better than ± 10 per cent under ideal conditions and may be ± 20 per cent if insufficient control is maintained. A second and less important limitation is the time required to dry the lacquer before tests can be conducted. These factors do not prevent the brittle-lacquer method from being a useful and versatile technique for investigating countless strain problems.

Attempts to develop a satisfactory strain-indicating brittle coating date back to 1932 in Germany. No marked commercial success was achieved in this country prior to the work of Greer Ellis at Massachusetts Institute of Technology in 1939. Ellis developed a brittle-lacquer composition sufficiently sensitive to crack at strains below the yield point of most metals. Because the brittleness and crack sensitivity of the lacquer are affected drastically by temperature and humidity, it has been found necessary to compound a series of lacquers, each with slightly different characteristics, for use over a range of atmospheric conditions.

Basically, the Stresscoat lacquers are made from certain wood resins dissolved in carbon disulfide. Plasticizers are added in varying amounts during the formulating process to produce coatings with differing rupture characteristics. The lacquers are designed to crack at approximately 800 micro-inches per in. of strain, corresponding roughly to a stress of 25,000 psi in steel. If a lacquer is strained at a temperature above that for which its use is prescribed, a greater strain will be required to produce cracks; if at a lower temperature, a lesser strain. Extremely low temperatures will cause the lacquer to craze (or crack all over in a random manner) without the presence of strain. Humidity variations have similar effects in that the sensitivity of the lacquer is decreased with high humidity and increased with low humidity. Rupture of the lacquer is essentially independent of the coating thickness, provided it is between 0.003 and 0.006 in. A typical Stresscoat crack pattern is shown in Fig. 13-1, illustrating the cracks on a crankshaft after loading in a manner simulating that in an engine. The cracks visible in the illustration have been darkened for photographic purposes by the application of a special dye etchant supplied by the manufacturer of Stresscoat.

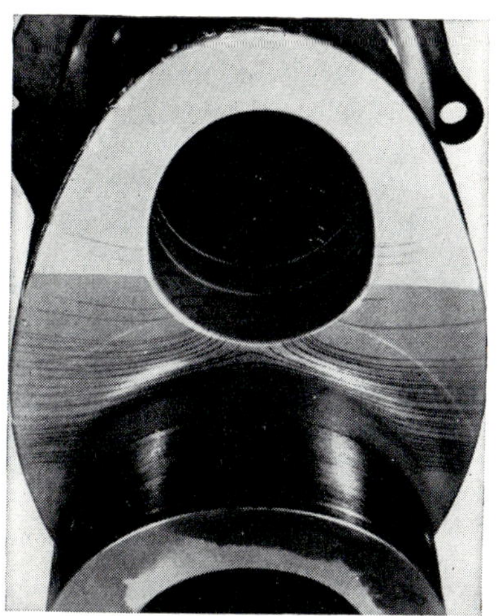

FIG. 13-1. Typical Stresscoat crack pattern on an engine crankshaft. The cracks have been intensified with dye etchant for photographic purposes. (*Courtesy of Magnaflux Corporation.*)

BASIC STRESSCOAT TECHNIQUES

In addition to an indication of the distribution and direction of strains, the fundamental quantity which can be determined with Stresscoat is the magnitude of the principal tensile strain (indicated by incipient cracking of the lacquer) corresponding to a definite load on the member under test. Once the correspondence between load and strain is established, the strain at any load is determinate so long as the entire test piece stays within the elastic range. This is based on the premise that all local strains vary in direct proportion to the load under the prescribed conditions of complete elasticity.

There are seven major steps in performing a strain analysis with brittle lacquers. These are as follows:

1. Preparation of the test-piece surface by cleaning and spraying with a reflective coating.
2. Selection of the appropriate lacquer for the expected test conditions.
3. Application of the lacquer to the test piece and calibrating strip.
4. Curing the lacquer.
5. Loading the test piece and observing the cracks.
6. Loading the calibration strip to determine the strain corresponding to incipient cracking.
7. Treating with dye etchants or Statiflux for improved crack visibility when desired.

LACQUER SELECTION

The principal factors affecting the choice of a lacquer are the expected temperature and humidity in the laboratory or other area where the test will be conducted. The Stresscoat kit includes a sling psychrometer, with which wet- and dry-bulb temperatures can be measured. With the kit is also included a chart, shown in Fig. 13-2, for selecting the lacquer on the basis of the wet- and dry-bulb readings. One item which the Stresscoat kit significantly lacks is an instrument for detecting at the time of lacquer selection what the wet- and dry-bulb temperatures will be 14 to 28 hr later when the actual tests are conducted. This minor indeterminancy must, however, be accepted with composure by the strain analyst as he commits himself to a particular lacquer. Organizations actively engaged in Stresscoat strain analysis will find it advantageous to provide a temperature- and humidity-controlled room for this work.

Lacquer selection is accomplished by establishing the point on the chart of Fig. 13-2 at which the wet- and dry-bulb temperature coordinates intersect. The area between any two of the curves on the chart corresponds to the lacquer indicated by the number found in that area. For example, if the laboratory in which the Stresscoat tests are to be conducted has a dry-bulb temperature of 70°F and a wet-bulb temperature of 56°F, the 1203 lacquer would ordinarily be selected. This

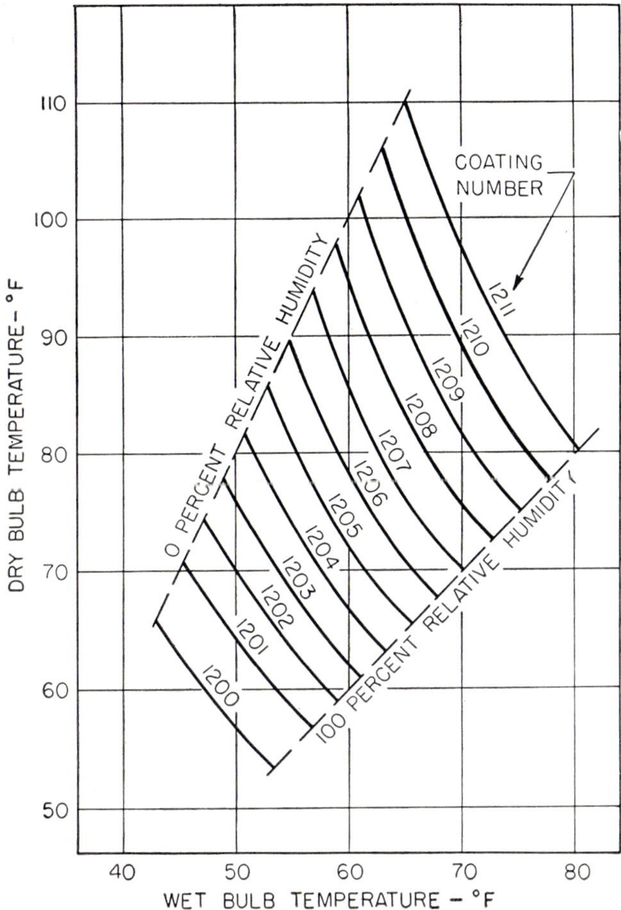

FIG. 13-2. Temperature and humidity chart for Stresscoat lacquer selection.

lacquer should crack at a strain of 700 to 800 micro-inches per in. The lacquer selection may often be modified somewhat to alter the sensitivity for a particular test. As an example, if the strains are expected to be quite low, one can select a higher lacquer number than that indicated for the expected atmospheric conditions. When the lacquer is tested at a temperature or humidity lower than the one for which it is designed, the Stresscoat cracks occur at a correspondingly lower strain. Thus, the selection of a 1204 lacquer for the above case would increase the lacquer sensitivity, so that cracks could be expected at approximately 600 micro-inches per in. This technique must be used with caution because of the danger of crazing if the temperature or humidity drops much lower than anticipated.

Because the lacquer will craze at reduced temperatures, it is imperative in storing a freshly sprayed specimen overnight that temperatures be kept well above the crazing point. For those occasions when a temperature- and humidity-controlled room is not available, the specimen should be stored in an oven or other container which can be kept warm enough to provide an ample margin of safety. Moderate overtemperatures (to 100°F) will not harm the lacquer; in fact, curing the lacquer at slightly above room temperature may actually increase the strain sensitivity. The possible effects of lacquer-curing conditions on the final strain sensitivity emphasize the need for exposing both the specimen and the calibrating strip to the same curing cycle.

LACQUER APPLICATION

The procedure for applying the lacquer is as follows: first, the test piece is thoroughly cleaned and degreased. After this, a coat of aluminum paint is sprayed over the surface. The aluminum paint serves to increase undersurface reflectivity and thus heightens crack visibility. After the aluminum paint has dried for approximately 15 min, the brittle lacquer can be applied. The particular brittle lacquer selected under step 1 is then sprayed over all surfaces to a thickness between 0.004 and 0.006 in. Although proper spraying requires a certain amount of technique, persons with previous spray-gun experience will ordinarily be able to apply Stresscoat satisfactorily after a few trials. Since it is difficult to determine the coating thickness during the spraying operation, the technician must learn to associate the color of the deposited wet lacquer with thickness. The novice can accomplish this by spraying several calibration strips to well-defined color differences and measuring with a micrometer the corresponding coating thicknesses when dry.

Manipulation of the spray gun is of paramount importance. If the gun is held too far from the surface, the lacquer tends to dry out in passage from the nozzle and is deposited in a powdery form. If the spray gun is held too close, the lacquer will run and form an uneven coating, requiring a longer time for drying and resulting in less predictable characteristics. Particular attention is necessary in spraying in the vicinity of sharp fillets and along the edges of surfaces in order to maintain a coating of uniform thickness. The lacquer should be dried 15 to 24 hr before loading the test specimen, although tests can be run in as little as 6 hr after spraying if necessary. The Stresscoat should not be left on the part for over 48 hr prior to testing, since with greater periods of time the consistency of rupture is less certain. If more than 48 hr must elapse before testing, a thicker coating will improve crack consistency.

TEST PROCEDURE AND CRACK OBSERVATION

The actual test procedure consists in applying a reasonable load to the structure or specimen and, while holding the load, making a search for any crack patterns which may have appeared. The boundaries of the crack patterns are then quickly marked and the load released. The specimen is subsequently left unloaded for at least three times the time involved in the preceding loading cycle, after which the load is again

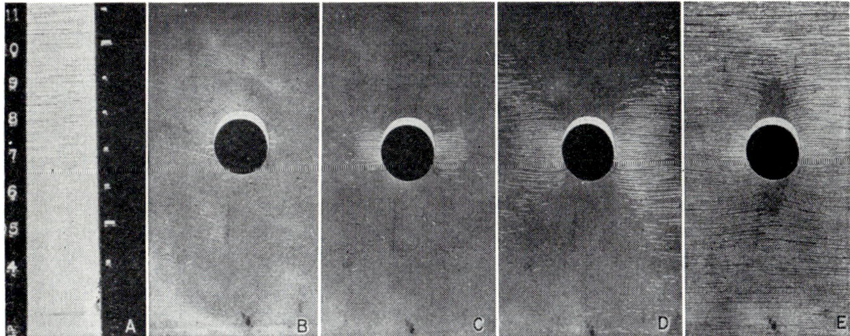

FIG. 13-3. Growth of crack pattern with load for plate with hole. Note that when the cracks have spread to the portion of the plate where $\sigma = P/A$, the ratio of the respective loads is the stress concentration factor. (*Courtesy of Magnaflux Corporation.*)

applied until it is 10 to 30 per cent greater than the previous value. The boundaries of new crack patterns are marked and identified with the corresponding load, and the load is released once more. This process of applying and releasing loads at increasing magnitudes is continued until crack patterns have appeared and have been identified on all areas of interest. Figure 13-3 illustrates the manner in which the crack pattern grows with load.

The procedure for indicating compressive strains is very similar to that for tensile strains. In determining compressive strains, the Stresscoated member is loaded to the maximum expected value and held in this condition for 3 hr. During this time, all tension patterns should be marked and identified. Upon release of the load, the lacquer will crack in the areas which were highly stressed in compression by the initial

FIG. 13-4. Stresscoat kit, including lacquers, solvents, spray guns, air compressor, calibrating equipment, and accessories. (*Courtesy of Magnaflux Corporation.*)

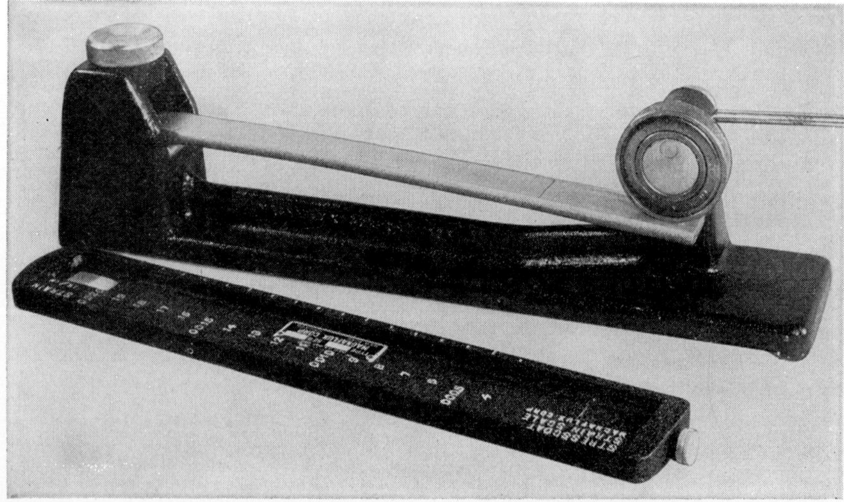

FIG. 13-5. Calibration fixture with a calibrating strip being strained by the loading cam. (*Courtesy of Magnaflux Corporation.*)

load. As in the case of tensile strain, the load can be released until cracks appear, and these marked and identified, after which the load is again applied and held for three times the release time. The load is then released to a greater extent and the new cracks marked and identified. This procedure is continued in a manner parallel to that for tensile strains until all areas of interest have been investigated or until the load is completely released.

In indicating dynamic strain with Stresscoat, it is common to find that by the time the testing mechanism is brought to rest, the cracks will have closed and will no longer be visible. In this case it will be necessary to apply one of the crack-intensification treatments to the surfaces of interest. With cyclic loading the member can be viewed under stroboscopic light, which will make the cracks appear to persist.

CALIBRATION OF LACQUER STRAIN SENSITIVITY

Calibration is accomplished with a calibrating fixture, calibrating strip, and strain scale supplied with the Stresscoat kit (Fig. 13-4). The calibrating strip consists of a bar of steel or aluminum, 12 in. long, 1 in. wide, and ¼ in. thick. This strip, after having been sprayed with the same lacquer as the test specimen and dried, is mounted in a special loading fixture as a cantilever beam (Fig. 13-5) and subjected to a fixed deformation at its free end. As a matter of sound technique, the lacquer should be scraped from the calibrating strip at the end which is to be clamped in the loading fixture and at the point of contact with the loading cam. When clamping the strip in the calibrating fixture, the locking screw should be tightened until the strip just touches the bottom of the loading cam. This procedure will ensure consistency of strain between the calibrating fixture and the calibrating scale. The load is applied to the calibrating strip in the same length of time as that used in loading the test specimen. The point on the strip at which the cracks commence is marked and represents the section where the strains are equal to the crack sensitivity of the lacquer. The calibrating strip can then be removed from the loading fixture and placed alongside a calibrated scale, from which the incipient cracking strain can be read. Figure 13-6 shows a calibration strip which has been

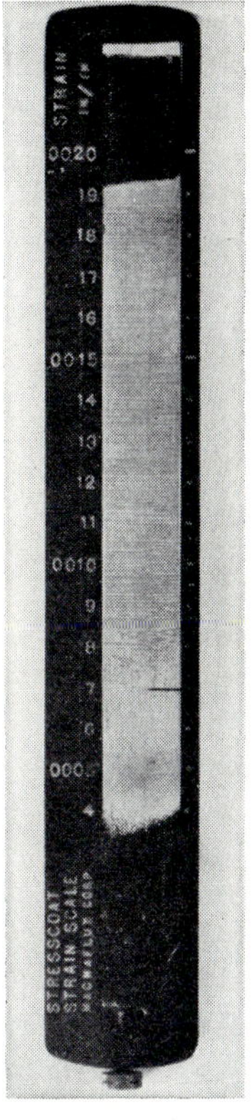

Fig. 13-6. Calibrating strip being compared with the strain scale. The incipient cracking strain in this case is 0.0007 in. per in. (*Courtesy of Magnaflux Corporation.*)

loaded and is being compared with the strain scale. The indicated strain to initiate cracking is, in this case, 0.0007 in. per in.

CRACK INTENSIFICATION

If a permanent record of the crack pattern is desired, it may be found necessary to etch and dye the cracks in order to increase their visibility for photographing. This is accomplished by applying a small quantity of dye-etchant solution, supplied with the Stresscoat kit, to the surfaces of interest. The dye etchant is left on the Stresscoat for approximately 5 min, after which it is removed with an emulsifying agent. Removal of the dye etchant, incidentally, will be facilitated if the surface of the

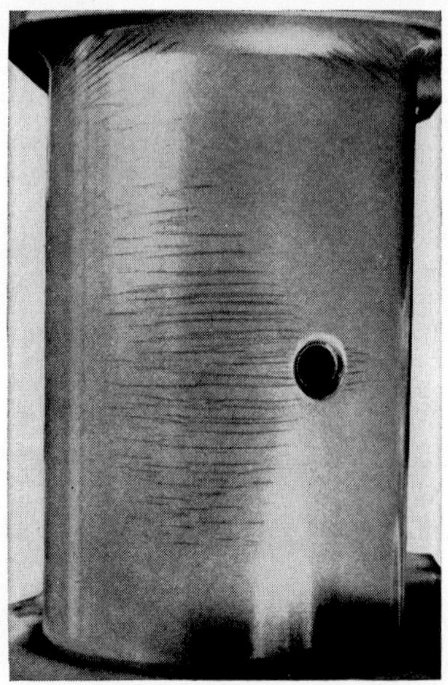

FIG. 13-7. Stresscoat pattern on a crankshaft journal after crack intensification. (*Courtesy of Magnaflux Corporation.*)

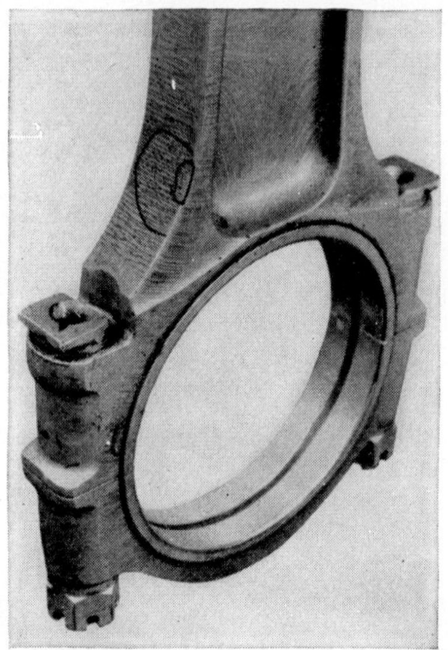

FIG. 13-8. Typical crack pattern on a connecting rod after crack intensification. (*Courtesy of Magnaflux Corporation.*)

part is kept wet with that solution during the period of etching activity. The Stresscoat cracks now appear as dark red lines which are easily photographed. The dye etchant can also be used to show cracks which have closed due to plastic flow in the Stresscoat. This procedure for increasing the visibility of the cracks must be used only after all tests have been completed, since the dye etchant destroys the sensitivity of the lacquer. Examples of the appearance of Stresscoat patterns after crack intensification are shown in Figs. 13-7 and 13-8.

Another method for detecting cracks in Stresscoat (and in other objects) involves a technique for crack intensification which overcomes many of the difficulties associated with the dye etchants. This new method is known as Statiflux and is a form of electrified-particle inspection. Basically, the procedure involves applying a special Statiflux penetrant to the Stresscoated test piece; the surface is then superficially dried, leaving the penetrant in the Stresscoat cracks; and finally, an ionized Statiflux powder is blown over the part. The powder particles, which have obtained an electrostatic charge in being blown from a special gun, are electrically attracted to the cracks. When dynamic strains are being studied, or when coatings with high threshold strains are used, it will often be necessary to apply the Statiflux penetrant before initiating the test and to keep the coating wet with the penetrant during the test. Upon completion of the test, the part is dried and the Statiflux powder applied in the normal manner. The outstanding feature of Statiflux is that this treatment does not destroy the sensitivity of the Stresscoat lacquer for further testing, as does the older dye-etchant method.

The general techniques for employing Stresscoat for various types of strain indication have been summarized in tabular form by Ellis, as shown in Table 13-1. The individual strain analyst will find that modifications and extensions of these techniques may be necessary for particular applications.

RESIDUAL-STRESS STUDIES

Stresscoat has been used to indicate the presence of residual stresses in metals, the nature of the stresses (uniaxial, biaxial, tension, compression, etc.), and, to some degree, the stress magnitudes. Gadd first demonstrated that the crack pattern produced by drilling a shallow hole in the coated surface is indicative of the residual stresses. Subsequent attempts were made to establish a quantitative relationship between the size of the crack pattern and the magnitude of the residual stress.

The technique involves coating the test piece with a lacquer having a threshold cracking strain between 300 and 600 micro-inches per in. (by selection of a lacquer several numbers higher than that indicated in Fig. 13-2 for the prevailing temperature and humidity). After the lacquer is cured, holes not larger than ⅛ in. in diameter are drilled ⅛ in. deep in the surface of the part to relax the stresses. Dye etchant is applied to the coating immediately after drilling. Within several minutes the sensitizing action of the dye etchant will normally have produced a distinct pattern of cracks surrounding the hole. The patterns have

TABLE 13-1. SUMMARY OF STRESSCOAT TECHNIQUES*

Technique No.	Strain	Loading	Coating No.	Loading Procedure	Calibration	Computations	Use of red dye etchant†
1	Tension	Controlled static within elastic limit	Normal—indicated by chart	Increments—10 to 30% additional each load. Rest at zero load for 3 × loading time between increments	Loading time of calibration strip same as that of structure	Assume local strains proportional to loads. Compute all strains to working load, and multiply by tension modulus of elasticity to get apparent stress	Use after completion of test
2	Compression	Controlled static within elastic limit	Normal—indicated by chart	Hold 3 hr at maximum load. Have all tension strain patterns identified. Release load in increments. Return to maximum load for 3 × loading time between increments	Load calibration strip, coating down, in calibrator while maximum load is on structure. Release in same time as structure	Effective load is the release from maximum. Otherwise computation same as tension analysis	Wait 3 hr after completion of test before using
3	Tension	Controlled rotating dynamic loading	Normal—indicated by chart	Increments—10% additional speed increase each increment. Rest at zero load between increments	Load in same time to get to speed	Local strain proportional to square of speed. Compute to working speed	Must be used after completion of test

4	Tension	Dynamic cyclic	Two numbers less than normal	Operate	View under stroboscopic light	Catch deflections or phases at which patterns just open at different areas. Stress ratios are inverse of deflections	Use after completion of test
5	Tension	Uncontrolled dynamic. Actual operating load	On unsymmetrical part use normal coat indicated by chart	Operate minimum time	Load calibration strips in same time as dynamic loading of structure	Presence of patterns indicates maximum tension is above initial calibrated amount	Must be used after completion of test
6	Tension	Uncontrolled dynamic. Actual operating load	If part is symmetrical place bands of normal coating, 1 number above and 1, 2, and 3 numbers below	Operate minimum time	Load all strips in same time as dynamic loading of structure	See where coating just starts pattern	Must be used after completion of tests
7	Yield indicator	Any	Four numbers above normal	Not critical	Observe flaking off of coating	Indicates 1% compression strain component	Not used

* Greer Ellis.

† This table of techniques was developed prior to the introduction of the Statiflux method of crack intensification. Detailed instructions for the use of Statiflux are supplied by the manufacturer.

the general appearance of those shown schematically in Fig. 13-9, according to the type of residual stress present. The radial extent of the crack pattern increases with the residual-stress magnitude. Tokarcik and Polzin observed residual strains of roughly 500 to 700 micro-inches per in. per hole diameter that the pattern extended from the hole edge.

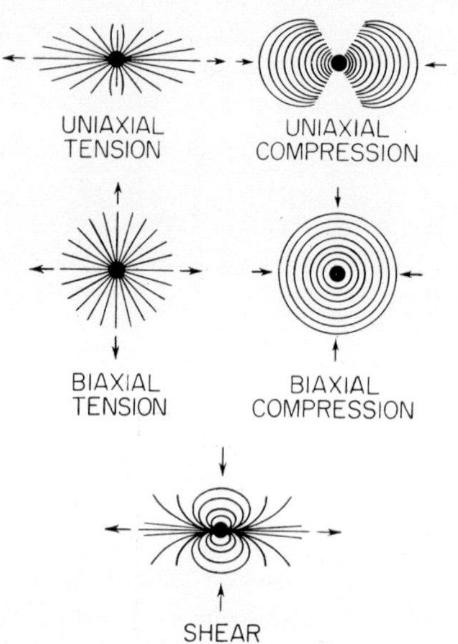

FIG. 13-9. Characteristic Stresscoat patterns which appear when various types of stresses are relieved by drilling a small hole in the coated member. (*After Tokarcik and Polzin.*)

THE USE OF STRESSCOAT ON NONMETALLIC MATERIALS

The greatest use of Stresscoat is on metal parts, since the majority of load-carrying members in mechanical devices where stress is important are made of metal. Stresscoat can be used with any material which is subjected to strains as high as the minimum cracking strain of approximately 500 micro-inches per in. Examples of the application of Stresscoat to nonmetallics might include glass, paperboard, plastics, wood, and fiberboard. An advantage of Stresscoat when used on such low-modulus-of-elasticity materials is that the lacquer does not appreciably alter the mechanical properties of the part.

QUANTITATIVE PRECISION OF STRESSCOAT

When viewed superficially, Stresscoat is a very simple medium for indicating the direction, magnitude, and distribution of strains. The Stresscoat cracks presumably occur along lines normal to the principal tensile strain and at a strain magnitude determined by the type of lacquer and the ambient temperature and humidity. By employing the basic loading and calibrating techniques already described, it is possible to map the strains over the entire surface of the test piece. These strains are then commonly converted to stresses by multiplying by the modulus of elasticity of the material being tested. As stated earlier, this method can ideally produce results with an accuracy of ± 10 per cent.

Actually there are two separate fundamental sources of error in this process. One is that the strain corresponding to the cracking threshold may be different in the calibrating strip from that in the test piece (for any of several reasons to be mentioned later); and the other may arise from a condition in which the stress in the test piece is not directly obtainable from knowledge of the algebraically maximum principal strain. The latter problem occurs because of the presence of a biaxial stress field. The elastic ramifications of such a stress condition were discussed in Chap. 6. The greatest stresses in a machine part are ordinarily in the neighborhood of any stress concentrations which may be present, and the stress concentrations in turn are apt to be of such geometrical configuration that biaxial stresses exist. These and other considerations have led to a number of studies to determine precisely what information Stresscoat gives and how the quantitative accuracy of this information is affected by the variables under which the lacquer is used.

The primary requirement for obtaining equality in the threshold cracking strain of the calibrating strip and the test piece is that all variable conditions be identical in both cases. This refers to the manner of spraying, coating thickness, temperature, humidity, time of drying, and rate of loading. The strain sensitivity of the coatings will be modified by variations in any of these factors. Concerning spraying technique, it has been found that greatest consistency in duplicating a definite strain pattern occurs when the coating contains a formation of fine bubbles. This condition will ordinarily be obtained when the special spray gun supplied by the Stresscoat manufacturer is employed for applying the lacquer. Spray-gun technique is important in controlling the thickness of the coating. Tests conducted to determine the effect of coating thickness on strain sensitivity have shown that the strain necessary to initiate cracks is essentially independent of the coating thickness if that thickness is between 0.003 and 0.006 in. Thicker and thinner coats require a higher strain to cause rupture of the lacquer. This effect is modified somewhat by the time allowed for the coating to dry before straining. Figure 13-10 illustrates the combined effects of drying time and coating thickness on the strain sensitivity of a Stresscoat lacquer. It can be seen that for a drying time of less than 12 hr the coating thickness is quite critical in determining the strain sensitivity. Because it is almost impossible to apply identical thicknesses to both the calibrating strip and the test specimen, it is evident from the figure that drying the coating at least 18 hr will improve the consistency of rupture between the two.

Figures 13-11 and 13-12 demonstrate the variation in strain sensitivity of a particular coating with temperature and humidity. These figures show that the strain necessary to produce cracks decreases as temperature or humidity decreases. Extremely low values of either parameter will result in crazing the lacquer. At the other extreme the lacquer may

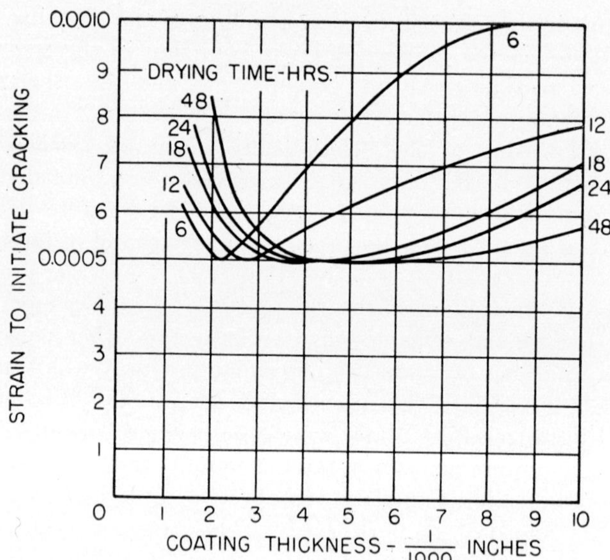

Fig. 13-10. Variation of strain sensitivity with coating thickness for different drying times. (*Ellis.*)

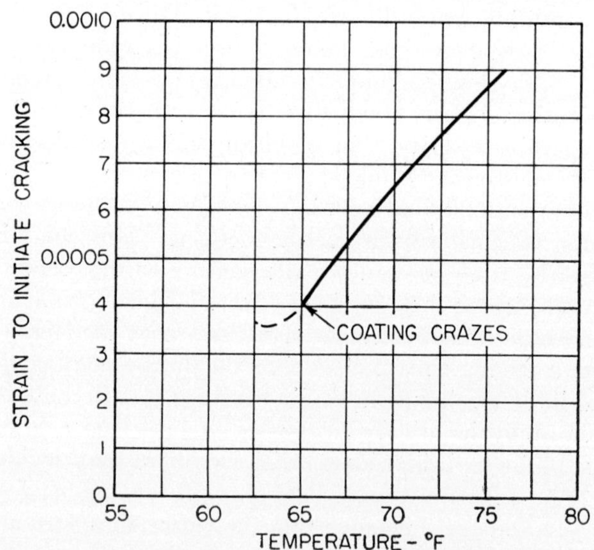

Fig. 13-11. The manner in which the strain sensitivity of a particular Stresscoat lacquer (1204) varies with temperature at constant absolute humidity. (*Ellis.*)

become so soft that it flows, instead of rupturing. The necessity for maintaining the same ambient conditions for both the calibrating strip and the test specimen is very apparent from the figure. Errors may also arise from differences in thermal inertia, as in testing a very thin specimen. The thin member may fluctuate in temperature because of drafts or the mere closeness of the operator's body.

Although the Stresscoat lacquers are known as brittle coatings, they are actually quite plastic and subject to creep over periods of time. This makes it necessary to load the calibrating strip in approximately the same length of time as the test specimen. If the loading occurs in

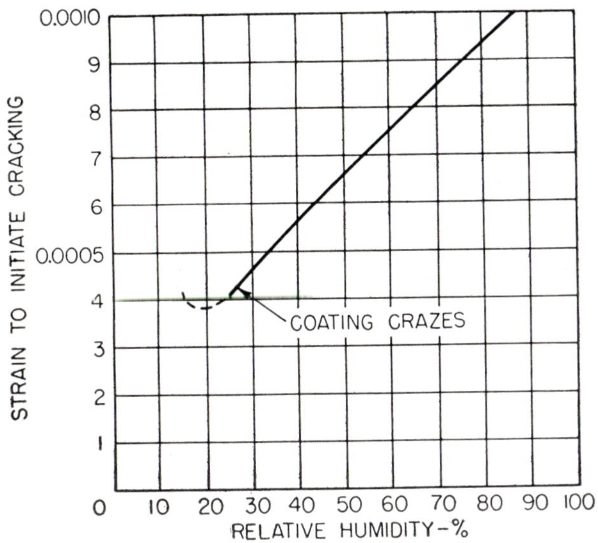

FIG. 13-12. The manner in which the strain sensitivity of a particular Stresscoat lacquer (1204) varies with relative humidity at constant temperature. (*Ellis.*)

less than 10 sec, this factor is not particularly significant, but for greater loading times the strain necessary to initiate cracking increases with time, as shown in Fig. 13-13.

It has been shown that to obtain the same threshold strain in both the calibrating strip and test member requires close control of a number of variables. Lack of control can result in sizable errors in the strain indicated in the test specimen. Assuming that all conditions have been maintained so that the strain indication is very nearly true, there still remains the problem of translating the strain into the corresponding stress. The procedure of multiplying the threshold strain by the modulus of elasticity is valid in certain cases, such as in uniaxial stress fields, but does not give the correct value in a biaxial stress field.

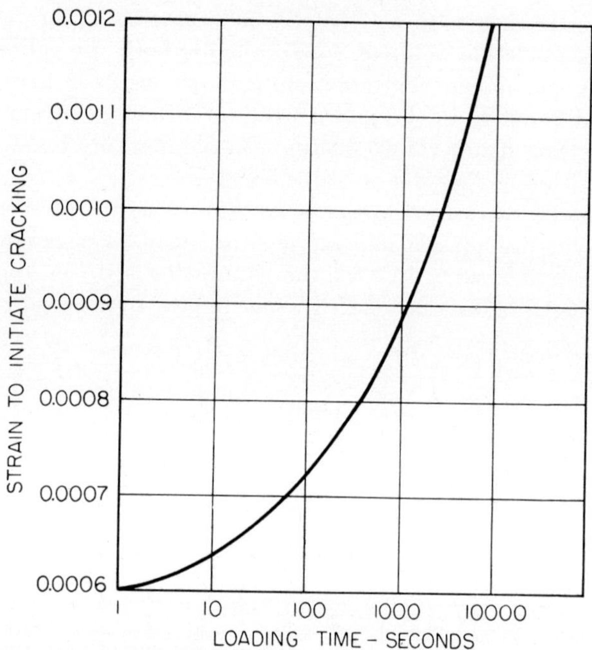

FIG. 13-13. The manner in which the strain sensitivity of Stresscoat lacquer varies with loading time. (*Ellis.*)

CERAMIC COATINGS

One of the primary sources of inaccuracy in the use of Stresscoat, that is, sensitivity to temperature and humidity, has been overcome by the development of a ceramic brittle coating. This coating is cured at an elevated temperature after spraying and produces a strain indicator of greater rupture consistency over the commonly encountered range of atmospheric conditions.

The Magnaflux Corporation markets a ceramic brittle coating known as Stresscoat AllTemp. This material is a porcelain enamel which is applied to the test piece and subsequently fired at 1000°F for approximately 15 min (varying somewhat with the size of the part). The resultant coating is usable over a temperature range from −50 to +600°F and is virtually unaffected by water, oil, and most common solvents. Stresscoat AllTemp is available in coatings having strain sensitivities varying from 0.0002 to 0.002 in. per in. These coatings are satisfactory for use on steels, cast iron, titanium, and other metals with similar thermal expansion coefficients which can withstand the coating curing temperature of 1000°F.

BIBLIOGRAPHY

Birdsall, G. W.: Developing Parts for Production, *Steel,* vol. 117, no. 25, pp. 104–108+, 1945.

Clark, E. C.: Letter to the Editor: Advances in the Art of Stresscoat Analysis, *Proc. SESA*, vol. 13, no. 1, p. 59, 1955.

Dally, J. W., and A. J. Durelli: Prediction of Brittle Coating Strain Sensitivity Based on a Statistical Regression Analysis, *Proc. SESA*, vol. 13, no. 1, p. 169, 1955.

Dally, J. W., and A. J. Durelli: Variables Affecting Brittle Coating in Stress Analysis, *Product Eng.*, vol. 30, pp. 302–305, Mid-September, 1959.

Dally, J. W., A. J. Durelli, and V. J. Parks: Further Studies of Properties of Stresscoat under Dynamic Loading, *Proc. SESA*, vol. 15, no. 2, p. 57, 1958.

Durelli, A. J.: Experimental Determination of Isostatic Lines, *Trans. ASME*, vol. 64, pp. A-155 to A-160, 1942.

Durelli, A. J.: What Kind of Information Does Brittle Coating Give? *Product Eng.*, vol. 19, no. 6, pp. 86–91, June, 1948; no. 7, pp. 133–136, July, 1948.

Durelli, A. J., and J. W. Dally: Some Properties of Stresscoat under Dynamic Loading, *Proc. SESA*, vol. 15, no. 1, p. 43, 1958.

Durelli, A. J., and T. N. DeWolf: Law of Failure of Stresscoat, *Proc. SESA*, vol. 6, no. 2, pp. 68–83, 1949.

Durelli, A. J., R. H. Jacobson, and S. Okubo: Further Studies of Properties of Stresscoat, *Proc. SESA*, vol. 13, no. 1, p. 35, 1955.

Durelli, A. J., and S. Okubo: Influence of Strain Gradient on Brittle Coating Sensitivity, *Product Eng.*, vol. 24, no. 1, pp. 136–137, January, 1953.

Durelli, A. J., and S. Okubo: Heat Treated Brittle Coating Increases Sensitivity, *Product Eng.*, vol. 22, no. 12, pp. 144–147, December, 1951.

Durelli, A. J., and S. Okubo: Crack Density Studies in "Stresscoat," *Proc. SESA*, vol. 11, no. 2, p. 153, 1954.

Durelli, A. J., S. Okubo, and R. H. Jacobson: Study of Some Properties of Stresscoat, *Proc. SESA*, vol. 12, no. 2, p. 55, 1954.

Durelli, A. J., and C. H. Tsao: Discussion of Paper Entitled: Quantitative Evaluation of Residual Stresses by the Stresscoat Drilling Technique, *Proc. SESA*, vol. 10, no. 1, pp. 237–242, 1953.

Durelli, A. J., and C. H. Tsao: Use of Brittle Coating Data in Stress Analysis, *Proc. SESA*, vol. 11, no. 1, p. 181, 1954.

Ellis, G.: Method of Determining Strain Concentration in Rigid Articles, U.S. patent No. 2,294,897, Sept. 8, 1942. Also U.S. patent Nos. 2,310,845 and 2,325,116.

Ellis, G.: Practical Strain Analysis by Use of Brittle Coatings, *Proc. SESA*, vol. 1, no. 1, pp. 46–53, 1943.

Ellis, G., and F. B. Stern: Dynamic Stress Analysis with Brittle Coatings, *Proc. SESA*, vol. 3, no. 1, pp. 102–111, 1945.

Gadd, C. W.: Residual Stress Indications in Brittle Lacquer, *Proc. SESA*, vol. 4, no. 1, pp. 74–77, 1946.

Geschelin, J.: Continental Finds Stresscoat Analysis Valuable Guide in Redesigning Engine Parts, *Automotive and Aviation Indus.*, vol. 95, no. 4, pp. 36–39, 100, Aug. 15, 1946.

Hetenyi, M., and W. E. Young: Application of the Brittle Lacquer Method in the Stress Analysis of Machine Parts, *Proc. SESA*, vol. 1, no. 2, pp. 116–129, 1944.

Linge, J. R.: Some Developments and Applications of Brittle Lacquers, *Aircraft Eng.*, vol. 30, nos. 350, 351, 352, pp. 94–100, April, 1958; pp. 142–148, May, 1958; pp. 173–179, June, 1958.

Salmon, B.: Stress Analysis with Brittle Lacquers, *Aircraft Eng.*, vol. 22, no. 259, pp. 256–263, September, 1950.

Staats, H. N., and S. J. Baranowski: Calibrated Porcelain Enamel Coatings, *Am. Ceram. Soc. Bull.*, vol. 35, no. 4, pp. 143–146, April, 1956.

Stern, F. B.: Ceramic Coatings for Experimental Stress Analysis, *Machine Design*, vol. 30, pp. 147–149, May 29, 1959.

Teague, J. M., Jr., and H. H. Blau: Investigations of Stresses in Glass Bottles under Hydrostatic Pressure; Electric Strain Gauge and Brittle Coating Studies, *J. Am. Ceram. Soc.*, vol. 39, pp. 248–252, July 1, 1956.

Tokarcik, A. G., and M. H. Polzin: Quantitative Evaluation of Residual Stresses by the Stresscoat Drilling Technique, *Proc. SESA*, vol. 9, no. 2, pp. 195–207, 1952.

EXERCISES

13-1. Apply the appropriate Stresscoat lacquer to 10 or 12 calibration bars in graded coating thicknesses from, say, 0.003 to 0.020 in. After properly curing the coatings, test for the effect of coating thickness on strain sensitivity. Plot threshold cracking strain versus coating thickness.

13-2. Stresscoat an expendable C clamp and test for the presence of residual stresses in the manner described in this chapter. Estimate the magnitude of the stress.

13-3. Apply the proper coating as indicated by Fig. 13-2 to one of seven calibration bars. On the remaining six bars use the three higher- and lower-numbered coatings. After curing the lacquers, test for the threshold cracking strain.

13-4. Conduct a stress analysis of any hand tool (such as a pipe wrench) with Stresscoat. Make recommendations for improving the stress distribution in the tool, keeping in mind that understressed areas may be as undesirable as overstressed areas.

13-5. Prepare a summary of the findings of Durelli and his coworkers on the behavior of Stresscoat under biaxial stress, impact, etc.

13-6. Tabulate the sources of variability and error which can affect Stresscoat results, and for each item suggest the optimum remedy or control procedure.

13-7. Coat 10 calibration bars with the same Stresscoat lacquer. Make every effort to maintain all conditions identical among the bars (coating thickness, spraying technique, curing time and procedure, etc.). Test the bars identically in the calibration fixture and record your results. Calculate the average sensitivity (threshold cracking strain) and the confidence limits on the average. What assessment can you make of the precision of Stresscoat under these circumstances?

13-8. Conceive and conduct a test which quantitatively evaluates the relative capacities of Statiflux and the dye etchant for detecting hidden cracks in the lacquer.

13-9. Test for the effect of ambient humidity on the performance of Statiflux. What effect, if any, does grounding the Statiflux gun and/or the test member have on its performance?

13-10. Examine a test piece for compressive stress distribution by applying a maximum load to the Stresscoated part and holding it for about 3 or 4 hr before releasing it in increments.

13-11. Using a number of Stresscoated calibration bars, determine the variation in lacquer sensitivity due to the rate of load application in the calibration-test fixture, by loading very rapidly and very slowly (over a period of 5 min).

14 PHOTOELASTIC STRAIN GAGES

The history of photoelasticity proper goes back to the beginning of the nineteenth century, and that of photoelastic coatings to the experiments of Mesnager in 1930. Mid-twentieth century saw the introduction of commercially practicable photoelastic coatings, due in a large measure to the efforts of Zandman. The photoelastic strain gage (Fig. 14-1) is an outgrowth of these coatings. It consists of a small coupon of birefringent plastic (usually circular or rectangular in shape) approximately 0.1 in. thick, with an integral polariscope for direct indication of strain. The photoelastic gage is cemented to the test piece in about the same manner as the resistance strain gage in order to measure the strain in a particular locality.

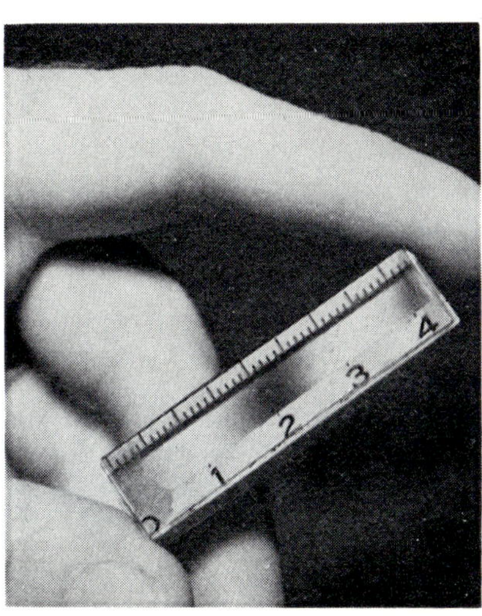

Fig. 14-1. Photoelastic strain gage. (*Courtesy of The Budd Company.*)

The principal advantage of the photoelastic strain gage lies in its direct-reading characteristic. No instruments or other equipment items are needed for the installation or use of the gage, nor is training in the theory of photoelasticity necessary to understand the gage indications. Its disadvantages and limitations include a minimum gage length of approximately 3/4 in., very limited applicability to curved surfaces, a sensitivity of from 40 to 75 microinches per in., a maximum operating temperature of 120°F, and, of course, the fact that the gage requires direct or optical observation and does not produce an electrical signal for remote recording.

Since the photoelastic strain gage does not require knowledge of photoelastic theory for its proper use, and since adequate texts on this subject are readily available (including Frocht's modern classic), no treatment of such theory will be undertaken here.

GAGE CONSTRUCTION

The photoelastic strain gage is constructed as shown in Fig. 14-2. The birefringent plastic (frequently an epoxy resin) is coated on its undersurface with a reflecting layer, while the upper surface carries a thin polarizing film and sometimes a quarter-wave plate. Strain scales or other indicial marks are provided on the face of the gage for translating fringe positions into strains. The net effect is that of a calibrated photoelastic specimen with a built-in plane or circular polariscope.

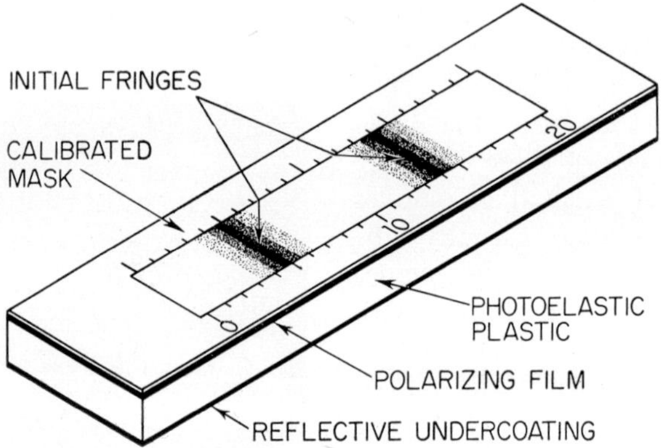

FIG. 14-2. Typical construction of rectangular photoelastic strain gages.

Gages are manufactured in two most common shapes—rectangular and circular. The rectangular gage indicates the strain along its primary axis, while the circular gage functions in the manner of a rosette and indicates principal strain magnitudes and/or directions. The rectangular gages are ordinarily prestressed during manufacture to "freeze in" an initial fringe pattern. Shift of the fringe pattern with further deformation of the installed gage is interpreted in terms of strain in the underlying specimen. Circular gages intended to indicate both the direction and magnitude of principal strains also have initial fringe patterns locked in during manufacture, while those designed to show only principal-strain directions can be free of initial strains or fringes.

There are several variations on the basic gage construction described above which allow increased sensitivity, indications proportional to stress rather than strain, and other refinements.

RECTANGULAR GAGES

The rectangular photoelastic strain gage commonly has an initial pattern consisting of from two to three transverse fringes as shown in Fig. 14-3*A* for an unstrained gage. The application of longitudinal strain to the gage causes the fringes to shift along the gage axis. The fringe movement is proportional to the strain in the gage. Compressive strain causes a movement in one direction, while tensile strain reverses the direction of movement. Figure 14-3*B* illustrates the gage appearance when strained to, say, 500 micro-inches per in. in compression. The fringe labeled No. 1 has disappeared to the left, and a new fringe, No. 3, has appeared on the right. The total movement of fringe No. 2 corresponds to seven of the small marks on the gage scale. Assuming that the gage calibration is 70 micro-inches per in. per unit of fringe shift, the apparent strain is 490 micro-inches per in. Similarly, a tensile strain (Fig. 14-3*C*) produces a shift to the right. Fringe No. 2 disappears, and a new fringe, No. 0, appears on the left. The indication on the scale for this instance is 11 units, or 770 micro-inches per in.

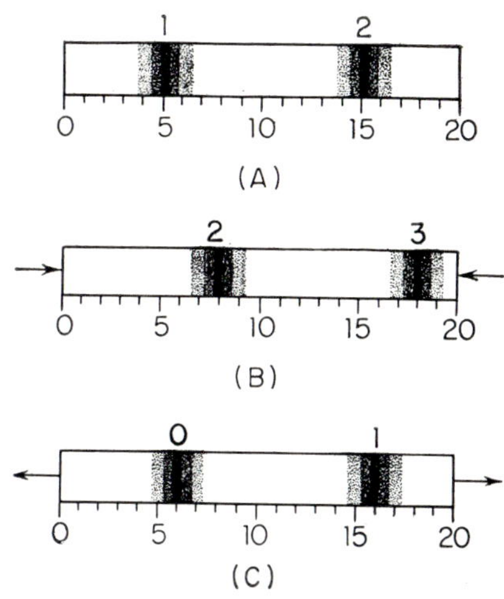

FIG. 14-3. Photoelastic strain gage indication: (*A*) initial fringe position with zero strain; (*B*) all fringes shift seven units to the left due to 490 micro-inches per in. compressive strain; (*C*) all fringes shift eleven units to the right because of 770 micro-inches per in. tensile strain.

The fringes seen in the photoelastic strain gage under white light consist of a series of repetitive color bands. In order to measure with reasonable precision the fringe movement due to strain, it is necessary to follow a "fringe index line" or "tint of passage." Both these terms refer to the narrow border line between red and blue bands or between red and green bands. In practice, especially for color-blind individuals, it is sometimes a little difficult to establish accurately the magnitude of the fringe shift. Maximum accuracy is achieved by bright illumination, nearly normal observation, and, if necessary, a magnifying glass for the smaller gages. Monochromatic light will also add contrast and definition to the fringes.

The strain sensitivity of the rectangular gage is dependent upon the manner of bonding to the test piece. If the gage is cemented only at its ends (Fig. 14-4), it will respond only to the strain along its axis. If bonded over its complete area, the gage output is proportional to the difference in strains along and perpendicular to the gage axis. For the normal application the photoelastic strain gage will be aligned with a principal axis as determined from other considerations. In a general biaxial stress field it is necessary to employ two gages, one along each principal axis, just as with electrical resistance gages. For this case the photoelastic gages should be bonded only at their ends in order to indicate the two principal strains. Principal stresses are calculated from the conventional expressions

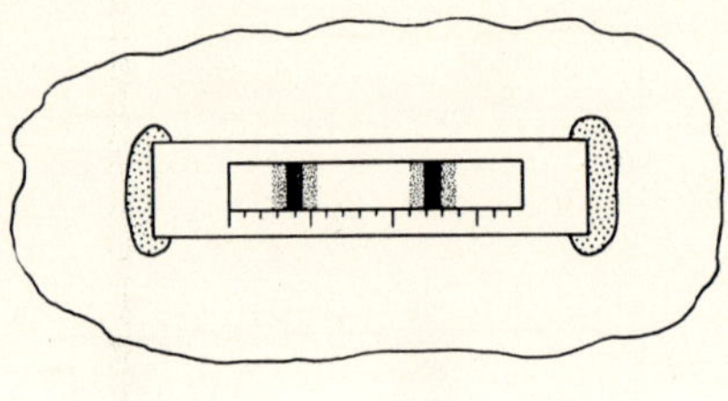

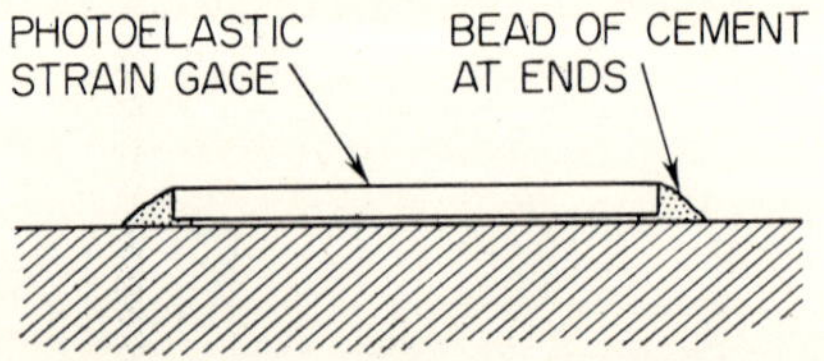

FIG. 14-4. Method of cementing rectangular photoelastic strain gage for uniaxial sensitivity.

$$\sigma_x = \frac{E}{1 - \mu^2} (\epsilon_x + \mu\epsilon_y)$$
$$\sigma_y = \frac{E}{1 - \mu^2} (\epsilon_y + \mu\epsilon_x) \tag{14-1}$$

The gage should be cemented along its complete length only when it is to be bonded to a surface with a known relationship between the principal strains, i.e., uniaxial stress as in a simple tension member ($\epsilon_y = -\mu\epsilon_x$), etc.

If subjected to bending in the plane of the gage or to shear stresses, the fringes become skewed or tilted (Fig. 14-5) and the calibration factor is no longer valid. Special gages are manufactured for use in pure shear, and have the initial frozen-in fringes already tilted at 45° with respect to the gage axis. Under applied shear stress, the fringes in these gages shift without further tilting. In this instance the gage must be bonded over its entire surface.

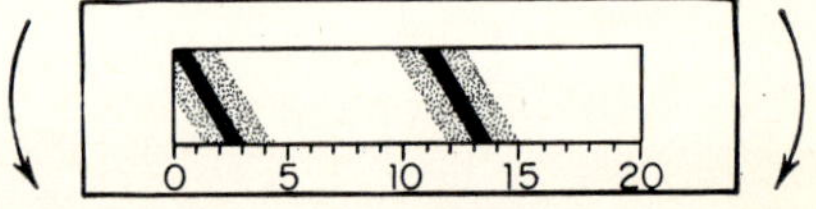

FIG. 14-5. Tilting of fringes due to bending in the plane of the gage or to shear stress.

Photoelastic strain gages can be employed for studying dynamic as well as static strains. For cyclic or repetitive phenomena the gage is viewed under synchronized stroboscopic lighting. Motion pictures can be used to obtain a permanent record, and high-speed motion pictures for impact or shock loading.

Because of its thickness, the photoelastic strain gage can produce a noticeable reinforcing effect when bonded to a thin and/or narrow member subjected to a bending moment. A further error is introduced because of the distance of the gage from the neutral axis of the member. The indicated strain, for example, when using a photoelastic strain gage on a steel member of the same width and thickness in pure bending, is approximately 60 per cent too high. For members subjected to plane strain with no bending, the error is ordinarily negligible. Detailed information on the errors introduced when the gages are bonded to various thicknesses of different metals can be obtained from the gage manufacturer.

GAGE-INSTALLATION TECHNIQUE

While the details of the installation technique for photoelastic strain gages vary somewhat according to the manufacturer, the general principles parallel those for resistance strain gages. The one major difference arises from the lack of conformability of the photoelastic strain gages. They must be used on flat or nearly flat surfaces. The surface on which the gage is to be mounted should be thoroughly cleaned with a volatile solvent and should be free of scale. Abrading with emery cloth prior to cleaning is usually recommended. For mounting on a porous surface, a thin precoat of cement (allowed to cure fully before bonding the gage in place) is good practice. Cleaning the back of the gage with a solvent prior to installation will also promote adhesion.

Cements used for photoelastic strain gages are commonly the room-temperature-curing epoxy type, although cyanoacrylate contact cement has also been used for applications on very flat surfaces, allowing intimate contact between the gage and test specimen. A generous amount of epoxy cement is spread over the gage area on the specimen, and the gage set firmly in place. Sufficient finger pressure is applied to the gage to squeeze out the excess cement and leave a uniform bond layer of 0.005 to 0.010 in. thickness. Extra beads of cement are built up at the ends of the gage as shown in Fig. 14-4 to augment the transfer of strain from the test surface to the gage. The cement is allowed to cure according to the manufacturer's recommendation, and the gage is ready for use.

The photoelastic strain gages are capable of indicating strains as high as 1.5 per cent (15,000 micro-inches per in.), but the usual limitation on an installed gage is the adhesive strength. With the latter consideration, the maximum allowable strain may be in the order of 7,000 micro-inches per in. for epoxy cements and about half of this for cyanoacrylate contact cement.

CIRCULAR GAGES

Circular photoelastic strain gages are commercially available in two principal types—with and without frozen-in fringe patterns. Both types are similar in construction, consisting of a ring of photoelastic plastic approximately 0.1 in. thick, backed by a reflective coating, and covered on the face with a disk of circularly polarizing film (Fig. 14-6).

The type having no initial fringe pattern is intended only for indicating the directions of the principal axes in the test piece on which it is mounted. Strain in the test piece is transmitted to the gage through the adhesive bond, and produces a fringe pattern which is always symmetrical about the principal axes. An asymmetrical pattern on the

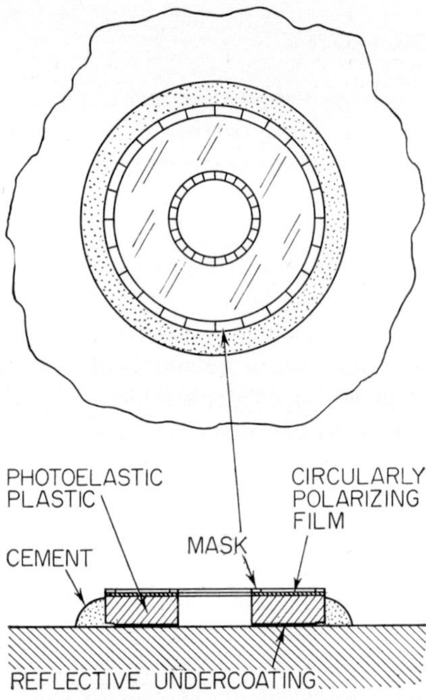

FIG. 14-6. Typical construction of circular photoelastic strain gages and method of cementing.

gage indicates either improper bonding or a severe strain gradient across the gage diameter. In the former case a new installation is required, and in the latter case either a smaller photoelastic strain gage or a conventional resistance strain gage of a size appropriate to the strain gradient should be used. Figure 14-7 illustrates the idealized fringe pattern in a circular gage subjected to uniaxial tensile strain. The periphery of the gage is graduated in equal increments as an aid in determining the angular orientation of the axes. No provision is made in these gages for quantitative measurement of strain magnitudes.

Circular gages which have initial fringe patterns locked in during manufacture can be used to indicate both the directions and magnitudes of the principal strains. The zero-strain fringe pattern consists of one or two circular fringes concentric with the axes of the gage as shown in Fig. 14-8*A*. After cementing the gage to the test piece and applying loads, the strain transmitted to the gage causes the pattern to distort symmetrically about the principal axes. The resulting fringe shifts along the axes of symmetry can be interpreted in terms of principal strain magnitudes.

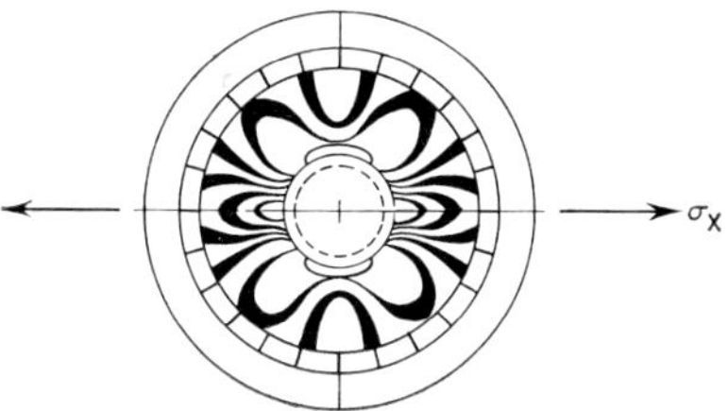

FIG. 14-7. Idealized fringe pattern in circular gage subjected to uniaxial tension. (*Courtesy of Baldwin-Lima-Hamilton Corporation. After Oppel.*)

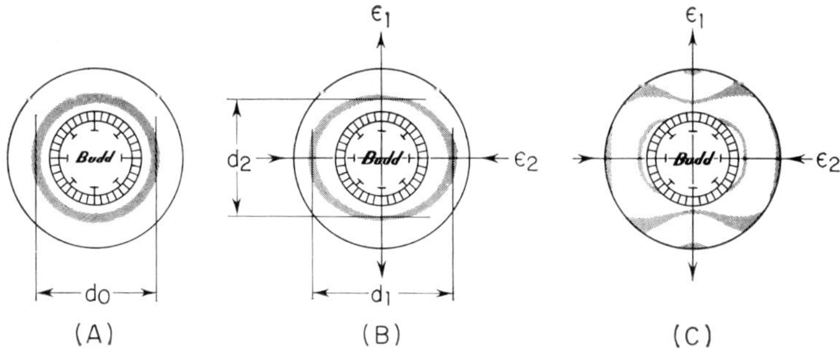

FIG. 14-8. Circular photoelastic strain gage indication: (*A*) initial fringe with zero load; (*B*) fringe displacement at low load; (*C*) fringe displacement for high load. (*Courtesy of The Budd Company.*)

Figure 14-8 shows the pattern changes accompanying increasing load on a test piece. In Fig. 14-8*B* the distance d_1 minus the original strain-free distance d_0 can be measured with an illuminated optical comparator. ϵ_1 is then a function of $d_1 - d_0$. Similarly, ϵ_2 is a function of $d_2 - d_0$. The functional relationship between fringe shift and principal strain is supplied by the gage manufacturer in the form of a graph. At all but low strains the original fringes may be displaced beyond immediate identification. Fringe order numbers can be determined readily, however, by locating the black spot (just beginning to appear along the ϵ_1 axis in Fig. 14-8*C*) and counting from that point as a zero. After identifying the order number of any fringe, the position of which can be measured conveniently along an axis of symmetry from the reference diameter d_0, the measured shift and fringe number are entered in the manufacturer's chart and the strain read directly. This process is repeated for the second axis of symmetry, and the results used with Eqs. (14-1) to calculate the principal stresses. A strain resolution of approximately 50 micro-inches per in. can be achieved with this system.

Installation procedure for the circular gages parallels that for the rectangular gages. Both types of circular gage described here are intended, however, to be cemented only around the periphery, as shown in Fig. 14-6. Some gage types may be provided with a vinyl or rubber mask over most of the bottom of the gage to prevent adhesion in this region.

PHOTOELASTIC STRESS GAGES

Zandman has extended the principle of the photoelastic strain gage to perform the function of a stress gage. He notes that the degree of birefringence is proportional to the difference in the principal stresses existing in a plane perpendicular to the direction of observation. If a circular piece of photoelastic plastic is illuminated and observed as in Fig. 14-9, the birefringence will be proportional to $\sigma_x - \sigma_z$. But σ_z is obviously zero, and thus, under these conditions, the birefringence is directly proportional to the stress σ_x. Photoelastic stress gages operating on this principle can be produced in a variety of forms, including rectangular and circular.

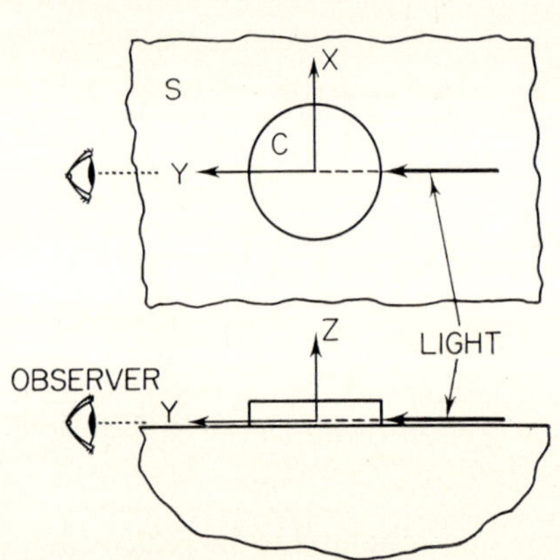

FIG. 14-9. Principle of photoelastic stress gage. (*After Zandman.*)

One version of the circular photoelastic stress gage consists of a ring of photoelastic plastic coated with a reflective layer on its inner surface and having a stress scale marked on its outer surface as shown in Fig. 14-10. The gage is viewed radially—in a plane parallel to the surface on which the gage is mounted. The stress in a direction tangential to the ring periphery is proportional to the fringe shift at every point on the outer surface of the ring. This gage is therefore capable of indicating the stress in any direction. A survey of stresses over a portion of the ring circumference will yield principal stress magnitudes and directions.

The same principle has been applied in a linear photoelastic stress gage. The gage is composed of a strip of photoelastic plastic with a reflector on one side and a stress scale on the other side (Fig. 14-10). The shift of the initial fringe pattern with strain is directly proportional to the stress along the gage axis.

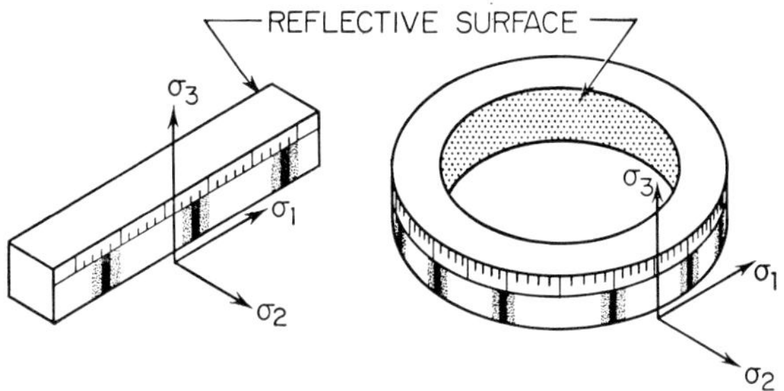

FIG. 14-10. Early commercial versions of rectangular and circular photoelastic stress gages. Fringe shift at any point on either gage is proportional to σ_1, the stress in a direction tangent to the indicating surface. (*Courtesy of The Budd Company.*)

TRANSDUCER APPLICATIONS

Both photoelastic strain gages and stress gages lend themselves to use as sensitive elements in transducers. A photoelastic gage bonded to a stressed area can be used to indicate pressure, force, torque, and numerous other mechanical variables. Photoelastic transducers are particularly simple and do not require power supplies, amplifiers, or

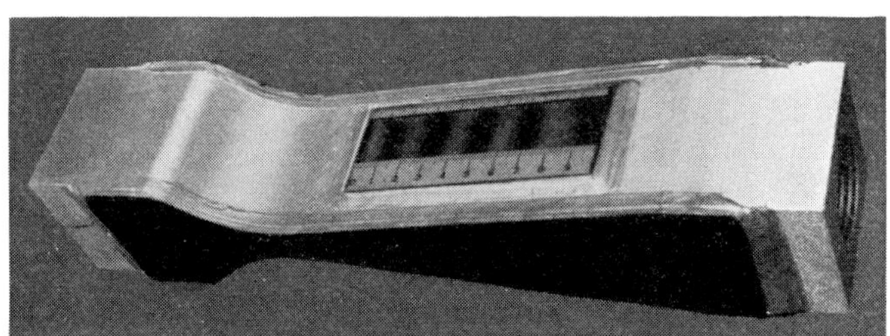

FIG. 14-11. A 60,000-lb tension load cell with a photoelastic strain gage as sensitive member. Accuracy is 1.5 per cent of full scale load. (*Courtesy of The Budd Company.*)

other instruments. Figure 14-11 illustrates a tension load-measuring transducer employing a rectangular photoelastic strain gage.

BIBLIOGRAPHY

Oppel, G. U.: Photoelastic Strain Gages, *Experimental Mechanics*, vol. 1, no. 3, pp. 65–73, March, 1961.

Post, Daniel, and Felix Zandman: Accuracy of Birefringent-coating Method for Coatings of Arbitrary Thickness, *Experimental Mechanics,* vol. 1, no. 1, pp. 21–32, January, 1961.

Zandman, F.: Visual Strain Gage Does Work of Three, *Product Eng.*, vol. 31, pp. 42–44, Oct. 24, 1960.

Zandman, F., and M. R. Wood: PhotoStress; New Technique for Photoelastic Stress Analysis, *Product Eng.*, vol. 27, pp. 167–178, September, 1956.

EXERCISES

14-1. Bond a rectangular photoelastic strain gage to a tensile specimen. Attach resistance strain gages to the same specimen, and load the specimen in increments, recording both sets of strain indications. Evaluate the precision, sensitivity, and repeatability of the two methods.

14-2. Derive an expression for predicting the error in the strain indication from a rectangular photoelastic strain gage due to bending strains, writing the expression as a function of the elastic moduli of the gage and underlying metal and of the relative dimensions of the gage and the member to which it is attached.

14-3. After reading the literature on frozen-stress photoelastic techniques, attempt to fabricate your own photoelastic strain gage from a piece of birefringent epoxy plastic.

14-4. What configuration might be taken by a "strain-multiplying" photoelastic strain gage for use on understressed members?

14-5. Apply two rectangular photoelastic strain gages on a test specimen, mounting one gage by cementing at the ends only, and the other by cementing along the complete length. Apply loads and record the strain indications. Evaluate the observed difference in the light of the applied stress field.

14-6. Analytically predict the behavior of a rectangular or circular photoelastic strain gage applied to a member with a strain gradient. In the case of the rectangular gage, let the axis of the strain gradient correspond to the gage axis.

14-7. How would you use photoelastic strain gages in the study of residual stresses?

14-8. Attach a circular photoelastic strain gage to a biaxially strained member and experimentally determine the sensitivity in terms of principal-stress magnitude and location of principal axes.

INDEX